New Views
In Mathematics
Course 2

Connections in Arithmetic, Algebra, & Geometry

by
Merv Edwards

Educational Design, Inc.   EDI 202

To Fay

Educational Consultant

Dr. Robert R. Jones
former Director of Mathematics
North Carolina Department of Public Instruction

Editorial Advisor

Dr. Cleo Meek
former Assistant Director of Mathematics
North Carolina Department of Public Instruction

Acknowledgments

The author is deeply indebted to the creative editorial guidance of *Caleb E. Crowell*. He shows the educational insight of a master mathematics teacher.

Lindley Robinson of Shore Regional High School, West Long Branch, and *Jean Norris* of Wall Township High School, Wall Township, meticulously prepared and checked answers to the student and teacher's edition of this textbook.

The publisher and author wish to thank the following teachers and administrators in New Jersey who helped pilot *New Views in Mathematics, Course 2* and whose suggestions and corrections have improved upon the original manuscript:

Carol De Cuzzi, Audubon High School, Audubon

Michael Burke, Math Supervisor, and *LaKay Reilly,*
Gloucester City Jr-Sr High School

John Lavagnino, Math Dept. Head, *Ciel Butka, Maria Caffrey, Edward Cappelutti, Barbara Teller, Joseph Dobish,* Hoboken High School, Hoboken

Lindley Robinson, Shore Regional High School, West Long Branch

Andrew Kazimer, Calvin Mayley, Hamilton East-Steinert High School, Trenton

Patrick Lamberti, Math Supervisor, *Margaret Roma, Edward Rosen, Michael Jordan, Greg Musselman,* Toms River High School System, Toms River

Louis Limongelli, Supervisor of Mathematics, Wall Township High School

About the Author

Merv Edwards was Mathematics Department Chairman for 30 years at Shore Regional High School, West Long Branch, New Jersey. He retired in June, 1992. Mr. Edwards taught all levels of math, General Math as well as Advanced Placement Calculus for all 30 years. He currently teaches *Methods of Teaching Mathematics* to Math Education majors at Trenton State College. Merv Edwards has given mathematics education workshops throughout the country for the past twenty years.

He is co-author of nine Algebra and Geometry textbooks published by Harcourt-Holt Rinehart and Winston. His most recent texts published by Educational Design include:

New Views in Mathematics, Course 1
New Views in Mathematics, Course 2
The HSPT Coach: Mathematics
The EWT Coach: Mathematics

To the Student

This book provides a new view of mathematics.

The main objectives of this book are for you to understand and to learn mathematics.

Here are some features of this text that are designed to help you:

- ❑ Most lessons include Discovery activities allowing you to explore mathematical concepts on your own or in a group.

- ❑ Classroom Practice and Written Exercise sections are similar to the Examples and Solutions worked out in the lesson. If you have difficulty solving a problem, refer to an example for help.

- ❑ Answers to the odd numbered Written Exercises are given in the back of the book in the Selected Answers section. After doing each exercise, look up the answer to see if you have solved the problem correctly. Do not wait until you have done all of the exercises before checking your answers. You don't want to waste time doing all the problems incorrectly.

- ❑ Every chapter ends with a review of not only the current chapter, but also every chapter from the beginning of the book. This will help you retain what you have learned. This is important because each lesson builds on the previous lessons.

- ❑ This book is a blend of arithmetic, algebra, and geometry. You will be able to see connections between various branches of mathematics.

- ❑ You will learn a variety of strategies for problem solving and you will see that there is more than one way to solve a problem.

- ❑ You will solve problems that apply to real life situations.

- ❑ You will explore interesting patterns in mathematics.

- ❑ You will gain experience in communicating with your peers orally and in writing.

- ❑ The calculator will be a valuable tool to help you with your homework. You will learn to estimate answers so that you can check if your calculator answer is reasonable; you may have accidently pressed the wrong key.

- ❑ Manipulative devices will be used throughout the course to help you discover mathematical concepts.

- ❑ Summary activities at the end of each lesson will help you to organize on your own the main ideas of the lessons.

- ❑ Every lesson contains an Open-Ended Question to encourage you to think creatively.

We hope you will enjoy *New View Mathematics*!

Merv Edwards
September, 1993

Contents

Chapter 5   Connecting Geometry and Algebra:
Like Terms, Factors, Multiples

Chapter 6   Connecting Algebra to Geometry and Statistics

Chapter 7   Angles

Chapter 8   Angles Part II

Chapter 9   Geometric Transformations

Chapter 10   Parallel Lines

Chapter 11   Graphing Lines

Chapter 12   Area and Volume

Chapter

1

Discovering Applications

1.1 Number Patterns

OBJECTIVE   To recognize and extend number patterns

Look at the sequence of numbers 4, 6, 8, 10, 12, ...

It is easy to see that the numbers are **increasing** by 2.

That is, each number is 2 bigger than the number before it.

So, the next number in the sequence will be 12 + **2**, or 14.

We call a sequence like this a ***number pattern***.

Frequently, when the numbers are small, you can guess the pattern.

Other times it is helpful to look for a pattern involving a repeated arithmetic operation such as addition, subtraction, multiplication, or division.

DISCOVERY   If the pattern of numbers below is continued, what will be the seventh number?   5, 9, 13, 17, ...

          HINT: What can you add to, or subtract from, 5 to get 9?

                       What can you add to, or subtract from, 9 to get 13?

                       What can you add to, or subtract from, any number of the sequence to get the next number?

EXAMPLE 1   If the following pattern is continued, what will be the next number?
        3, 10, 17, 24, 31, ...

Strategy   First look for the simplest type of pattern. Look for a pattern that involves only **one** operation, like addition.

Test to see if the pattern is formed by addition.

Find the **difference** between each term and the next one.

    10 - 3 = **7**   17 - 10 = **7**   24 - 17 = **7**

The difference is always **7**.

This shows that you **add 7** to any number to get the next number.

    3 + 7 = 10   10 + 7 = 17   17 + 7 = 24   24 + 7 = 31

Solution   Therefore, the number following 31 in the sequence is 31 + **7** = 38.

EXAMPLE 2   Find the eighth term of the sequence 3, 10, 17, 24, 31, ...

Strategy   In Example 1 of page 1 you saw that **7** must be added to any number
                       to get the next number in that sequence.

3,	10,	17,	24,	31,	31 + **7**,	38 + **7**,	45 + 7
1st	**2nd**	**3rd**	**4th**	**5th**	**6th**	**7th**	**8th**

Solution   Thus, the **8th** term of the sequence is 45 + 7, or **52**.

Sometimes **multiples** of a number play an important role in finding a number pattern.
What is meant by a **multiple** of some number, say, **7**?
Multiply 7 by any number, for example, **3**.
Recall that **multiplication** can be indicated by a **raised dot**.

$$7 \cdot 3 = 21 \qquad\qquad \textbf{7} \cdot \textbf{3 means 7 times 3.}$$
                       21 is called a **multiple** of 7.

DISCOVERY   How do you determine if a number is a multiple of another?
                       Is 128 a multiple of 8? Why?

EXAMPLE 3   Which of the following is **NOT** a multiple of 4?
                       (A)   12   (B)   17   (C)   16

Strategy   12 is a **multiple** of 4 if 12 is exactly divisible by 4: that is, there is no
                       remainder.
                       $12 \div 4 = 3$. There is no remainder, So, 12 is a multiple of 4.

                       $16 \div 4 = 4$. There is no remainder. So, 16 is a multiple of 4.

                       $17 \div 4 = 4$ with a **remainder of 1**. There is a **remainder**.

Solution   So, 17 is **NOT** a multiple of 4. The solution is **(B)**.

EXAMPLE 4   What is the next number in the pattern 2, 6, 18, 54, ...?

Strategy   First try subtraction of successive terms as you did in Example 1.

           6 - 2 = **4**   18 - 6 = **12**   54 - 18 = **36**

You can see that the difference between successive terms is **NOT** the same. So the pattern is **NOT** formed by adding the same number.

If the pattern is not formed by addition, maybe it is formed by **multiplying**.
Test by **division** of successive terms.

           6 ÷ 2 = **3**   18 ÷ 6 = **3**   54 ÷ 18 = **3**

Division works! The division shows that you **multiply** each number by **3** to get the next number.

Solution   Therefore, the number following 54 is 54 · **3 = 162**.

Sometimes a calculator is helpful in discovering a pattern.

EXAMPLE 5   What is the next number in the pattern 347, 4164, 49968, 599616, ... ?

Strategy   First try addition of successive terms.

          Use a calculator:
ENTER 4164 **ENTER** - **ENTER** 347 **ENTER** = READ 3817
By calculator, 49968 - 4164 = 45804. This is **NOT** the same as 3817.
Thus the pattern is **NOT** addition.

Use the calculator to determine if the pattern is **multiplication**.
ENTER 4164 **ENTER** ÷ **ENTER** 347 **ENTER** = READ 12
Then by calculator, 49968 ÷ 4164 = **12**.
By calculator, 599616 ÷ 49968 = **12**.
Thus the pattern is to multiply any number by **12** to get the next one.

Solution   Therefore, the number following 599616 is 599616 · **12 = 7195392**.

DISCOVERY   A thirteenth-century mathematician, Leonardo Fibonacci, came up
with the following sequence of numbers: 1, 1, 2, 3, 5, 8, 13, ...
This is called the **Fibonacci Sequence**.
What is the next term in this sequence?

EXAMPLE 6   What is the next number in the sequence 5, 7, 12, 19, 31, ... ?

Strategy   Note that 12, the third number in the sequence, is the sum of the
previous two numbers, 5 and 7. And so forth.

5, 7, 12, 19, 31,   **12 = 5 + 7**

5, **7, 12**, 19, 31   **19 = 7 + 12**

5, 7, **12, 19**, 31   **31 = 12 + 19**

Solution   Therefore, the next number in the sequence must be 19 + 31 = **50**.

The illustrations in the examples above involve only **one** arithmetic operation.

   Adding the same number to get the next number in the pattern.   (Examples 1 and 2)

   Multiplying by the same number to get the next term.   (Examples 3 and 4)

   Adding two successive numbers in the pattern to get the next term   (Example 5)

Some patterns involve **two** arithmetic operations.

The next example shows how to discover a pattern involving two arithmetic operations.

EXAMPLE 7   What is the next number in the sequence 3, 7, 15, 31, ... ?

Strategy   First check for a pattern involving only one operation.

Subtract successive terms.

7 - 3 = **4**   15 - 7 = **8**   31 - 15 = **16**

Subtraction does **not** give the same result each time.

You cannot find terms in this sequence by **adding** the same number
to successive terms.

(continued on next page)

Try **dividing** successive terms.

$7 \div 3 = \mathbf{2}$ with **1** left over.

$15 \div 7 = \mathbf{2}$ with **1** left over.

$31 \div 15 = \mathbf{2}$ with **1** left over.

So, the pattern is **NOT** just addition or just multiplication.

The pattern is to **multiply a term by 2** and then **add 1** to get the next term.

$3 \cdot \mathbf{2} + \mathbf{1} = 7$	**3**, 7, 15, 31, ...
$7 \cdot \mathbf{2} + \mathbf{1} = 15$	3, 7, **15**, 31, ...
$15 \cdot \mathbf{2} + \mathbf{1} = 31$	3, 7, **15, 31**, ...

Solution   Thus, the next term in the sequence 3, 7, 15, 31, ... is

$31 \cdot \mathbf{2} + \mathbf{1} = 62 + 1$ or **63**.

SUMMARY

Consider the sequence 4, 7, 10, 13, 16, ...

1.   How can you determine if the pattern involves addition or multiplication?
2.   How can you find the seventh number if the pattern is continued?

Consider the sequence 2, 8, 32, 128, ...

3.   How can you determine if the pattern involves addition or multiplication?
4.   How can you find the sixth number if the pattern is continued?

5.   How can you make up a sequence involving multiplication as well as addition?
6.   What is the Fibonacci sequence?
7.   How can you make up a sequence which behaves like a Fibonacci sequence?

CLASSROOM PRACTICE

Find the next term in each sequence.

1.   2, 4, 6, 8, 10, ...
2.   5, 8, 11, 14, 17, ...
3.   15, 12, 9, 6, ...
4.   24, 20, 16, 12, 8, ...
5.   1, 2, 4, 8, 16, ...
6.   1, 5, 25, 125, ...
7.   2, 5, 11, 23, ...
8.   1, 4, 13, 40, 121, ...

9.   9, 19, 39, 79, ...   10.   4, 17, 69, 277, ...
11.   5, 5, 10, 15, 25, 40, ...   12.   4, 1, 5, 6, 11, 17, ...

13.   Find the seventh term in the sequence 2, 5, 11, 23, ...
14.   Find the sixth term in the sequence 7, 22, 67, 202, ...

 Use a calculator to find the next term in each sequence.
15.   378, 677, 976, 1275, ...   16.   1275, 1019, 763, 507, ...

17.   49, 1127, 25921, 596183, ...   18.   78, 1092, 15288, 214032, ...

WRITTEN EXERCISES

Find the next term in each sequence.
1.   5, 7, 9, 11, 13, ...   2.   6, 9, 12, 15, 18, 21, ...
3.   25, 22, 19, 16, 13, ...   4.   30, 25, 20, 15, 10, ...
5.   1, 3, 9, 27, 81, ...   6.   2, 8, 32, 128, 512, ...
7.   3, 10, 31, 94, 283, ...   8.   2, 5, 11, 23, 47, 95, ...
9.   4, 4, 8, 12, 20, 32, ...   10.   5, 2, 7, 9, 16, 25, ...
11.   3, 8, 18, 38, 78, ...   12.   3, 13, 53, 213, 853, ...

13.   Find the seventh term in the sequence 3, 17, 87, 437, ...
14.   Find the sixth term in the sequence 6, 17, 39, 83, ...

 Use a calculator to find the next term in each sequence.

15.   496, 713, 930, 1147, ...   16.   1123, 1940, 2757, 3574, ...
17.   249, 2988, 35856, 430272, ...   18.   432, 3888, 34992, 314928, ...

OPEN-ENDED QUESTION (WRITING IN MATHEMATICS)

For the next question, write the answer. Also write an explanation of your solution. The explanation should be clear enough for anyone reading it to understand how to solve the problem.

19.   The following sequence is different from the ones you have seen, but it still
      involves two arithmetic operations: 4, 5, 7, 11, 19, 35, ... Find the eighth term.

1.2 Geometric Patterns

OBJECTIVE   To recognize and extend geometric patterns

One of the central themes of mathematics and science is the recognition of patterns. In the last lesson you worked with arithmetic patterns. In this lesson you will extend your ideas of patterns to geometric shapes. In most lessons in this course, you will be encouraged to **discover** how a process works before being shown a method of solution. You saw this in the first lesson where you were given **DISCOVERY** activities. The idea is illustrated below. Also, you can recognize from past experience triangles, squares, and circles. These shapes will be formally defined in later chapters.

DISCOVERY   If the pattern indicated below were continued, how many circles would be in the fourth figure of the pattern?

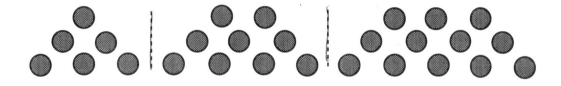

EXAMPLE 1   If the pattern indicated below were continued, how many blocks would be in the sixth figure of the pattern?

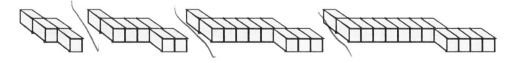

Strategy   Write the number of blocks in each of the 4 groups of blocks.

1st group	2nd group	3rd group	4th group
4,	**7,**	**10,**	**13**

Now look for an **arithmetic** pattern as in the last lesson.

(continued on next page)

4, 7, 10, 13, **?, ?,**

7 - 4 = **3,**   10 - 7 = **3,**   13 - 10 = **3**

The pattern is adding **3** to any number to get the next number.

Thus the sequence will be:

4,	7,	10,	13,	13 + **3,**	**16 + 3**
4,	7,	10,	13,	16,	**19**
1st	**2nd**	**3rd**	**4th**	**5th**	**6th**

Solution   Thus, the 6th figure in the pattern will contain **19** blocks.

EXAMPLE 2   The spiral below indicates a repeating pattern.

Which symbols are missing from the pattern at the positions x and y?

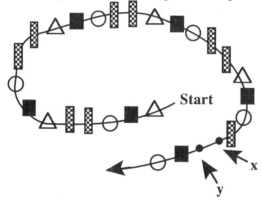

Strategy   First find the repeating pattern. What marks its beginning and end?

What block of symbols is being repeated over and over?

The pattern is displayed below.

Beginning of
pattern

End of
pattern

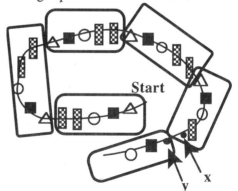

Solution   In the next to the last block, the missing symbol for **x** is:

The missing symbol for **y** is the first symbol in the pattern:

Sometimes a pattern like the spiral of Example 2 is altered by a slight, but consistent, change each time the pattern is repeated. For example, every time a block of figures is repeated, an extra triangle or circle is added. Then the problem becomes a combination of **geometric** and **arithmetic** patterns. This is illustrated in the next example.

EXAMPLE 3   Which symbols are missing from the pattern at the positions x and y?

Strategy   First look for a repetitive pattern.

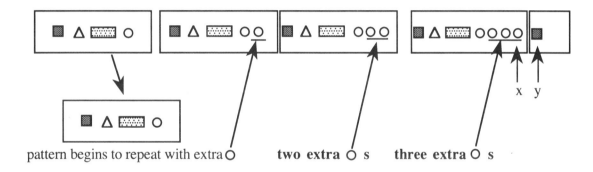

Solution   So, the x position is a ○.
                                                    The y position is a ▓
                                                    as pattern repeats again.

SUMMARY

The figures below suggest a pattern. Use the pattern to answer Exercises 1-4.

1.   Explain how the pattern works.

2.   How many triangles will be in the first row of the fourth figure if the pattern repeats?

3.   How can you use the pattern to determine the number of triangles in the fourth figure?

4.   How can you predict the number of triangles in the eleventh figure of the pattern?

Use the figure below to answer exercises 5-7.

5.   How can you determine the pattern in the figure?

6.   What is the pattern?

7.   If the pattern continues, what will the next 4 symbols be?

Use the figure below to answer exercises 8-11.

8.   How can you determine the pattern of the figure?

9.   Describe the pattern.

10. How can you predict the total number of blocks in the fourth figure if the pattern continues?

11. How can you use the pattern to predict the total number of blocks in the sixth figure if the pattern continues?

CLASSROOM PRACTICE

Use the pattern indicated in the figure below to answer exercises 1-4.

1.   How many rectangles will be in the first row of the fourth figure if the pattern continues?

2.   Find the number of rectangles in the fourth figure.

3.   How many rectangles will be in the sixth figure if the pattern continues?

4.   How many rectangles will be in the eighth figure if the pattern continues?

What symbols are missing from each pattern below at the locations x and y? (Ex. 5-7)

5.   6.

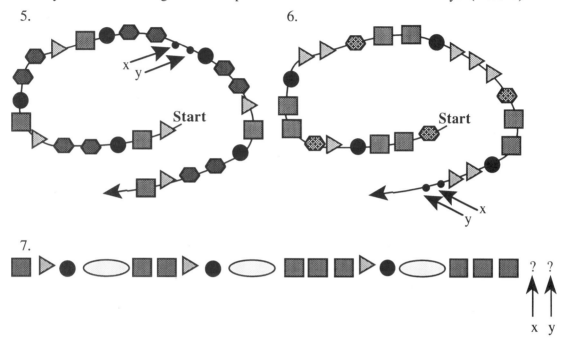

7.

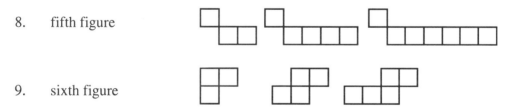

If the pattern indicated below were continued, how many blocks would be in the indicated figure?

8.   fifth figure

9.   sixth figure

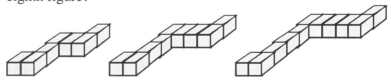

10.   If the pattern indicated below were continued, how many blocks would be in the eighth figure?

WRITTEN EXERCISES

Use the pattern indicated in the figures below to answers exercises 1-4.

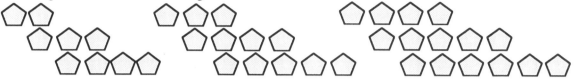

1.   How many pentagons will be in the first row of the fourth figure?
2.   Find the total number of pentagons in the fourth figure of this pattern.
3.   How many pentagons will be in the sixth figure of the pattern?
4.   Find the total number of pentagons in the eighth figure of the pattern.

Use the pattern indicated in the figures below to answer exercises 5-8.

5.   How many circles will be in the first row of the fourth figure?
6.   Find the total number of circles in the fourth figure of this pattern.
7.   How many circles will be in the sixth figure of the pattern?
8.   Find the total number of circles in the eighth figure of the pattern.

What symbols are missing from each pattern below at the locations x and y? (Ex. 9-10)

9.   10.

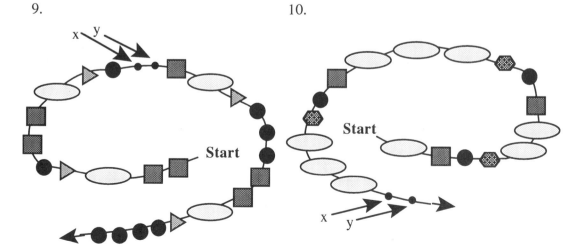

If the patterns below were to continue, how many squares would be in the sixth figure? (Ex. 11-12)

11.

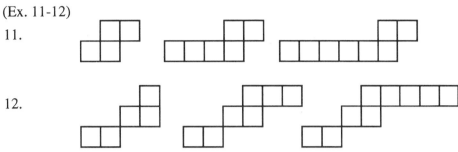

12.

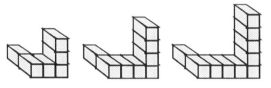

If the patterns below were to continue, how many blocks would be in the sixth figure?

13.

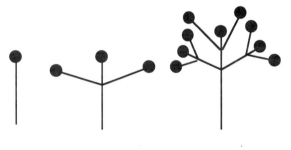

OPEN-ENDED QUESTION

14.   The first three figures of a pattern are shown at the right. Figure 1 begins with a single segment with **one tip**. Figure 2 shows two segments added, and therefore has **three tips**. Each new figure shows repetition: each segment has two new segments with tips added. How many tips will appear in the fifth figure of the pattern? Explain your answer.

1st figure 2nd figure   3rd figure

REVIEW

Find the next term of each sequence.

1.   8, 11, 14, 17, ...   2. 6, 6, 12, 18, 30, ...   3. 7, 15, 31, 63, ...

4.   19, 15, 11, 7, ...   5. 5, 13, 29, 61, ...   6. 1, 6, 7, 13, 20, ...

1.3 Patterns: Palindromes and Repeating Blocks of Symbols

OBJECTIVES   To predict an indicated symbol in a pattern of repeating blocks of symbols

To find the next palindrome number after a given palindrome number

In the last two lessons you studied arithmetic and geometric patterns. In the example below you are introduced to another type of pattern. You will be given a pattern of repeating blocks of symbols and asked to find which symbol will be in a particular position.

EXAMPLE 1   Examine this pattern:

ANGLESANGLESANGLESANGLES...

If this pattern keeps repeating, what symbol will be in the 20th position?

Strategy   This pattern consists of a block of letters repeated over and over: **ANGLES**.

Each block consists of **6** symbols. So it repeats in groups of **6**.

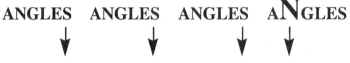

6th position	12th position	18th position	**20th** position
1st block	2nd block	3rd block	

But suppose you wanted to find what symbol is in the 20th position without counting.

You could **divide 20** by **6,** the number of symbols in **one block**.

The answer is **3** with a **remainder** of **2**.

The remainder is the key to the answer.

It tells you that the symbol you want is the **2nd** symbol after the **3rd** block: the letter **N**.

Solution   Either way, the symbol in the 20th position is **N**.

EXAMPLE 2   What symbol is in the 158th position of

ALGEBRAIIALGEBRAIIALGEBRAII ... ?

ALGEBRAII   ALGEBRAII   ALGEBRAII ...

There are **9** symbols to a **block**.

Divide 158 by **9** (the

number of symbols in a

repeating block).

$$\begin{array}{r} 17 \\ 9\overline{)158} \\ 9 \\ \hline 68 \\ 63 \\ \hline \end{array}$$

5 remainder

The division shows that the block of symbols repeats 17 times with **remainder 5**.

The fifth symbol in the block **ALGEBRAII** is **B**.

Solution   Therefore, the symbol in the 158th position is **B**.

The next examples will introduce you to an unusual number pattern that frequently occurs on standardized exams and proficiency tests.

Consider the following numbers:

The number 131 reads the same backward as forward.

The number 14541 reads the same backward as forward.

The number 4774 reads the same backward as forward.

Such numbers are called **palindrome** numbers.

DISCOVERY   The number 242 is a palindrome number.

What is the very next larger palindrome number?

In many cases you will be able to see the next larger palindrome without any work.

For example, the next number after   363   that is a palindrome is

373   **(Add 1 to the middle digit.)**

For more complex types of palindromes you might need a **strategy**.

The next examples illustrate a strategy for a palindrome with a
single middle digit NOT 9:   43634   or   with **several middle digits NOT 9:**   5775.

EXAMPLE 3   Find the next palindrome number after 43634.

Strategy   For the palindrome   43634   **6** is the middle digit.

                                                    ↓

                   Next palindrome: 43734   Add 1 to **6** to get the next palindrome.
Solution   So, the next palindrome after 43634 is **43734.**

EXAMPLE 4   Find the next palindrome number after 5775.

Strategy   For the palindrome   5775   there are **two "middle"** digits: **77.**

                                                    ↓

                   Next palindrome: 5**885**   Add **11** to **77** to get the next palindrome.
Solution   So, the next palindrome after 5775 is **5885.**

Trial and error will lead you to the pattern for palindromes with middle digit 9 or several
middle digits 9.
Consider the palindrome 595. Bigger numbers 596, 597, 598, and 599 are **NOT**
palindromes. So, the next palindrome must be a number in the 600s.
The first number in the 600s that is a palindrome is **606.**
Notice the pattern.   palindrome: **5 9 5**
                                         ↓ ↓↓

                          next palindrome: **6 0 6**   **The middle digit 9 is changed to a 0**
                                                            and 1 is added to the digit on either side.

EXAMPLE 5   Find the next palindrome after 3499943.

Strategy   palindrome: 3499943
                                      3**500**05**3**   **Change 9s to 0s and add 1 to**
                                                         each 4.
Solution   Thus, the next palindrome after 3499943 is **3500053.**

SUMMARY

1. Explain the strategy for determining which symbol will be in the 43rd position for the following pattern: **greatergreatergreater...**

2. How do you recognize a palindrome number?

Explain how to find the next palindrome number after each of the following numbers.

3. 3256523   4. 472333274   5. 1299921

CLASSROOM PRACTICE

For each of the following, if the pattern is continued, what symbol will be in the indicated position?

1. HSPT11HSPT11HSPT11...   37th position
2. exponentexponentexponent ...   106th position
3. trianglestrianglestriangles ...   121st position
4. volumevolumevolume ...   135th position
5. obtuseobtuseobtuse ...   89th position

For each palindrome number below, find the next larger palindrome number.

6. 343   7. 5665   8. 2569652   9. 249942
10. 49994   11. 525   12. 2399932   13. 74599547

WRITTEN EXERCISES

For each of the following, if the pattern is continued, what symbol will be in the indicated position?

1. parallelparallelparallel ...   49th position
2. perpendicularperpendicularperpendicular ...   97th position
3. quadrilateralquadrilateralquadrilateral ...   83rd position
4. algebra1algebra1algebra1 ...   117th position
5. part12fpart12f ...   112th position

For each palindrome number below, find the next larger palindrome number.

6.	787	7.	4884	8.	5289825	9.	439934
10.	89998	11.	1256521	12.	9499949	13.	399993

REVIEW

Find the next term in each sequence.

1.   4, 7, 10, 13, ...   2.   18, 15, 12, 9, ...

3.   4, 4, 8, 12, 20 ...   4.   9, 19, 39, 79, ...

5.   2458, 2845, 3232, 3619, ...   6.   587, 7044, 84528, 1014336, ...

7.   If the pattern below were to continue, how many squares would be in the sixth figure?

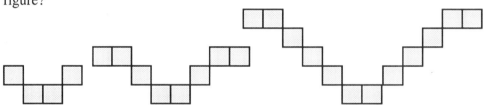

OPEN-ENDED QUESTION

For the next question, write the answer. Also write an explanation of your solution. The explanation should be clear enough for anyone reading it to understand how you solved the problem.

8.   If you fold a sheet of paper in half, the largest part of the paper that is not folded is $\frac{1}{2}$ a sheet. If that sheet of paper is folded in half again, the largest part not folded is $\frac{1}{4}$ of the original sheet. If the sheet of paper is folded in half exactly 5 times, what fractional part of the original sheet is the largest part not yet folded?

1.4 Patterns in Three Dimensions

OBJECTIVES   To predict, given three views of a die, which number or letter must be on the face you cannot see

To identify the correct three-dimensional image formed by folding along the dotted lines of a given plane figure

Many patterns in mathematics involve three-dimensional visualization.

You will now take a look at one such pattern.

The example below shows three views of a die (**one of a pair of dice**).

The digits 1-6 appear exactly once on the faces of this die.

You will be asked to predict which number must be on a face you cannot see.

EXAMPLE 1   What number is opposite the 5?
What number is opposite the 1?
What number is opposite the 2?

1st view   2nd view   3rd view

Strategy   Notice that the **2** is on the top in all three views.

Let's think of **1** as the **front** of the die, and label the other faces in terms of the front and top.

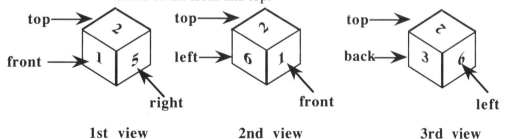

1st view   2nd view   3rd view

The **left** is opposite the right.   The **back** is opposite the front.

6 is opposite 5.   **3** is opposite 1.

The **bottom** is opposite the top.

Solution   **4** is the only number remaining. Therefore, **4** is opposite 2.

The box at the right can be formed by drawing a plane figure and folding up its sides. The shape of the plane figure can be discovered by cutting along certain edges of this box and folding up the sides or faces to form a single plane figure.

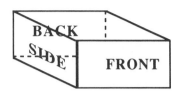

Cut along the bottom edge and the two vertical edges of the **FRONT** of the box. Fold up the **FRONT** flap of the box.

Repeat the process above for the **BACK** flap of the box.

Cut along the right edge of the **BOTTOM** of the box. Fold the **BOTTOM** down in line with the **LEFT SIDE** of the box.

Finally, fold up the **remaining** flaps in line with the **TOP** of the box.

These figures are **slanted** to give the drawings a 3-dimensional look. An unslanted version of the plane figure that would fold into a box is shown on the next page.

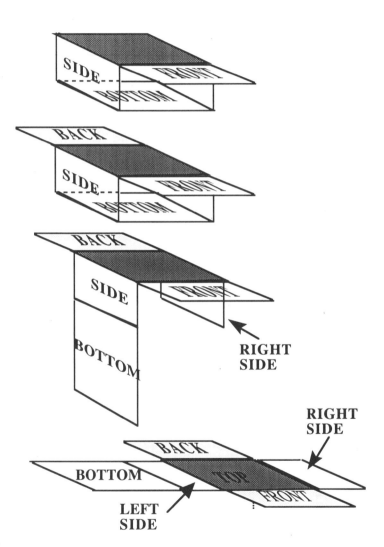

Notice the following pattern.

The front and back are **NOT** joined.

The sides are **NOT** joined.

The top and bottom are **NOT** joined.

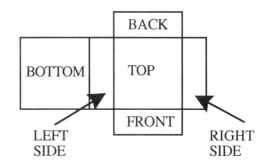

It is sometimes difficult to visualize how the plane figure above could actually fold into a box. It may be helpful to actually do the folding so you can see that it really works.

MANIPULATIVE DISCOVERY

Copy each of the figures below on a sheet of paper.

(Your teacher may give you an enlarged copy.)

Cut out each figure.

Fold along the dotted lines to try to form a box that can be taped together.

Which figure can be formed into a box?

Can you explain why one does not work?

FIGURE (A)

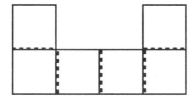

FIGURE (B)

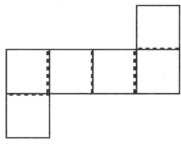

EXAMPLE 2   Which of the plane figures below cannot be folded to form a box?

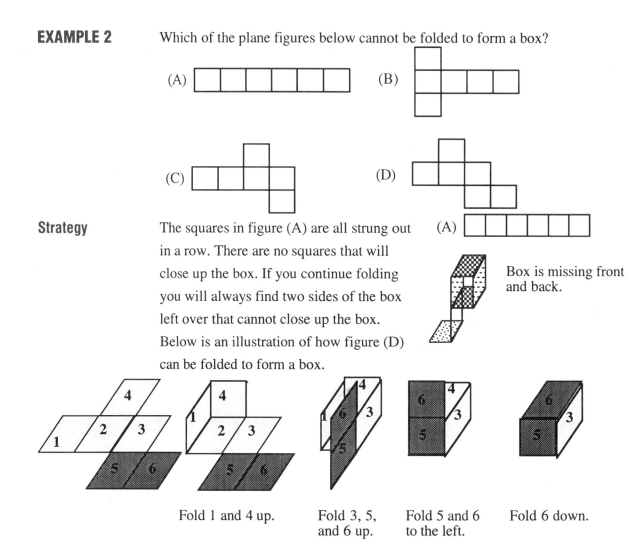

Strategy   The squares in figure (A) are all strung out in a row. There are no squares that will close up the box. If you continue folding you will always find two sides of the box left over that cannot close up the box. Below is an illustration of how figure (D) can be folded to form a box.

Box is missing front and back.

Fold 1 and 4 up.   Fold 3, 5, and 6 up.   Fold 5 and 6 to the left.   Fold 6 down.

Solution   Similarly, figures (B) and (C) can be folded to produce a box.

Therefore, figure (A) is the only one that cannot be folded to produce a box.

EXAMPLE 3   The plane figure at the right can be folded into a

box. Which of the figures below is a possible box

that can be made this way??

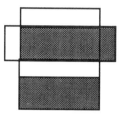

(A)   (B)   (C)   (D)

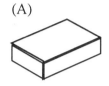   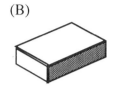   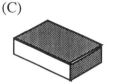   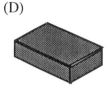

Strategy   Note that when the pattern is folded, the figure it forms will have three gray

surfaces. You may not be able to see one of these if, for example, it is on

the bottom.

Also notice that a long narrow surface is **NOT** shaded gray.

It is a short narrow side that is shaded gray.

Figure (A) is wrong. The top (large wide surface) is **not shaded gray.**

Since both of the large wide surfaces in the original pattern are shaded gray,

any large wide surface must be shaded gray in the 3-D drawing.

Figures (B) and (D) are not possible since each displays a long narrow side

that is shaded gray.

This leaves figure (C) as the remaining choice.

Figure (C) displays a **short narrow** side and a **large wide** surface that are

shaded gray.

Assume that the other large wide surface that cannot be seen, the bottom of

the box, is **shaded gray**. Also assume that the other short narrow side is

shaded gray.

Solution   Therefore, (C) is the only possible figure.

The explanation demonstrated in Example 3 above illustrates an important technique in

answering multiple-choice questions.

First try to eliminate impossible choices. If there are 4 multiple choices, elimination of

three of them as impossible implies that the fourth choice must be correct.

SUMMARY

At the right are three views of a die.
The digits 1-6 appear exactly once on the
faces of this die.

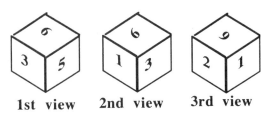

1st view   2nd view   3rd view

1.   What digit is on the top face of the
     die?

2.   What digit is in the front of the die?

3.   How do you find the number
     opposite the 3?

4.   Tell how to fold the plane figure at
     the right to make a box.

	6		
1	2	3	4
		5	

CLASSROOM PRACTICE

At the right are three views of a die.
The digits 1-6 appear exactly once on the
faces of this die.

1. What digit is opposite 5?
2. What digit is opposite 3?
3. What digit is opposite 2?

1st view   2nd view   3rd view

The letters A, B, C, D, E, and F appear
exactly once on the faces of this die.

4. What letter is opposite F?
5. What letter is opposite D?
6. What letter is opposite C?

1st view   2nd view   3rd view

Which of the plane figures below cannot be folded to form a box or cube? (Ex. 7-8)

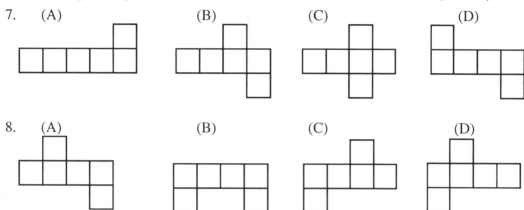

7.   (A)   (B)   (C)   (D)

8.   (A)   (B)   (C)   (D)

If the plane figure on the left is folded to form a box, which figure on the right is a possibility?

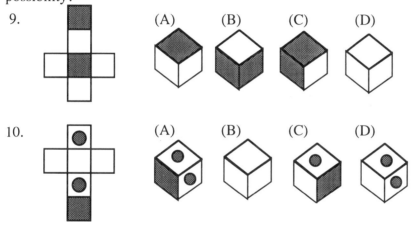

9.   (A)   (B)   (C)   (D)

10.   (A)   (B)   (C)   (D)

WRITTEN EXERCISES

At the right are three views of a die.
The digits 1-6 appear exactly once on the
faces of this die.

1. What digit is opposite 5?
2. What digit is opposite 3?
3. What digit is opposite 2?

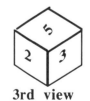

1st view   2nd view   3rd view

The letters A, B, C, D, E, and F appear
exactly once on the faces of three views of
a die.

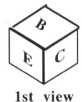  

    4. What letter is opposite E?

1st view **2nd view** **3rd view**

    5. What letter is opposite C?

    6. What letter is opposite B?

Which of the plane figures below cannot be folded to form a box or cube? (Ex. 7-8)

  7.   (A)   (B)   (C)   (D)

  8.   (A)   (B)   (C)   (D)

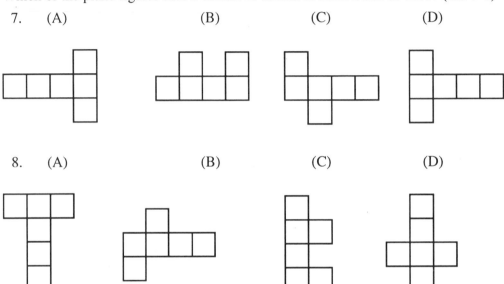

If the plane figure on the left is folded to form a box, which figure on the right is a
possibility?

  9.

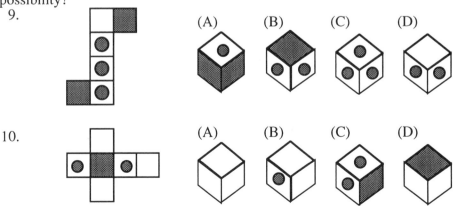

  10.

To the right of each pattern there are four 3-dimensional figures.

Which figure is the result of folding the pattern shown?

11.   (A)   (B)   (C)   (D)

12.   (A)   (B)   (C)   (D)

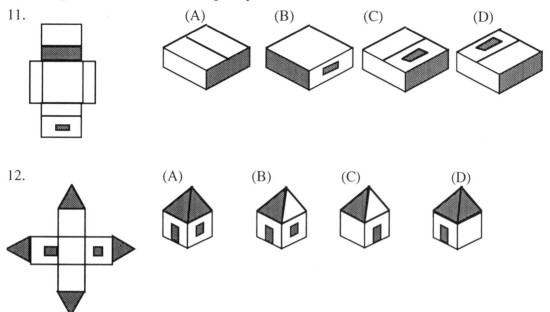

OPEN-ENDED QUESTION

13.   The cube at the right has a number on each of its six faces. If
       the sum of the numbers on each pair of opposite faces is 10,
       what is the sum of the numbers on the faces not shown?
       Write an explanation of how you got your answer.

REVIEW

1.   If the following pattern is continued, what symbol will be in the 95th position?
      arithmeticarithmeticarithmetic ...

2.   The number 46399364 is a palindrome number. What is the next larger
      palindrome?

Find the next term of each sequence.

3.   8, 17, 35, 71, ...   4. 4, 7, 11, 18, 29, ...   5. 4, 11, 25, 53, ...

1.5 Patterns Involving Exponents

OBJECTIVES   To evaluate arithmetic expressions involving exponents

To use a calculator to determine whether an expression like 1.5^6 is less than, greater than, or equal to an expression like 2.1^3

To use inequality symbols to compare arithmetic expressions involving exponents

To use rounding to the leftmost place to estimate computations

Recall that numbers can be compared using **inequality** symbols.

For example, you know that 4 <u>**is less than**</u> 8. This can be written as

$$4 \quad < \quad 8$$

9 <u>**is greater than**</u> 5

$$9 \quad > \quad 5.$$

EXAMPLE 1   Insert the appropriate inequality symbol, < or >.

(A)   7 ? 2   (B)   5 ? 10

Strategy   7 **is greater than** 2   5 **is less than** 10

Solution   7 > 2   5 < 10

In an expression like 4^3, the **3** is called an **exponent**.

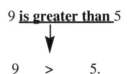

4^3 means $4 \cdot 4 \cdot 4$

$$4 \cdot 16$$

$$64$$

4^3 is **NOT** 12.

EXAMPLE 2   Find the value of 2^5.

Strategy   Think: 2^5 means $2 \cdot 2 \cdot 2 \cdot 2 \cdot 2$

                                    $4 \cdot 2 \cdot 2 \cdot 2$

                                        $8 \cdot 2 \cdot 2$

                                           $16 \cdot 2$

Solution 32

Sometimes you will be asked to compare two expressions involving exponents.

For example, is 1.5^6 greater than or less than 2.1^3?

This is easiest to do using the exponential key of a calculator: y^x.

For example, to find the value of 1.5^6:

Enter 1.5   **Press** the y^x key   **Enter** 6   **Enter** =   **Read the answer:** 11.390625

Some calculators might use a device other than an exponential key.

If your calculator does not have an exponential key, ask your teacher for assistance.

EXAMPLE 3   Insert the appropriate inequality symbol: $<$, $>$, or $=$.
                     1.5^6 ? 2.1^3

Strategy   Use a calculator to find the value of each expression.
                     1.5^6 ? 2.1^3

                     11.390625   ?   9.261

                     You can see that $11.390625 > 9.261$.

Solution   So, the correct symbol is $>$.

You have studied a number of mathematical patterns in this lesson.

The next example involves a repeating pattern in a set of numbers with exponents.

Note first that from now on we will use the word **evaluate** to mean **find the value of**.

Recall the idea of **digits** of a number. For the number 147:

> 1 is the **hundreds digit**.
>
> 4 is the **tens digit**.
>
> 7 is the **units digit**.

Notice that the question in the following example is an **OPEN-ENDED QUESTION**. You are asked to write the answer to a problem **and** then write an explanation of how you got your result. The example shows you how a student might correctly answer such a question.

EXAMPLE 4   What is the pattern of the units digit in the following sequence?

$$3^1, 3^2, 3^3, 3^4, \ldots$$

Explain how you discovered this.

Possible Student Response

Step 1	First, I write out several terms in the sequence.
	$3^1, 3^2, 3^3, 3^4, 3^5, 3^6, 3^7, 3^8, \ldots$
Step 2	Then I figure the value of each term (**evaluate**).
	$3^1 = 3$
	$3^2 = 9$
	$3^3 = 27$, etc.
	The values of the terms from 3^1 to 3^8 are
	3, 9, 27, 81, 243, 729, 2187, and 6561.
Step 3	I see a pattern in the units digits. I have blackened these with my pencil.
	3, **9**, 2**7**, 8**1**, 24**3**, 72**9**, 218**7**, 656**1**
Answer	The pattern is repetition of the block of digits **3, 9, 7, 1.**

OPEN-ENDED QUESTIONS give you practice in an important skill for real life. Many jobs call for a worker to explain how something works to either another worker or a customer. For example, an appliance sales person might have to **clearly** explain to a customer how to operate a washing machine. A nurse is frequently required to clearly explain in writing the progress of a patient.

The next example is very similar to a type you studied in Example 1 of Lesson 1.3. You learned to predict the symbol in the 20th position of a repeating block of symbols like **ANGLESANGLESANGLES ...**

EXAMPLE 5   What is the units digit in the 95th term of the sequence $3^1, 3^2, 3^3, 3^4, ...$?

Strategy   First look for a pattern of the units digits of successive terms.

In Example 4 you saw the pattern of the units digits.

They repeat in blocks of **3, 9, 7, 1**.

Number	$3^1,$	$3^2,$	$3^3,$	$3^4,$	$3^5,$	$3^6,$	$3^7,$	$3^8,$ ...
	1st	2nd	3rd	4th	5th	6th	7th	8th
Units digit of number	**3**,	**9**,	**7**,	**1**,	**3**,	**9**,	**7**,	**1**, ...

There are 4 digits in a block.

Divide 95 by **4**.(the number of digits in a repeating block).

The division shows that the block of units digits repeats 23 times with **3** left over.

The **3rd** digit in the block **3971** is **7**.

$$\begin{array}{r} 23 \\ 4\overline{)95} \\ \underline{8} \\ 15 \\ \underline{12} \\ \mathbf{3} \text{ remainder} \end{array}$$

Solution   Therefore, **7** is the units digit of the 95th term.

The following evaluation applies the idea of exponents to fractions.

EXAMPLE 6   Evaluate $(\frac{3}{4})^2$.

Strategy   First rewrite using the meaning of exponents.

$$(\frac{3}{4})^2 = \frac{3}{4} \cdot \frac{3}{4}$$

$$= \frac{3 \cdot 3}{4 \cdot 4} \qquad \text{Multiply the numerators. Multiply the denominators.}$$

Solution $$= \frac{9}{16}$$

When working with a calculator, you must to be able to use **rounding** to estimate your answer. This way you can at least tell if your **calculator** answer is **reasonable**.

Recall the rule for **rounding to the leftmost place:**

> To round to the leftmost place:
>
> 1. If the second digit in the numeral is **5** or more, round **up**.
>
> 2. If the second digit in the numeral is less than **5,** round **down**.

EXAMPLE 7   Round 3,984 and 438 to the leftmost place.

Strategy   **3**,984   **4**38

3 is the leftmost place.   4 is the leftmost place.

3, **9**84   4 **38**

↓   ↓

more than 5   less than 5

Solution   Therefore, round **up** to **4,000**   Therefore, round **down** to **400.**

EXAMPLE 8   Estimate 39.4^2. Then compare with the result you get withg a calculator.

Strategy

Round 39.4 to the leftmost place.

3**9**.4 rounds to **40.**   **9 is 5 or greater. Round 3 up to 4.**

So, to **estimate** 39.4^2,

use 40^2.

$$40^2 = 40 \cdot 40$$

$$= 1600 \quad \textbf{(4} \cdot \textbf{4 = 16, and add two zeros.)}$$

Solution   Now, by **calculator,** 39.4^2 is 1552.36.

The estimated answer, 1600, is a reasonable approximation of the calculator answer, 1552.36.

SUMMARY

1. How do you read the expression $7 < 12$?

2. How do you read the expression $9 > 4$?

3. What does the word **evaluate** mean?

4. How do you evaluate 7^3?

5.   How do you use a calculator to evaluate 1.8^6?

6.   How do you determine whether 1.8^6 is less than or greater than 2.3^2?

7.   What is the units digit of the number 1783?

8.   How can you find the units digit in 75th term of the sequence $3^1, 3^2, 3^3, 3^4, ...$?

9.   How do you round a numeral to the leftmost place?

10.   How do you estimate 28.6^3?

CLASSROOM PRACTICE

Insert the appropriate inequality symbol, < or >.

1. 5 ? 12   2. 4 ? 2   3. 15 ? 24   4. $3\frac{1}{2}$? $3\frac{1}{4}$

Evaluate each.

5. 6^3 6. 5^3 7. 2^4 8. 4^4

9. $(\frac{2}{3})^2$ 10. $(\frac{3}{4})^3$ 11. $(\frac{4}{5})^2$ 12. $(\frac{2}{5})^4$

Insert the appropriate inequality symbol, < or >.

13. 1.7^5 ? 2.7^2 14. 2.8^2 ? 2.1^2

15.   What is the units digit in the 113th term of the sequence $3^1, 3^2, 3^3, 3^4, ...$?

16.   What is the units digit in the 113th term of the sequence $8^1, 8^2, 8^3, 8^4, ...$?

Round each number to the leftmost place.

17.   489.1452   18.   25.23254   19.   74.7768

Estimate each answer and compare with the result you get with a calculator.

20. 59.231^2 21. 19.651^3

WRITTEN EXERCISES

Insert the appropriate inequality symbol, < or >.

1. 22 ? 29   2. 4.06 ? 4.6   3. 0.08 ? 0.008   4. $3\frac{5}{6}$? $3\frac{1}{10}$

Evaluate each.

5. 2^6 6. 8^3 7. 7^3 8. 4^5

9. $(\frac{4}{5})^3$ 10. $(\frac{1}{5})^4$ 11. $(\frac{2}{3})^6$ 12. $(0.03)^4$

Insert the appropriate inequality symbol, < or >.

13. 1.6^5 ? 2.1^3 14. 2.01^5 ? 3.1^3

15.   What is the units digit in the 94th term of the sequence $7^1, 7^2, 7^3, 7^4, ...$?

16.   What is the units digit in the 88th term of the sequence $4^1, 4^2, 4^3, 4^4, ...$?

Round each number to the leftmost place.

17.   548.665   18.   558.665   19.   598.665

Estimate each answer and compare with the result by using a calculator.

20. 51.4324^2 21. 1.93245^5

OPEN-ENDED QUESTION

22. 4^2 is called the **2nd power** of 4.

      8^5 is called the **5th power** of 8.

      7^9 is called the **9th power** of 7.

      As the power of a number increases, what happens to the results?

      For example, consider $2^3, 2^4, 2^5, 2^6$, etc. Are these results getting bigger or smaller?

      Can you find a number that when raised to larger powers gets smaller?

      If so, generalize what kind of number this must be.

*There is **no** review lesson at the end of the last lesson of a chapter.*

*Instead, there is a review of the entire chapter and **all previous chapters**.*

Review: Chapter 1

1.   If the pattern indicated below were continued, how many squares would be in the sixth figure?

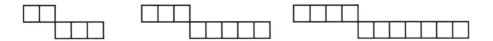

Find the next term in each sequence. (exercises 2-7)

2.   2, 7, 22, 67, 202, ...   3.   7, 7, 14, 21, 35, 56, ...

4.   46, 41, 36, 31, ...   5.   7, 16, 34, 70, 142, ...

6.   496, 709, 922, 1135, 1348, ...

7.   718, 22976, 735232, 23527424, ...

8.   What symbol is in the 135th position of the following pattern?
HISTORYHISTORYHISTORY ...

9.   What symbol is in the 119th position of the following pattern?
EXPONENTEXPONENTEXPONENT ...

For each palindrome number below, find the next larger palindrome.

10.   4375734   11.   256999652

At the right are three views of a die. The digits 1-6 appear exactly once on the faces of this die.

1st view   2nd view   3rd view

12.   What digit is opposite 6?

13.   What digit is opposite 4?

14.   What digit is on the bottom of the die?

Insert the appropriate inequality symbol, < or >.

15.   4.04 ? 4.004   16. $2\frac{1}{3}$? $2\frac{1}{2}$

At the right are three views of a die. The
letters P, Q, R, S, T, and U appear exactly
once on the faces of this die.

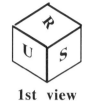

1st view   2nd view   3rd view

17.   What letter is opposite P?

18.   What letter is opposite Q?

19.   What letter is on the bottom of the
       die?

20.   Which of the plane figures below can be folded to form a box or cube?

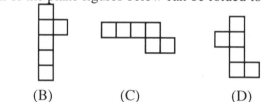

       (A)   (B)   (C)   (D)

21.   Which of the plane figures below **cannot** be folded to form a box or cube?

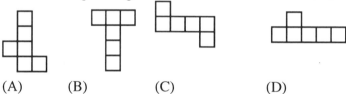

       (A)   (B)   (C)   (D)

22.   If the plane figure on the left is folded to form a box, which figure on the right is a
       possibile result?

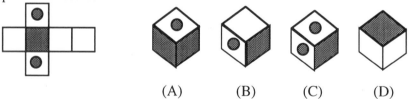

                   (A)   (B)   (C)   (D)

Evaluate the following.

23. 6^2 24. $(\frac{2}{5})^3$

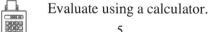   Evaluate using a calculator.

25. 3.85^5 26. 2.003^6

Insert the appropriate inequality symbol < or >.

27. 1.7^7 ? 2.9^3 28. 0.0042^4 ? 0.042^4

Estimate each. Then compare with the result you get with a calculator.

29. 3.9876^4 30. 308^3

31.   What is the units digit in the 74th term of the sequence $3^1, 3^2, 3^3, 3^4, 3^5, ...$?

32.   What is the units digit in the 95th term of the sequence $2^1, 2^2, 2^3, 2^4, 2^5, ...$?

33.   What symbols are missing from the spiral pattern at the locations x and y?

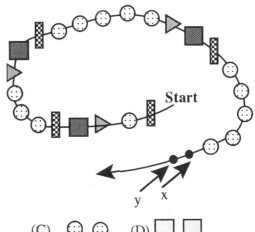

Start

y   x

(A) x y   (B) ☺ ▷ x y   (C) ☺ ☺ x y   (D) ☐ ☐ x y

OPEN-ENDED QUESTION

34.   If the pattern along three diagonals below is continued, describe what will be contained in a fourth diagonal of figures? Explain how you came to your conclusion.

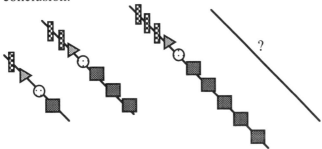

?

Chapter

▶ **2**

Connections with Algebra:
Evaluations, Signed Numbers

2.1 Order of Operations

OBJECTIVES   To simplify expressions using the Order of Operations Rule

To verify computations with a calculator

An expression like $3 \cdot 5 + 2$ involves two arithmetic operations:
multiplication and **addition**.

Recall that in such a case you do the **multiplication first** and **then** the **addition**.

$$3 \cdot 5 + 2$$
$$\downarrow$$
$$15 + 2$$
$$17$$

You can verify this with a calculator.

 Enter 3   Enter X   Enter 5   Enter +   Enter 2   ENTER =   READ 17

Order of Operations

When several operations occur—

1. Compute all multiplications and divisions first in order from left to right,

2. Then compute all additions and subtractions in order from left to right.

EXAMPLE 1   Simplify $45 \div 5 - 4 \cdot 2 + 12$.

Strategy   Do multiplications and divisions first in order from left to right.

$$45 \div 5 - 4 \cdot 2 + 12$$

$\quad\quad\quad\quad 9 \; - \quad 8 \; + 12$ **Do additions and subtractions in order from**

$\quad\quad\quad\quad\quad 1 \quad\quad + 12$ **left to right.**

Solution $\quad\quad\quad 13$

Recall that $\frac{18}{6}$ means $18 \div 6$, or 3. A fraction bar can be used to indicate division.

EXAMPLE 2   Simplify $\frac{18 + 2 \cdot 3}{8 \cdot 2 - 4}$.

Strategy   First use the rule for Order of Operations to simplify

$18 + 2 \cdot 3$ and $8 \cdot 2 - 4$.

Then divide the results. $18 + 2 \cdot 3$ $8 \cdot 2 - 4$

$\frac{18 + 2 \cdot 3}{8 \cdot 2 - 4} = \frac{24}{12} = 2$ $18 + 6$ $16 - 4$

                                         24   **12**

Solution   Thus, 2 is the simplified result.

In mathematics **parentheses** are used for grouping.

To simplify or evaluate the expression above by calculator, think of the expression as:

     numerator (top) **divided** by the **denominator** (bottom).

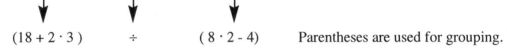

     $(18 + 2 \cdot 3)$ $\div$ $(8 \cdot 2 - 4)$ Parentheses are used for grouping.

Enter the expression as written above into a **calculator**.

Then **Enter** = to get the same result, **2**, found in Example 2.

Can you guess the Order of Operations Rule when the rule is extended to include

operations with **exponents**?

DISCOVERY

To evaluate $4 \cdot 2^3$

Do you multiply first,   or   Find 2^3 first,

then use the exponent?   then multiply the answer by 4?

$4 \cdot 2 = 8$ $2^3 = 8$

$8^3 = 8 \cdot 8 \cdot 8 = 512$ $4 \cdot 8 = 32$

Use a calculator to determine which result is correct, 32 or 512.

Using a calculator, you should have discovered from the previous page that $4 \cdot 2^3 = 32$.

Enter 4   Enter X   Enter 2   Enter y^x Enter 3   Enter =   READ 32

Thus, to evaluate $4 \cdot 2^3$, you first compute 2^3. Then multiply the result by 4.

This suggests extending the rule for Order of Operations to include expressions involving exponents.

Order of Operations

When several operations occur—

1. Compute all expressions containing exponents first in order from left to right,

2. Then compute all multiplications and divisions in order from left to right,

3. Then compute all additions and subtractions in order from left to right.

EXAMPLE 3   Simplify $60 - 6 \cdot 2^3 + 15 \div 3$

Strategy

$60 - 6 \cdot 2^3 + 15 \div 3$ **Use the exponent first:**

$60 - 6 \cdot 8 + 15 \div 3$ $2^3 = 2 \cdot 2 \cdot 2 = 8$

$60 - 48 + 5$ **Do multiplications and divisions next.**

$12 + 5$ **Do additions and subtractions next.**

Solution 17

The next example applies the Order of Operations to expressions involving multiplication of fractions. Recall first how to simplify products of fractions.

For example, to simplify $\frac{3}{4} \cdot 8$:

$$\frac{3}{4} \cdot 8 = \frac{3}{4} \cdot \frac{8}{1} = \frac{3}{\cancel{4}} \cdot \frac{\cancel{8}^{2}}{1}$$

First rewrite 8 as $\frac{8}{1}$.

Divide **numerator 8** and **denominator 4** by the largest common divisor of both: **4.**

$$= \frac{3 \cdot 2}{1 \cdot 1} = \frac{6}{1} = 6$$

EXAMPLE 4   Simplify $\frac{3}{4} \cdot (\frac{2}{3})^3$.

Strategy   First apply the Order of Operations.

$\frac{3}{4} \cdot (\frac{2}{3})^3$ **Compute $(\frac{2}{3})^3$ first.**

$\frac{3}{4} \cdot \frac{8}{27}$ $(\frac{2}{3})^3 = \frac{2}{3} \cdot \frac{2}{3} \cdot \frac{2}{3} = \frac{2 \cdot 2 \cdot 2}{3 \cdot 3 \cdot 3} = \frac{8}{27}$

$\frac{3}{\cancel{4}} \cdot \frac{\cancel{8}^{2}}{27}$ **Do the multiplication.**
$\quad\,_1$ **Simplify the product of the two fractions.**
                                  Divide 4 and 8 by 4.

$\frac{\cancel{3}^{1}}{\cancel{4}} \cdot \frac{\cancel{8}^{2}}{\cancel{27}_{9}}$ **Divide 3 and 27 by 3.**
$\quad\,_1$

$\frac{1 \cdot 2}{1 \cdot 9}$ **Multiply the numerators and**
                                  denominators.

Solution $\frac{2}{9}$

SUMMARY

How do you use the Rule for the Order of Operations to simplify each expression below?

1. $23 - 4 \cdot 3$ 2. $7 + 5 \cdot 3 - 28 \div 14$ 3. $4 \cdot 6^2$ 4. $7 + 3^2 + 9 \cdot 6$

5. How do you use a calculator to evaluate $\frac{8 + 4 \cdot 7}{9 - 2 \cdot 3}$?

How do you simplify each of the following products?

6. $\frac{4}{5} \cdot 35$ 7. $\frac{7}{8} \cdot \frac{2}{21}$

CLASSROOM PRACTICE

Simplify.

1. $9 + 7 \cdot 2$ 2. $38 - 6 \cdot 4$ 3. $24 \div 6 + 9$

4. $49 \div 7 - 2 \cdot 3 + 12$ 5. $49 - 50 \div 10 + 28 \cdot 2$ 6. $18 - 45 \div 9 + 7 \cdot 6$

7. $\dfrac{8 \cdot 5 + 16}{34 - 3 \cdot 2}$ 8. $\dfrac{8 \cdot 4 + 12}{31 - 5 \cdot 4}$ 9. $\dfrac{12 \cdot 4 - 6}{1 + 3 \cdot 2}$

10. $4 \cdot 3^2$ 11. $7 \cdot 2^3$ 12. $6^2 \cdot 3$

13. $\dfrac{4}{5} \cdot 20 + 8$ 14. $16 + \dfrac{2}{3} \cdot 12$ 15. $\dfrac{4}{15} \cdot \left(\dfrac{5}{4}\right)^2$

16. $70 - 2 \cdot 3^3 + 28 \div 4$ 17. $3 \cdot 2^5 - 48 \div 16 + 7 \cdot 6$

WRITTEN EXERCISES

Simplify. Verify with a calculator.

1. $12 + 8 \cdot 6$ 2. $45 - 7 \cdot 3$ 3. $39 \div 3 + 29$

4. $38 - 60 \div 10 + 17 \cdot 2$ 5. $54 \div 9 - 2 \cdot 2 + 14$ 6. $32 - 72 \div 6 + 8 \cdot 7$

7. $\dfrac{18 - 4 \cdot 2}{8 - 2 \cdot 3}$ 8. $\dfrac{5 \cdot 4 + 2}{17 - 2 \cdot 3}$ 9. $\dfrac{8 + 4 \cdot 6}{4 \cdot 3 - 8}$

10. $8 \cdot 2^3$ 11. $4^4 \cdot 2$ 12. $4 \cdot 2^5$

13. $\dfrac{5}{6} \cdot 12 + 8$ 14. $28 - \dfrac{4}{7} \cdot 21$ 15. $\dfrac{9}{4} \cdot \left(\dfrac{2}{3}\right)^4$

16. $200 - 4 \cdot 3^3 + 64 \div 16$ 17. $2 \cdot 3^5 + 8 \cdot 9 - 68 \div 4$

OPEN-ENDED QUESTION

18.   Parentheses are used in mathematics for grouping. Compute each of the following: (A) $7 \cdot 4 + 8$ (B) $7 \cdot (4 + 8)$

Explain why the results are different. Do the results contradict the Order of Operations Rule? Why or why not?

REVIEW

Find the next term in each sequence.

1.   45, 41, 37, 33, ...   2.   8, 9, 17, 26, 43, 69, ...   3.   8, 25, 76, 229, ...

2.2 Variables

OBJECTIVES   To evaluate algebraic expressions for given values of the variables

To estimate computations involving variables

To evaluate expressions with a calculator

A mathematical pattern frequently suggests a new concept.

What is the pattern below?

$$6 \cdot 2 + 7$$
$$6 \cdot 3 + 7$$
$$6 \cdot 4 + 7$$
$$6 \cdot 5 + 7$$

In each of the above expressions, the number multiplied by 6 changes or **VARIES**.

A letter, such as **n**, can be used to represent the **number** that changes or **VARIES**.

For example, 6 times a **number** plus 3 becomes

6 · **n** + 3, or   When you are multiplying by a variable, the

6n + 3   raised dot can be dropped.

The **n** is called a **variable.**

A **variable** is a letter that can be replaced by a number.

The value of **6n** + 3 depends upon the number that is substituted for the **variable n.**

This is illustrated in Example 1 below.

EXAMPLE 1   Evaluate 6n + 3 for n = 7.

Strategy   To **evaluate** 6n + 3 for n = 7 means to replace n by 7 and then compute the result.

6n + 3

6 · n + 3   **6n means 6 times n or 6 · n.**

6 · 7 + 3   **Replace n by 7 (or substitute 7 for n).**

42 + 3   **Use Order of Operations. Multiply first.**

Solution   45   **Then add.**

EXAMPLE 2   Which of the following is the approximate value of 0.6899a for
                 a = 0.03214?

                 (A)   0.021   (B)   0.018   (C)   0.21   (D)   0.018

Strategy   0.6899**a** becomes

                0.6899 · **0.03214**   **Substitute 0.03214 for a.**

                To approximate, use rounding.

                0.6**8**99 rounds to 0.7.   **8 is 5 or greater. Round 6 up to 7.**

                0.03**2**14 rounds to 0.03.   **2 is less than 5. Leave 3 unchanged.**

                Multiply: 0.7 · 0.03   0.03   **2 decimal places**
                                                x 0.7   **1 decimal place**
                          0.021   0.021   **2 + 1 or 3 decimal places**

Solution   Thus, (A) is the answer.

Throughout this text you will **CONNECT** algebraic ideas with geometric concepts.
You will formally study the idea of perimeter in Chapter 5.
However, the idea is introduced now to show an application of **variables**.
The distance around a rectangle is called the **perimeter**.
The formula for the perimeter of a rectangle is

            P = 2L + 2W,

where **P** is the **P**erimeter, **L** is the **l**ength, and **W** is the **w**idth.

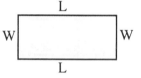

EXAMPLE 3   Find the perimeter of a rectangle with length 8 ft and width 6 ft.

Strategy   **Evaluate** P = 2L + 2W for L = 8 and W = 6.

                P   =   2L   +   2W

                P   =   2· **8**   +   2· **6**   **Substitute 8 for L and 6 for W.**

                P   =   16   +   12   **Do multiplications first.**

                P   =   28   **Then add.**

Solution   Thus, the perimeter is 28 ft.

The next application of variables involves exponents in a formula for the area of a circle.

In the figure of the circle at the right, **R** represents the length of the **R**adius of the circle.

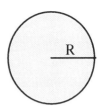

The formula for the area of a circle is:

$A = \pi R^2$ or $A = 3.14 R^2$, where 3.14 is the approximate value of π.

EXAMPLE 4   Find the area of a circle with radius 4 cm.

Strategy   Use the formula for the area of a circle.

Evaluate $A = 3.14 R^2$ for $R = 4$.

$A = 3.14 \cdot 4^2$

$A = 3.14 \cdot 16$ $4^2 = 4 \cdot 4 = 16$

$A = 50.24$

Solution   Thus, the area is 50.24 cm^2.

The cm^2 indicates the units for area: **centimeters square.**

$$\begin{array}{r} 3.14 \\ \times\ 16 \\ \hline 1884 \\ 314\ \\ \hline 50.24 \end{array}$$

Let's now look at the **connection** between **variables** and **real-life applications.**

Workers who repair appliances usually charge a fixed rate or **service charge** just to examine the item to be repaired. Then they charge a rate for each hour they actually work on the repair.

EXAMPLE 5   An electrician charges $40 an hour plus an additional service charge of $35. If C represents the electrician's total charge in dollars, and h represents the hours worked, write a formula that could be used to calculate C.

Strategy   Make up an actual problem. Its solution will suggest a general formula. Find the total charge for 3 hours at $40 an hour and a service charge of $35.

(continued on next page)

Think: $40 an hour for 3 hours <u>plus $35 service charge</u>

Total charge is: 40   ·   3   +   35

Total **C**harge is rate per hour times **h**ours worked + service charge,

C   =   40   ·   h   + 35

Solution   Thus, the formula is C = 40h + 35.

Notice the strategy used in the Example above .

You formed a **MODEL** of the problem.

You made up an actual example of the general problem.

You used finding the total charge for $40 an hour for 3 hours plus $35 service charge

to discover the **general** formula.

This method is called **MODELING** a problem.

This technique can be used to solve many problems.

You will be asked to use **MODELING** to solve Exercise 30 in the written exercises of

this lesson.

EXAMPLE 6   An electrician charges $24 an hour plus an additional $12 service

charge. At that rate how much would he charge the Martuscellis

for doing $3\frac{1}{2}$ hours work at their home? Use a calculator.

Strategy   This problem is similar to that of Example 5 above.

Total **C**harge is rate per hour times **h**ours worked + service charge.

C   =   24   · $3\frac{1}{2}$ + 12

 $C = 24 \cdot 3.5 + 12$ **Rewrite $3\frac{1}{2}$ as 3.5 for ease of calculator use.**

$C = 96$ **Enter 24   Enter X   Enter 3.5 Enter + Enter 12**

Enter =   Read 96

Solution   Thus, the Martuscellis are charged $96.

EXAMPLE 7   Here is the formula for changing temperature from Celsius to Fahrenheit: $F = \frac{9}{5}C + 32$.

If the temperature of something is 80° Celsius, find its temperature in degrees Fahrenheit.

Strategy   This is equivalent to **evaluating** F for C = 80.

$$F = \frac{9}{5}C + 32$$

$$F = \frac{9}{5} \cdot \textbf{80} + 32 \qquad \textbf{Substitute 80 for C.}$$

$$F = \;144\; + 32 \qquad\qquad \frac{9}{5} \cdot 80 = \frac{9}{\cancel{5}} \cdot \frac{\overset{16}{\cancel{80}}}{1} = \frac{9 \cdot 16}{1} = 144$$

Solution $F = \qquad 176°$

SUMMARY

1. What is a variable?

2. What are the steps in evaluating 4a + 5 for a = 3?

3. How do you estimate the value of 0.0784235 · 0.0421678?

4. What are the steps in evaluating $16t^2$ for t = 5?

5. How do you write a formula for the perimeter of the rectangle at the right?

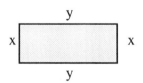

6. How do you simplify $\frac{5}{3} \cdot 12$?

7. A T.V. repair person charges a service charge of $25 and $40 an hour. How do you find the total charge for 4 hours work?

CLASSROOM PRACTICE

Evaluate for the given values of the variables.

1. 4n + 2 for n = 3   2. 28 - 3x for x = 5   3. 9 + 5r for r = 3

4. 7g + 6 for g = 3   5. 6 + 2n for n = 5   6. 24 - 2k for k = 5

7. $3a^2$ for a = 4   8. $3.14r^2$ for r = 6   9. $16t^2$ for t = 5

10. 2L + 2W for L = 7, W = 5   11. 3a + 4b for a = 6, b = 5

12.   The approximate value of 0.45678n for n = 0.02347 is ?

13.   The approximate value of 24.9a for a = 3.25672 is ?

14.   Find the perimeter of the rectangle
       with width 14 ft and length 29 ft.

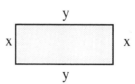

15.   The formula for the perimeter of
       this triangle is P = 2a + b.
       Find the perimeter if a = 9 cm and
       b = 4 cm.

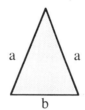

16.   Find the area of a circle with radius 8 in.

17.   If the temperature of a liquid is 35° Celsius, find its temperature in degrees
       Fahrenheit using the formula $F = \frac{9}{5} C + 32$.

WRITTEN EXERCISES

Evaluate for the given values of the variables.

1.   5x + 3 for x = 7   2.   43 - 4m for m = 5   3.   8 + 6t for t = 7

4.   9g + 5 for g = 4   5.   18 + 4k for k = 5   6.   62 - 5j for j = 7

7. $4x^2$ for x = 3   8. $3.14r^2$ for r = 5   9. $16t^2$ for t = 3

10. $\frac{3}{4}$ a + 10 for a = 12   11.   32 - $\frac{2}{3}$ m for m = 15   12. $\frac{2}{7}$ x for x = 21

13. 2L + 2W for L = 12, W = 6   14.   4a - 3b for a = 9, b = 5

15.   319x + 717 for x = 38   16.   243m - 119n for m = 13, n = 12

17.   3.245n + 214.7 for n = 0.32   18. $39k^2$ for k = 17

19.   The approximate value of 0.423451n for n = 0.046743 is ?

20.   The approximate value of 3.12749^5 is

      (A)   15   (B)   81   (C)   243   (D)   1024

21.   The approximate value of 2.93241^3 is

       (A)   9   (B)   27   (C)   64   (D)   none of these

22.   Find the perimeter of the rectangle
       with width 14 cm and length 33 cm.

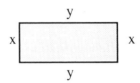

23.   The perimeter of this trapezoid is
       P = 2a + b + c. Find the perimeter if
       a = 13 in., b = 37 in., and c = 19 in.

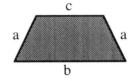

24.   An auto mechanic charges $40 for each hour worked plus an additional $20
       service charge. At that rate what would Maria be charged for $3\frac{1}{2}$ hours work?

25.   Mr. Sherafi is paid a weekly salary of $85 plus a commission of $6 on each
       camera he sells. If T represents his total pay for the week and N the number of
       cameras he sells, write a formula you could use to calculate his total pay for the
       week.

26.   The following procedure can be used to estimate the air temperature. Count
       the number of chirps made by a cricket in one minute. Add 37 to $\frac{3}{4}$ of that
       number to get the estimated temperature. If T represents the temperature and
       C the number of chirps counted, which formula below describes the procedure?

       (A) $T = \frac{3}{4}C + 37$ (B) $T = \frac{3}{4}(C + 37)$
       (C) $\frac{4}{3}C = T - 37$ (D) $T = \frac{3}{4}C - 37$

27.   When purchasing an item, Natasha gave a sales clerk a $20 bill. The clerk gave
       her the item and change consisting of d dollar bills, h half dollars, and n nickels.
       Which of the following expressions represents the cost in dollars of the item?

       (A)   20 - (d + h + n)   (B)   20 - d - 0.50h - 0.05n
       (C)   d + h + n   (D)   100d + 50h + 5n

28.   Which of the following formulas
       correctly represents the perimeter   a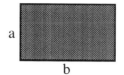
       of the rectangle?
                                                      b
       I   a + b + a + b
       II   ab
       III   4ab
       IV   2a + 2b
       (A)   I only   (B)   I and II only
       (C)   I and IV only   (D)   IV only

29.   On a multiple-choice test each correct response was assigned a value of 6 points.
       Incorrect responses got no points. Scores were based only on the number of
       correct responses and the 6 points assigned to each correct response. Which
       of the formulas below represents a relationship between the number of correct
       responses C on the test and the score S?
       (A) $S = C + 6$ (B) $S = \frac{1}{6}C$ (C) $C = 6S$ (D) $S = 6C$

OPEN-ENDED QUESTION

30.   In New Jersey a sales tax of $0.06 on every dollar is charged on certain items.
       Make up some sample **models** of this problem. For example, find the
       cost including sales tax of the following items:
       $300 television $40 camera $50 football
       Let T = the cost of an item excluding sales tax. Write a formula for the cost of
       any item including sales tax.

REVIEW

1.   What symbol is in the 79th position of the following pattern?
      LATINLATINLATIN...

2.   Insert the appropriate inequality symbol < or >: 2.8^3 ? 1.6^9

3.   What is the units digit in the 43rd term of the sequence of $4^1, 4^2, 4^3, 4^4, 4^5, ...$?

4.   What is the next larger palindrome after the palindrome number 5243993425?

2.3 Number Line Patterns

OBJECTIVES   To name the coordinate of a point on a number line

To use positive and negative numbers to describe real-ife situations

To insert the appropriate inequality symbol between two signed numbers

To graph points on a number line

DISCOVERY   Suppose someone said that the largest number in the world is 1,000,000. How could you prove that this statement is **false**?

Do this with an example of why you think you are correct.

Whole numbers can be written in order as 1, 2, 3, 4, 5, 6, 7, ...

The dots ... , as you have seen from examples of patterns, mean go on forever.

So, there is no such thing as a **largest** number.

The geometric figure at the right is called a **RAY**.
This ray begins at point A. The arrow indicates that the
ray goes on forever.

Whole numbers can be graphed on the ray as
shown at the right.

At the right, the point B is associated with or
COORDINATED with the number 8.

B is called the **graph** of the number 8.

8 is called the **COORDINATE** of the point B.

Sometimes you will be given a number line with only two numbers actually graphed.

You will then be asked to **estimate** the coordinate for an indicated point.

DISCOVERY   The coordinate of the point indicated by the arrow is between what two whole numbers?

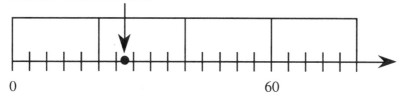

EXAMPLE 1   The coordinate of the point indicated by the arrow is between what two whole numbers? (Only a portion of the ray is shown.)

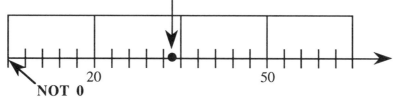

Strategy   First find the length of each of the tiny subdivisions between 20 and 50. The method is indicated in the diagram below.

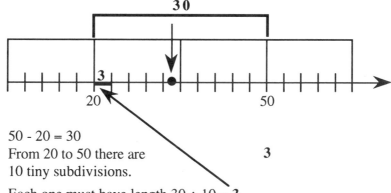

50 - 20 = 30
From 20 to 50 there are
10 tiny subdivisions.   **3**

Each one must have length 30 ÷ 10 = **3**.

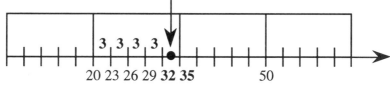

Solution   Therefore, the coordinate of the indicated point is between **32** and **35**.

A real-life example of a number ray is a thermometer.

The numbers on the ray below represent temperatures measured in degrees.

What would be wrong with the horizontal thermometer shown below if used to measure temperatures on very cold winter days?

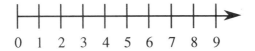

You would not be able to measure temperatures **below zero**!

So, let's extend the ray in the **opposite** direction.

Then point B corresponds to 1 degree **below zero**:   **-1 degrees**.

-1 degree is read as **negative 1 degree**.

Point D corresponds to a temperature of 4 degrees **above 0**.

The temperature is read as **positive 4 degrees.**

Point C corresponds to a temperature of 4 degrees **below 0**.

The temperature is read as **negative 4 degrees.**

The number line below shows the following:

        zero: the number corresponding to the point called the **origin,**

        negative numbers to the left of zero,

        positive numbers to the right of zero.

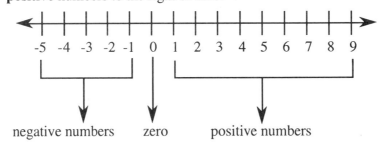

The numbers ... -4, -3, -2, -1, 0, 1, 2, 3, 4, ... are called **integers.**

Integers are whole numbers and their **opposites**. For example, the opposite of 2 is -2.

The **negative** integers -1, -2, and -3 are read as negative 1, negative 2, and negative 3.

The **positive** integers 1, 2, and 3 are read as positive 1, positive 2, and positive 3.

Zero is neither positive nor negative.

Integers can be used to describe real-life situations.

EXAMPLE 2   Name the integer that describes each situation.

          (a)   a loss of 4 points in a game   (b)   a gain in weight of 3 lb

Solution   (a)   -4   (b)   3

                        Read as **negative** 4.   Read as **positive** 3.

                                                     or simply 3.

EXAMPLE 3   Name the coordinates of the points graphed.

Solution   0 is the coordinate of A.

                6 is the coordinate of B.

                -3 is the coordinate of C.

EXAMPLE 4   Graph the points with coordinates -5 , 2, and $-3\frac{1}{2}$.

                Label these points as P, R, and Q.

Solution

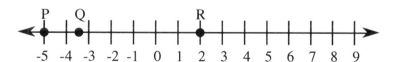

Inequalities can be used to describe the relationship between two integers.

On the number line above, 2 < 6.   On the number line, 8 > 3.

Notice that 2 is to the **left** of 6.   Notice that 8 is to the **right** of 3.

On a number line: numbers to the **left** of a number are **less** than that number, and

                         numbers to the **right** of a number are **greater** than that number.

EXAMPLE 5   Insert the appropriate inequality symbol to make each statement true.

-4 ? 3   -5 ? -1   3 ? -5

Solution
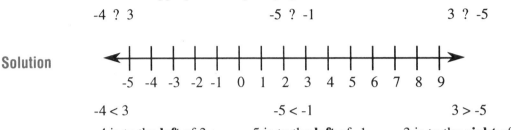
-5 -4 -3 -2 -1 0 1 2 3 4 5 6 7 8 9

-4 < 3   -5 < -1   3 > -5

-4 is to the **left** of 3   -5 is to the **left** of -1   3 is to the **right** of -5

You can insert the proper inequality betweeen two integers without using a number line. Think in terms of temperatures.

For example, -7 ? 4.

   7° **below zero** is **colder** than 4° **above zero**.

   7° **below zero** is a **lower** temperature than 4° **above zero**.

   Therefore, -7 **<** 4.

SUMMARY

Use the drawing below to answer exercises 1-2.

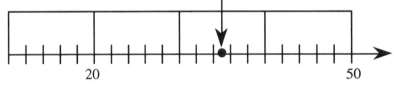
20   50

1.   How do you find the length of each tiny subdivision?
2.   How do you find what numbers the coordinate of the point indicated by the arrow is between?

3.   What kind of numbers are used to represent temperatures below zero?
4.   Give a practical illustration, other than temperature, of something that can be described by a negative number.
5.   How do you graph a point with coordinate - $4\frac{1}{2}$?
6.   How do you read each of the following?
   (a)   -6   (b)   8

7.   Is a number to the left of -8 greater than or less than -8?

8.   Explain, in terms of temperature, how to insert the correct inequality symbol to make -9 ? 12 true.

CLASSROOM PRACTICE

The coordinate of the point indicated by the arrow is between ? (Ex. 1-2)

1.

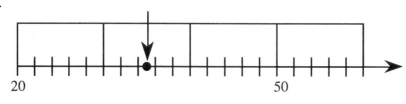

    (A)   20 and 22   (B)   30 and 32   (C)   31 and 33   (D)   34 and 36

2.

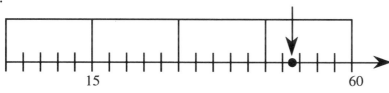

    (A)   33 and 36   (B)   45 and 48   (C)   48 and 51   (D)   50 and 53

Name the integer that describes each situation.

3.   a loss of 6 points in a game   4. a gain of 3 lb in weight

5.   130 meters below sea level   6. a drop of 4° in temperature

Name the coordinates of the points graphed. (Ex. 7-12)

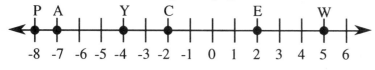

7.   A   8. W   9. P   10.   E   11.   Y   12.   C

Graph the points with the given coordinates on a number line. (Ex. 13-16)

13.   I: -3   14.   H: 5   15.   M: $-2\frac{1}{2}$ 16.   T: $5\frac{1}{2}$

Insert the correct inequality symbol to make each statement true. (Ex. 17-20)

17.   -5 ? -1   18.   7 ? -3   19.   -15 ? 12   20.   6 ? -8

WRITTEN EXERCISES

The coordinate of the point indicated by the arrow is between ? (Ex. 1-2)

1.

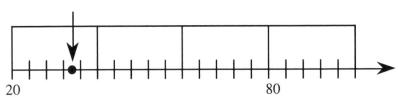

(A)   23 and 24   (B)   26 and 28   (C)   32 and 36   (D)   43 and 44

2.

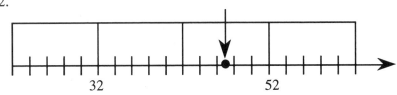

(A)   46 and 48   (B)   44 and 46   (C)   40 and 42   (D)   39 and 40

Name the integer that describes each situation.

3.   a rise of $0.10 in cost of gallon of milk   4.   800 meters below sea level

5.   a gain of 7 points in a stock   6.   a withdrawal of $80 from a
       on the stock exchange   checking account

Name the coordinates of the points graphed on the number line below. (Ex. 7-12)

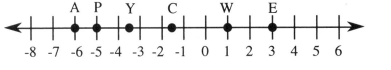

7.   W   8. E   9. Y   10.   P   11.   A   12.   C

Graph the points with the given coordinates on a number line. (Ex.13-16)

13.   J: -7   14.   B: 3   15.   R: $-3\frac{1}{2}$ 16.   U: $4\frac{1}{2}$

Insert the correct inequality symbol to make each statement true. (Ex. 17-20)

17.   -7 ? -3   18.   -5 ? 10   19.   15 ? -5   20.   -6 ? -8

OPEN-ENDED QUESTION

21.   Find the coordinate of the point indicated by the arrow.

        Write an explanation of how you solved this problem. Indicate each step so that
        another student unable to solve the problem could easily follow your method.

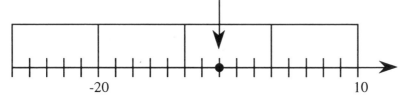

REVIEW

1.   The approximate value of 3.98745^4 is ?

Evaluate each for the given values of the variables.

2. $\frac{2}{3}$ x + 12 for x = 9   3. $4x^2$ for x = 2

4.   If the pattern below were continued, how many squares would be in the seventh
        figure?

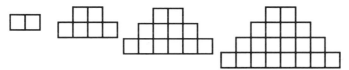

5.   At the right are three views of a die.

        The digits 1-6 appear once

        on the faces of the die.

        What digit is opposite the 3?

        1st view   2nd view   3rd view

2.4 Addition on a Number Line

OBJECTIVE   To add integers using a number line

To add integers using a calculator

You can use a number line to add numbers. For example, you can show the sum 4 + 3.

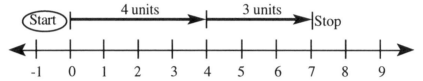

The addition is shown in terms of moves on a number line.

Start at 0, move 4 units to the right (*positive direction*) to 4.

Then move 3 more units to the right (*positive direction*) to 7.

So, 4 + 3 = 7.

This is read as **positive 4 plus positive 3 equals positive 7**.

The same procedure can be used to find the sum of two negative numbers, as shown in Example 1 below.

Notice that a *negative number* indicates a move to the *left* , which is the *negative direction* .

EXAMPLE 1   Add -5 + (-3) using a number line.

Strategy   Start at 0.

Move 5 units to the left (negative direction) to -5.

Then move 3 more units to the left (negative direction) to -8.

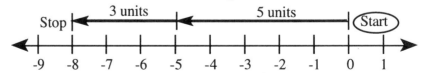

Solution   The sum is -8.

EXAMPLE 2   Add 5 + (-7) using a number line.

Strategy   Start at 0.

Move 5 units to the right (positive direction) to 5.

Then move 7 units to the left (negative direction) to -2.

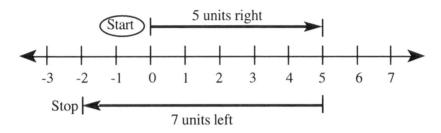

Solution   The sum is -2.

EXAMPLE 3   Add -8 + 9 using a number line.

Strategy   Start at 0.

Move 8 units to the left (negative direction) to -8.

Then move 9 units to the right (positive direction) to 1.

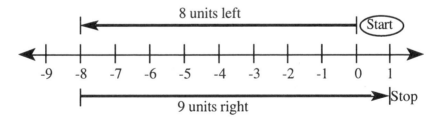

Solution   The sum is 1.

DISCOVERY   Find, on a calculator, the key marked **+/-**.

Enter 6   **Enter +/-**

What is the purpose of the **+/-** key?

How can you use this key to add -18 + 43?

EXAMPLE 4   Use a calculator to add -19 + (-49).

Enter 19   Enter +/-   Enter +   Enter 49   Enter +/-
Enter =   Read -68

Solution   So, by calculator, -19 + (-49) = -68.

SUMMARY

Tell how to use a number line to find each of the following sums. (Ex. 1-4)

1.   -7 + (-3)   2. -9 + 2   3. -8 + (-4)   4. -6 + 6

5.   How do you enter a negative number on a calculator?

How can you use a calculator to find each sum? (Ex. 6-8)

        6.   -83 + 19   7. -55 + (-49)   8. 102 + (-74)

CLASSROOM PRACTICE

Add.

1.   -8 + 12   2.   8 + 5   3.   -6 + (-8)   4.   7 + (-4)
5.   -6 + (-4)   6.   -1 + 7   7.   9 + (-2)   8.   -5 + (-3)
9.   7 + (-2)   10. 4 + 9   11. 6 + (-9)   12. -3 + (-7)
13. 8 + (-9)   14. 6 + (-2)   15. -4 + (-5)   16. 6 + 9

        17.   -89 + (-15)   18.   -79 + 123   19.   104 + (-59)

WRITTEN EXERCISES

Add.

1.   -4 + (-6)   2.   -6 + 2   3.   5 + (-9)   4.   3 + 8

5.	-10 + (-3)	6.	11 + 5	7.	12 + (-9)	8.	-3 + 11
9.	4 + 5	10.	-4 + 4	11.	-6 + (-1)	12.	-1 + (-8)
13.	-3 + 8	14.	2 + (-6)	15.	-6 + 2	16.	11 + (-3)
17.	-9 + 9	18.	-9 + 10	19.	-23 + 23	20.	-17 + (-5)

21.	-92 + (-35)	22.	-59 + 113	23.	204 + (-89)
24.	-1.07 + 83	25.	-1.12 + (-0.046)	26.	-0.0004 + 1.703

OPEN-ENDED QUESTION

27. Use a calculator to complete the table at the right. Look for a pattern for finding the sum without using a calculator or a number line.

If the signs are different for two integers being added, how do you get the numerical value of the answer? How do you know what sign to give the answer?

Repeat the work above for this table.

State a rule that appears to work for adding two signed numbers with different signs: one positive and one negative.

Use this rule to explain how to add -19 + 43 without using a calculator or number line.

Sum	Answer
5 + (-8)	?
5 + (-9)	?
5 + (-10)	?
5 + (-12)	?

Sum	Answer
-5 + 9	?
-5 + 10	?
-5 + 14	?
-5 + 16	?

REVIEW

1. Find the perimeter of the rectangle with length 18 ft and width 9 ft

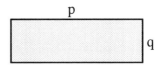

2. Mr. Tomlison is paid a weekly salary of $140 and a commission of $120 on each car he sells. If T represents his total pay for the week and C the number of cars he sells, which formula below describes the way to find his total weekly pay?

(A)   T = 120(C + 140)   (B)   T = 140 + 120C

(C)   T = 140C + 120   (D)   T = 1404 + 120 + C

Evaluate for the given values of the variables.

3.   5a - 7 for a = 9   4. $4t^2$ for t = 3

5.   Find the area of a circle with radius 6 cm.

$$A = 3.14r^2$$

6.   Simplify $35 - 4 \cdot 2^3 + 45 \div 9$.

Find the next term in each sequence.

7.   5, 9, 14, 23, 37, ...   8.   11, 23, 47, 95, ...   9.   28, 24, 20, 16, ...

10.   Which of the plane figures below can be folded to form a box or cube?

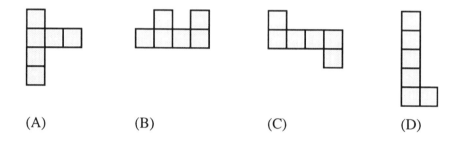

(A)   (B)   (C)   (D)

11.   There are four different figures in the spiral below. If they are labeled
       A, B, C, and D in the order in which they first appear, (beginning at **Start** and
       going clockwise), what letters represent the missing figures?

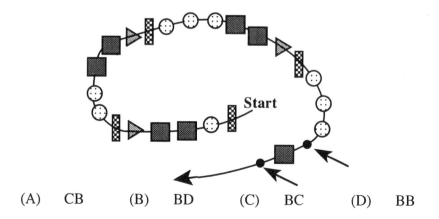

(A)   CB   (B)   BD   (C)   BC   (D)   BB

2.5 Rules for Adding Signed Numbers

OBJECTIVES   To use the rules for adding signed numbers to find the sum of two or more signed numbers

To solve word problems involving addition of signed numbers

On the number line below, notice that the integers **-5** and **5** are on opposite sides of 0 and are the same distance from 0: **5 units**.

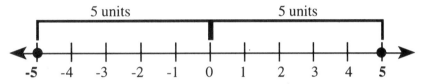

5 is **5 units** to the right of 0.

-5 is **5 units** to the left of 0.

To indicate distance only, and **NOT** direction, use the **absolute value** of a number.

You say that the absolute value of -5 ⎫
the absolute value of 5 ⎬➤ is 5.

There is a symbol for the phrase **the absolute value of.**

| |

So, you write **the absolute value of -5** this way:

|-5|

EXAMPLE 1   Find (a) |-8| and (b) |8|

Strategy |-8| is the **distance** of -8 from 0. |8| is the **distance** of 8 from 0.

Solution |-8| = 8 |8| = 8

You might think of the absolute value of a signed number as its value **without** the **sign**.

  |-13| = 13 |6| = 6 |-2| = 2 |7| is 7 |-23| = 23

To add -329 + 178 would be very difficult using a number line.

Now you will use the idea of **absolute value** of an integer to develop some simple rules for adding signed numbers **without** using a number line.

Recall from the last lesson, you found 4 + 3 using a number line.

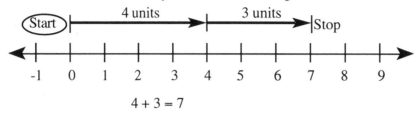

4 + 3 = 7

Also, from Example 2 of the last lesson, you found -3 + (-5) using a number line.

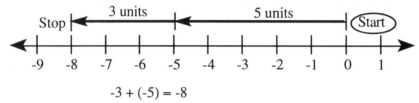

-3 + (-5) = -8

The two examples above suggest a pattern.

In each case the two numbers had the same sign: 4 + 3   -3 + (-5)

both numbers **positive**   both numbers **negative**

Pattern:

4 + 3 = 7   **RULE:**   **Add the absolute values.**

                        Give the sum the same sign as the sign of the numbers
                        being added.

-3 + (-5) = -8   **RULE:**   **Add the absolute values.**   **|-3| + |-5|**

                                            3 + 5 = 8

                        Give the sum the same sign as the sign of the numbers
                        being added: <u>negative</u>. So, -3 + (-5) = -8

Adding numbers   **To add two numbers with the same sign:**

with the same sign   **1. Add their absolute values.**

                        2. Give the sum the same sign as the sign of each number.

You can now find a sum like -24 + (-7) by using the rule from the previous page.

EXAMPLE 2   Add -24 + (-7).

Strategy   The signs are the same, both negative.

-24 + (-7)   **Add the absolute values: |-24| + |-7|**

24 + 7 = 31

Solution   -31   **Give the sum the same sign as the sign of each number, negative.**

Let's try to discover a rule for adding signed numbers with unlike or different signs.

DISCOVERY   Use either a number line or calculator to complete each table at the right.

Sum	Answer
5 + (-8)	?
4 + (-9)	?
6 + (-10)	?
8 + (-12)	?

Look for two patterns involving absolute values for each table:

(1)   How do you get the value of each sum **without** the sign?

Sum	Answer
-3 + 9	?
-7 + 10	?
-2 + 14	?
-8 + 16	?

(2)   How do you then determine the **sign** of the answer?

Try to write the rule for adding signed numbers when the numbers have different or unlike signs.

The **DISCOVERY** above suggests a rule for adding 6 + (-10) where the signs are **unlike**.

6 + (-10)   **Subtract the absolute values: |-10| - |6|**

10 - 6 = 4

-4   **Give the result the same sign as the sign of the number with the larger absolute value, ⁻10, <u>negative.</u>**

Below is the rule for adding signed numbers with **unlike** or **different** signs.

Adding numbers with unlike or different signs	To add two numbers with unlike or different signs: 1. **Subtract their absolute values.** 2. **Give the result the same sign as number with the larger absolute value.**

EXAMPLE 3   Add -26 + 5.

Strategy   The signs are **unlike**.

-26 + 5   **Subtract the absolute values: |-26| - |5|**
                           26 - 5 = 21
                           Give the result the same sign as the sign of
                           the number with the larger absolute value,
Solution   -21   **-26, <u>negative</u>.**

EXAMPLE 4   Add -16 + (-14).

Strategy   The signs are **like**.

-16 + (-14)   **Add the absolute values: |-16| + |14|**
                           16 + 14 = 30
                           Give the result the same sign as the sign of
Solution   -30   **each number, <u>negative</u>.**

Below, is a summary of the two rules for adding signed numbers.

RULES for ADDING SIGNED NUMBERS	
To add signed numbers with the same sign: 1. Add the absolute values. 2. Keep the same sign as the sign of each number.	To add signed numbers with different signs: 1. Subtract the absolute values. 2. Take the sign of the number with the larger absolute value.

Adding signed numbers has many real-life applications.

One of these is illustrated in the next example.

EXAMPLE 5   A submarine was at a depth of 300 m below sea level.

It rose 100 m. What number describes the new depth of the submarine?

Strategy   Represent the new position in terms of adding signed numbers.

300 m **below**   **rose** 100 m

-300 m + 100 m   **The signs are unlike.**

Subtract the absolute values: |-300| - |100|

300 - 100 = 200

Give the result the same sign as the sign of

the number with the larger absolute value,

Solution   -200 m   **-300, negative**

SUMMARY

1.   What is meant by the absolute value of a number?

2.   What is the absolute value of -8?

How do you apply the rules for adding signed numbers to finding each sum?

3.   -6 + (-8)   4. -9 + 10   5. 12 + (-8)   6. 5 + (-9)

CLASSROOM PRACTICE

Add.

1.   5 + 9   2.   -7 + (-8)   3.   -6 + (-8)   4.   6 + 9

5.   5 + (-8)   6.   -12 + 6   7.   6 + (-13)   8.   -14 + 9

9.   15 + (-9)   10.   -25 + 8   11.   14 + (-19)   12.   -13 + 6

13.   -17 + (-12)   14.   23 + (-50)   15.   -38 + 60   16.   -23 + (-32)

17.   In the morning, Mrs. Campbell withdrew $125 from her account. In the afternoon
she withdrew $225. What number describes the net change in her account?

18.   A football team had a 4-yard gain followed by a 7-yard loss.
        Find the resulting gain or loss.

WRITTEN EXERCISES

Add

1.	5 + 8	2.	-4 + (-6)	3.	-8 + (-2)	4.	5 + (-13)
5.	-11 + (-8)	6.	-22 + 4	7.	-23 + (-17)	8.	34 + (-54)
9.	32 + (-15)	10.	-16 + 43	11.	-18 + (-46)	12.	13 + (-40)
13.	-39 + (-31)	14.	43 + (-70)	15.	-41 + (-19)	16.	-70 + 39

17.   (-4.1) + (-3.99)   18.   (-3.6) + 40.0   19.   17.34 + (-20.0)

20.   The temperature was -5° at midnight. It dropped 7° by 3:00 A.M.
        Find the temperature at that time.

21.   Shirley gained 3 lb in one month. The next month she lost 7 lb.
        Find the net gain or loss.

REVIEW

Evaluate each for the given values of the variables. (Ex. 1-2)

1. $\frac{4}{5}x + 12$ for x = 15   2. $6x^2$ for x = 2

OPEN-ENDED QUESTION

3.   For the pattern below, the geometric process being repeated to get from each
       stage to the next stage is: *For each unshaded triangle, find the middle point of
       each of its sides, connect to form a new triangle, and shade the interior of that
       new triangle.* Sketch the next triangle. How many unshaded triangles are
       present in the figure at stage 4? Write an explanation of your solution.

     stage 1   stage 2   stage 3

2.6 A New Look at Adding Signed Numbers

OBJECTIVES   To add two or more signed numbers

To represent the sum of signed numbers without the parentheses symbol

To solve word problems involving signed numbers

In this lesson you will extend the idea of adding signed numbers to adding more than two numbers. You will also see a short cut for indicating addition of signed numbers without the need to write the + ( ) notation.

First, recall that 5 + 6 + 2 is the same as 2 + 6 + 5 or 5 + 2 + 6.

You can add in **any order**.

Assume that signed numbers can also be added in any order.

Sometimes it is easier to add signed numbers by grouping like signs together.

EXAMPLE 1   Add -3 + 8 + (-7).

Strategy	-3 + 8 + (-7)	**There are two negatives.**
	(-3 + (-7)) + 8	**Group the negatives together.**
	-10 + 8	**Use rule for adding integers with like signs.**
		Add absolute values. Keep same sign as that of each.
Solution	-2	**Use rule for adding integers with unlike signs.**
		Subtract absolute values. Take sign of larger.

In Example 1, you added the numbers -3, 8, and -7.

To simplify the writing, you can omit the + ( ) notation.

Thus, -3 + 8 + (-7) can be written as

-3 + 8 - 7.

Read -3 ⤴ + 8 ⤴ -7 as

negative 3 **plus** positive 8 **plus** negative 7.
The **plus ( )** is **omitted.**

EXAMPLE 2   Simplify 8 - 9 + 6.

Strategy   8 - 9 + 6
                      8 + 6 - 9   **Group positives together.**
                       14 - 9   **Think: 14 + (-9).**
Solution   5   **Use rule for unlike signs.**

EXAMPLE 3   Simplify -14 + 21 - 9.

Strategy   -14 + 21 - 9
                     -14 - 9 + 21   **Group negatives together.**
                       -23 + 21   **Think: -14 + (-9): Like signs.**
Solution   -2   **Use rule for unlike signs.**

EXAMPLE 4   Simplify -5 + 8 - 6 + 4.

Strategy   -5 + 8 - 6 + 4
                     -5 - 6 + 8 + 4   **Group like signs together.**

                       -11 + 12   **Think: -5 - 6 = -5 + (-6) = -11   8 + 4 = 12.**
Solution   1   **Use rule for unlike signs.**

EXAMPLE 5   An elevator on the eighth floor goes up 3 floors, then down 5 floors,

                     then up 2 floors, then down 7 floors. Where is the elevator now?

Strategy   on eighth floor   up 3   down 5   up 2   down 7
                            8   + 3   - 5   + 2   -7
                            8 + 3 + 2 - 5 - 7   **Group like signs together.**
                              13 -   12
                                   1
Solution   Thus, the elevator is now on the 1st floor.

SUMMARY

1. How do you read an expression like -5 + 4 - 8 - 2 + 5?
2. What is a good first step in simplifying an expression like -5 + 4 - 8 - 2 + 5?
3. What are the steps in simplifying the expression -7 + 6 - 5 + 4 - 8?

CLASSROOM PRACTICE

Simplify.

1.	3 - 8	2.	-7 + 6	3.	-5 - 9	4.	2 - 8
5.	4 - 3 + 10	6.	-8 + 12 - 7	7.	-3 - 1 - 6	8.	3 - 7 + 9
9.	4 - 10	10.	-9 + 3	11.	-3 - 9	12.	-8 + 13
13.	-6 - 9 + 1	14.	5 + 6 - 17	15.	-16 - 31 + 3	16.	-28 + 3 + 12

17. -8 + 9 - 7 + 12   18. -8 - 4 + 5 + 12   19. -19 + 13 - 4 + 4 - 6

20. In one month Mike gained 2 lb. The next month he lost 6 lb. He lost 3 more lb the third month. Find the net gain or loss.

21. A team scored 5 points. Then there was a 2-point penalty. This was followed by a 3-point score. Find the net gain or loss.

WRITTEN EXERCISES

Simplify.

1.	4 - 10	2.	-8 + 12	3.	-7 - 8	4.	3 - 11
5.	5 - 2 + 12	6.	-7 + 14 - 8	7.	-4 - 5 - 3	8.	2 - 8 + 12
9.	3 - 13	10.	-8 + 6	11.	-6 - 9	12.	-7 + 15
13.	-5 - 9 + 16	14.	4 + 9 - 16	15.	-18 - 33 + 5	16.	7 - 31 + 21

17. -9 + 5 - 74+ 16   18. -6 - 9 + 10 - 12   19. -29 + 13 - 5 + 5 - 8

20. The temperature was -5° Fahrenheit at midnight. It dropped 7° by 3:00 A.M. and then rose 15° by noon. Find the temperature at that time.

21. The lowest point in Death Valley, California, is 276 ft below sea level. A hot-air balloon was floating 83 ft above this point. It climbed 68 ft higher and then dropped 72 ft. Find the balloon's altitude relative to sea level.

OPEN-ENDED QUESTION

22.   You are playing a game in which you move a chip on a number line. Where you move the chip is determined by the cards you draw from a pack. Each card has an integer printed on it. Your chip is now at the location indicated below.

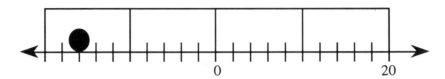

On each turn, you move your chip to the location with its coordinate equal to the sum of the coordinate of your current location and the integer on the card you draw.

(a)   Find the coordinate of the location of your chip now.

(b)   Suppose you got on your present location after 3 moves. What 3 integer cards might you have drawn?

REVIEW

1.   Simplify $44 - 4 \cdot 3^2 + 35 \div 7$.

2.   Evaluate $25 - \frac{3}{4}a$ for $a = 16$.

3.   What is the units digit in the 46th term of the sequence $7^1, 7^2, 7^3, 7^4, \ldots$?

4.   Juan got an answer of about 4.90 when he entered 24 on his calculator and pressed the $\sqrt{}$ key. He stopped to think if the answer was reasonable. Which of the following is the most likely explanation for him to believe that the calculator answer is or is not reasonable?

(A)   It is reasonable since 24 is an even number.

(B)   It is not reasonable since the answer should be only a little more than 4.

(C)   It is reasonable since 24 is a whole number.

(D)   It is reasonable since 4 squared is 16 and 5 squared is 25.

2.7 Multiplication of Signed Numbers

OBJECTIVES   To find the product of two or more signed numbers

To simplify products of signed numbers involving exponents

To simplify products involving variables

To estimate products of numbers on a number line

From arithmetic you know that the product of any two positive numbers is positive.

Thus, $8 \cdot 6 = 48$.

You have seen the importance of using patterns to discover rules.
The **DISCOVERY ACTIVITY** below will help you discover the rule for multiplying
signed numbers with **unlike** signs such as $-4 \cdot 5$.

DISCOVERY   Examine the pattern below.

Complete the pattern and use it to write the rule for multiplying
numbers with **unlike** signs.

$3 \cdot 3 = 9$

$3 \cdot 2 = 6$

$3 \cdot 1 = 3$ **The product <u>decreases</u> by 3 each time.**

$3 \cdot 0 = 0$

$3 \cdot -1 = ?$

$3 \cdot -2 = ?$

$3 \cdot -3 = ?$

Assume that the order of multiplication makes no difference in the product of two signed
numbers . Thus, $3 \cdot -2$ is the same as $-2 \cdot 3$. Each has the same answer, -6.

To multiply two numbers with unlike signs:

1. **Multiply their absolute values.**

2. **The sign of the product is negative**

    negative · positive = negative.   **positive · negative = negative**

$\quad$ **(-) · (+)   = (-)** $\qquad$ **(-) · (+)   = (-)**

EXAMPLE 1   Multiply each:

(a) 6 · -8   (b) -9 · 3

Solution   (a)   6 · -8 = -48   **pos. · neg. = neg.**

(b)   -9 · 3 = -27   **neg. · pos. = neg.**

EXAMPLE 2   Multiply $\frac{3}{4}$ · -20

Multiply absolute values.

Solution $\frac{3}{4}$ · -20 = - 15   **pos. · neg. = neg.** $\frac{3}{4}$ · 20 = $\frac{3}{\cancel{4}}$ · $\cancel{20}^{5}$ = 15

1

You already know that the product of two positive numbers is positive.

Now you will use a pattern to discover the rule for multiplying two negative numbers.

DISCOVERY   Examine the pattern below.

Complete the pattern and use it to write the rule for multiplying signed numbers with the **same** sign, such as -5 · -3 and 4 · 8.

The pattern uses what you have just learned: (-) · (+) = (-).

-3 · 3 = -9

-3 · 2 = -6

-3 · 1 = -3   **The product <u>increases</u> by 3 each time.**

-3 · 0 = 0

-3 · -1 = ?

-3 · -2 = ?

-3 · -3 = ?

To multiply two numbers with the same sign:
1. **Multiply their absolute values.**
2. **The sign of the product is positive.**

   negative · negative = positive   positive · positive = positive

   (-) · (-)   = (+)   (+) · (+)   = (+)

You have used a raised dot to indicate multiplication.

Multiplication can also be indicated by parentheses as shown below.

$$5 \cdot \text{-3 can be written as}$$

$$5(\text{-3}) \text{ which is read as 5 times negative 3.}$$

In this case there is no need to write a raised dot between 5 and the parentheses.

This second way of indicating multiplication is helpful when working with decimals.

For example, -7 · 0.54 might be confusing with **two dots.**

You could instead write -7(0.54).

The next example uses both ways of indicating multiplication .

EXAMPLE 3   Multiply each:

(a) -4(-8)   (b) 6 · -3

-4(-8) means -4 · -8   6 · -3

Solution   (a) 32   **(neg.) · (neg.) = (pos.)**   (b) -18   **(pos.) · (neg.) = (neg.)**

Notice the end results of the following patterns:

$7 = \mathbf{1} \cdot 7$

$4 = \mathbf{1} \cdot 4$

$12 = \mathbf{1} \cdot 12$ **Multiplication by 1 does not change the identity of a number.**

$\mathbf{a} = \mathbf{1} \cdot \mathbf{a}$

$\text{-7} = \mathbf{\text{-1}} \cdot 7$

$\text{-4} = \mathbf{\text{-1}} \cdot 4$

$\text{-12} = \mathbf{\text{-1}} \cdot 12$

$\mathbf{\text{-a}} = \mathbf{\text{-1}} \cdot \mathbf{a}$

The results above suggest the following rules.

It is understood that **a** means **1 times a**	It is understood that **-a** means **-1 times a**
a = **1**· a or 1a	-a = **-1** · a or -1a

EXAMPLE 4   Evaluate $(-x)(-x)$ for $x = -4$.

Strategy	$(-x)(-x) = (-1 \cdot x)(-1 \cdot x)$	**Use $-x = -1 \cdot x$.**
	$= (-1 \cdot -4)(-1 \cdot -4)$	**Substitute -4 for x.**
	$= \quad (4)(4)$	**(neg.) $\cdot$ (neg.) = (pos.)**
Solution	$= \quad\quad 16$	

EXAMPLE 5   Evaluate $(-x)^2$ for $x = -5$.

Strategy	$(-x)^2 = (-1 \cdot x)^2$	**Use $-x = -1 \cdot x$.**
	$= (-1 \cdot -5)^2$	**Substitute -5 for x.**
	$= \quad (5)^2$	**(neg.) $\cdot$ (neg.) = (pos.)**
Solution	$= \quad\quad 25$	

EXAMPLE 6   Evaluate $-x^2$ for $x = -2$.

Strategy	$-x^2 = -1 \cdot x^2$	**-1 is understood.**
	$= -1 \cdot x \cdot x$	
	$= -1 \cdot -2 \cdot -2$	**Substitute -2 for x.**
	$= -1 \cdot \quad 4$	**(neg.) $\cdot$ (neg.) = (pos.)**
Solution	$= \quad -4$	**(neg.) $\cdot$ (pos.) = (neg.)**

EXAMPLE 7   Evaluate $-2x^3$ for $x = -3$.

Strategy	$-2x^3 = -2 \cdot x \cdot x \cdot x$	**The exponent 3 effects only x, not -2.**
	$= -2 \cdot -3 \cdot -3 \cdot -3$	**Substitute -3 for x.**
	$= \quad 6 \cdot \quad 9$	**(neg.) $\cdot$ (neg.) = (pos.)**
Solution	$= \quad\quad 54$	

Estimation of products of signed numbers from a graph is illustrated in the next example.

EXAMPLE 8   Which point could represent
the product of the numbers
represented by T and V?

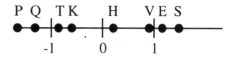

(A) E   (B)   H   (C)   K   (D)   Q

Strategy   Points between -1 and 0 could have coordinates -0.9, -0.8, -0.7, -0.6, ...etc.
T is negative, just to the right of -1. So, estimate T with coordinate **-0.9**.

V is close to 1 and positive. Estimate V with positive coordinate **0.9**.
Now, T · V is approximately -0.9 · 0.9 = **-0.81**.
On the number line, **-0.81** is to the **right** of **-0.9**.
Therefore, **K**, to the right of T, could represent the product.

Solution   The answer is choice (C).

SUMMARY

1.   What are two ways, indicated in this lesson, to write the product of the numbers
-8 and 5?

Tell how you detemine the sign of each of the following products.

2.   -5 · 6   3. 8 · -7   4. -6 · -9

5.   a can be written as ? · ?.
6.   -b can be written as ? · ?.

What are the steps in evaluating each of the following?

7.   -x² for x = -6   8. (-x)² for x = -7   9. (-a)(-a) for a = -9

10.   How can you estimate the
coordinate of the point Q?

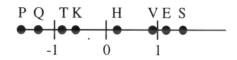

CLASSROOM PRACTICE

Multiply.

1. $-5 \cdot 8$ 2. $10(-1)$ 3. $6(-5)$ 4. $7 \cdot 8$

5. $6(-3)$ 6. $-8 \cdot 8$ 7. $4(-12)$ 8. $-6(-6)$

9. $8 \cdot 4$ 10. $-4 \cdot -7$ 11. $-10 \cdot 9$ 12. $(8)(-9)$

13. $-\frac{3}{4} \cdot 12$ 14. $-20 \cdot -\frac{4}{5}$ 15. $\frac{2}{7} \cdot -28$ 16. $(-\frac{2}{3})(-\frac{9}{10})$

17. $4(-3)^2$ 18. $-5(-2)^3$ 19. $-4(-3)^3$ 20. $-6(-4)^2$

Evaluate each for the given value of the variable.

21. $(-b)(-b)$ for $b = -9$ 22. $(-k)^2$ for $k = -8$ 23. $-a^3$ for $a = -3$

24. $-3c^5$ for $c = -2$ 25. $-6d^3$ for $d = -1$ 26. $-a^4$ for $a = -2$

Which point could represent the product of the numbers represented by:

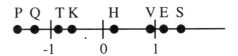

27.   T and H?

28.   Q and E?

WRITTEN EXERCISES

Multiply.

1. $-8 \cdot 7$ 2. $12(-2)$ 3. $-7(-4)$ 4. $8 \cdot 11$

5. $-9 \cdot 9$ 6. $9(-3)$ 7. $6(-12)$ 8. $-5 \cdot -9$

9. $6 \cdot 4$ 10. $-4(-13)$ 11. $-9 \cdot 7$ 12. $-13(-3)$

13. $-\frac{5}{9} \cdot 27$ 14. $\frac{3}{5} \cdot -35$ 15. $-21 \cdot \frac{3}{7}$ 16. $(-\frac{4}{5})(\frac{5}{12})$

17. $-6(-5)^2$ 18. $-2(-3)^3$ 19. $(-2)^3 \cdot (-4)^2$ 20. $(1)^5 \cdot (-3)^4$

Evaluate each for the given value of the variable.

21. $(-b)(-b)$ for $b = -8$ 22. $(-k)^3$ for $k = -5$ 23. $-a^3$ for $a = -7$

24. $-4c^7$ for $c = -2$ 25. $-d^3$ for $d = -6$ 26. $-a^4$ for $a = -3$

Which point could represent the product of the numbers represented by: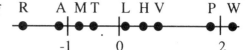

27.   M and W?

28.   H and V?

OPEN-ENDED QUESTION

29.   Numbers like 1, 3, 5, 7, 9, ... are called **odd** numbers.

Numbers like 0, 2, 4, 6, 8, ... are called **even** numbers.

Complete the data table at the right. Use the results to predict the values of $(-1)^{75}$ and $(-1)^{24}$. Explain how you reached your conclusion in terms of odd and even number exponents.

$(-1)^1$	?
$(-1)^2$	?
$(-1)^3$	?
$(-1)^4$	?
$(-1)^5$	?
$(-1)^6$	?
$(-1)^7$	?

REVIEW

Simplify.

1.   -8 + 5

2. -8 - 4 + 6

3. 9 - 12 + 5 - 4

4.   The coordinate of the point indicated by the arrow is between what two numbers ?

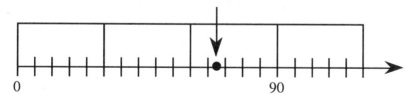

(A)   30 and 32   (B)   60 and 62   (C)   66 and 72   (D)   82 and 84

2.8 Division of Signed Numbers

OBJECTIVES   To divide signed numbers

To divide fractions

Recall the rules for **multiplying** signed numbers.

The product of two numbers with **like (same)** signs is **positive.**

(pos.)(pos.) = (pos.)   (neg.)(neg.) = (pos.)

(+)(+) = (+)   (-)(-) = (+)

The product of two numbers with **unlike** signs is **negative.**

(neg.)(pos.) = (neg)   (pos.)(neg.) = (neg.)

(-)(+) = (-)   (+)(-) = (-)

Recall how to **check** division. You check by multiplication.

For example $12 \div 4 = 3$ since $3 \cdot 4 = 12$.

Multiplication and division are **inverse** operations.

Division will **undo** multiplication.

MULTIPLICATION	**DIVISION**
$4 \cdot 2 = 8$	$8 \div 2 = 4$, or $\frac{8}{2} = 4$

You can use this relationship to discover the rules for dividing signed numbers.

MULTIPLICATION		**DIVISION**
Since $3 \cdot 2 = 6$	then	$6 \div 2 = 3$
Since $3 \cdot -2 = -6$	then	$-6 \div -2 = 3$
Since $-3 \cdot -2 = 6$	then	$6 \div -2 = -3$
Since $-3 \cdot 2 = -6$	then	$-6 \div 2 = -3$

These examples suggest that the rules for dividing signed numbers are the **same** as the rules above for multiplying signed numbers.

These rules are stated on the next page.

Dividing Numbers

The quotient of two numbers with **like** signs is **positive**.

$$\frac{\text{positive}}{\text{positive}} = \text{positive} \qquad \frac{\text{negative}}{\text{negative}} = \text{positive}$$

The quotient of two numbers with **unlike** signs is **negative**.

$$\frac{\text{negative}}{\text{positive}} = \text{negative} \qquad \frac{\text{positive}}{\text{negative}} = \text{negative}$$

EXAMPLE 1   Divide.   (a) $\dfrac{27}{3}$ (b) $-6 \div -2$

Solution   (a) $\dfrac{27}{3} = 9$ $\dfrac{\textbf{pos.}}{\textbf{pos.}} = \textbf{pos.}$

(b) $-6 \div -2 = 3$ **neg. ÷ neg. = pos.**

EXAMPLE 2   Divide.   (a) $\dfrac{-36}{4}$ (b) $2.4 \div -0.08$

Solution   (a) $\dfrac{-36}{4} = -9$ $\dfrac{\textbf{neg.}}{\textbf{pos.}} = \textbf{neg.}$

(b) $2.4 \div -0.08 = -30.$ **pos. ÷ neg. = neg.**

$$\begin{array}{r} 30. \\ 0.08\overline{)2.40.} \end{array}$$

EXAMPLE 3   Which of the following is not equivalent to the other three?

(A) $-\left(\dfrac{-5}{-2}\right)$ (B) $\dfrac{-5}{2}$

(C) $-\left(\dfrac{-5}{2}\right)$ (D) $\dfrac{5}{-2}$

Strategy   Use the rules for dividing signed numbers to find the sign of each.

(continued on next page)

(A) $-\left(\dfrac{-5}{-2}\right) = -\left(\dfrac{5}{2}\right)$ $\dfrac{\textbf{neg.}}{\textbf{neg.}} = \textbf{pos.}$

$= -1 \cdot \left(\dfrac{5}{2}\right)$ **-a = -1a: -1 is understood.**

$= -\dfrac{5}{2}$ **neg. · pos. = neg.**

(B) $\dfrac{-5}{2} = -\dfrac{5}{2}$ $\dfrac{\textbf{neg}}{\textbf{pos.}} = \textbf{neg.}$

(C) $-\left(\dfrac{-5}{2}\right) = -\left(-\dfrac{5}{2}\right)$ $\dfrac{\textbf{neg}}{\textbf{pos.}} = \textbf{neg.}$

$= -1 \cdot \left(-\dfrac{5}{2}\right)$ **-a = -1a: -1 is understood.**

$= \dfrac{5}{2}$ **neg. · neg. = pos.**

(D) $\dfrac{5}{-2} = -\dfrac{5}{2}$ $\dfrac{\textbf{pos.}}{\textbf{neg.}} = \textbf{neg.}$

Three of the choices are $-\dfrac{5}{2}$. But, choice (C) is $\dfrac{5}{2}$, **not** $-\dfrac{5}{2}$.

Solution   Thus, choice (C) is **not** equivalent to the other three.

Recall, any quotient or **division** can be expressed as a product or **multiplication**.

divide   multiply

$$\dfrac{3}{4} \div \dfrac{2}{7} = \dfrac{3}{4} \cdot \dfrac{7}{2}$$ **Multiply by the reciprocal of $\dfrac{2}{7}$.**

EXAMPLE 4   Divide. $\dfrac{10}{9} \div -\dfrac{5}{3}$

Strategy $\dfrac{10}{9} \div -\dfrac{5}{3} = -\left(\dfrac{10}{9} \div \dfrac{5}{3}\right)$ **pos. ÷ neg. = neg.**

$= -\left(\dfrac{10}{9} \cdot \dfrac{3}{5}\right)$ $\dfrac{10}{9} \cdot \dfrac{3}{5} = \dfrac{10}{\cancel{9}} \cdot \dfrac{\cancel{3}}{5} = \dfrac{\cancel{10}}{\cancel{9}} \cdot \dfrac{\cancel{3}}{\cancel{5}} = \dfrac{2 \cdot 1}{3 \cdot 1} = \dfrac{2}{3}$

Solution $= -\dfrac{2}{3}$

Recall, to simplify a quotient like $2\frac{2}{3} \div 4$ you first have to rewrite $2\frac{2}{3}$ as an improper fraction.

$$2\frac{2}{3} = \frac{3 \cdot 2 + 2}{3} = \frac{6 + 2}{3} = \frac{8}{3}$$

This idea is applied in the next example.

EXAMPLE 5   Divide. $-2\frac{2}{3} \div -4$

Strategy

$$-2\frac{2}{3} \div -4 = \left(2\frac{2}{3} \div 4 \right) \qquad \text{neg.} \div \text{neg.} = \text{pos.}$$

$$= \frac{8}{3} \div 4 \qquad \text{Rewrite } 2\frac{2}{3} \text{ as } \frac{8}{3} \text{ as shown above.}$$

$$= \frac{8}{3} \div \frac{4}{1} \qquad \text{Rewrite 4 as a fraction, } \frac{4}{1}.$$

$$= \frac{8}{3} \cdot \frac{1}{4} \qquad \text{Express division as multiplication.}$$

Solution

$$= \frac{2}{3} \qquad \frac{8}{3} \cdot \frac{1}{4} = \frac{\overset{2}{\cancel{8}}}{3} \cdot \frac{1}{\underset{1}{\cancel{4}}} = \frac{2}{3}$$

SUMMARY

1. What are the rules for dividing signed numbers?

2. How does the rule for division of signed numbers compare with the rule for multiplication of signed numbers?

3. How can $\frac{5}{7}$ be rewritten as a division problem?

4. How do you determine the sign of the number represented by $- \left(\frac{-5}{11} \right)$?

5. What is the first step in simplifying $\frac{4}{7} \div \frac{2}{21}$?

6. How do you write $3\frac{2}{5}$ as an improper fraction?

7. What will be the sign of the answer to $-3\frac{1}{2} \div 14$? What is each of the steps in actually doing the division?

CLASSROOM PRACTICE

Divide.

1. $\dfrac{12}{6}$ 2. $\dfrac{-18}{2}$ 3. $\dfrac{45}{-9}$ 4. $\dfrac{-60}{-5}$ 5. $\dfrac{-44}{11}$

6. $\dfrac{-48}{12}$ 7. $\dfrac{32}{-32}$ 8. $\dfrac{-80}{4}$ 9. $\dfrac{-28}{-14}$ 10. $\dfrac{46}{-23}$

11. $-24 \div 6$ 12. $38 \div -2$ 13. $-0.42 \div -0.2$ 14. $2.1 \div -0.07$

15. $\dfrac{4}{5} \div -\dfrac{8}{5}$ 16. $-\dfrac{5}{2} \div -\dfrac{25}{6}$ 17. $\dfrac{5}{9} \div -15$ 18. $-4 \div -\dfrac{2}{3}$

19. $-24 \div 1\dfrac{3}{5}$ 20. $-\dfrac{2}{5} \div -\dfrac{4}{15}$ 21. $2\dfrac{2}{3} \div -\dfrac{16}{9}$ 22. $-1\dfrac{1}{4} \div \dfrac{15}{8}$

Which of the following is not equivalent to the other three?

23.   (A) $-\left(\dfrac{-6}{7}\right)$ (B) $\dfrac{-6}{-7}$ (C) $-6 \div -7$ (D) $-\left(\dfrac{-6}{-7}\right)$

24.   (A) $5 \div -\dfrac{1}{2}$ (B) $-20 \div 2$ (C) $-2 \div -\dfrac{1}{5}$ (D) $-\left(\dfrac{-50}{-5}\right)$

WRITTEN EXERCISES

Divide.

1. $\dfrac{26}{13}$ 2. $\dfrac{-12}{3}$ 3. $\dfrac{32}{-8}$ 4. $\dfrac{-72}{-8}$ 5. $\dfrac{-40}{10}$

6. $\dfrac{-45}{9}$ 7. $\dfrac{46}{46}$ 8. $\dfrac{-100}{4}$ 9. $\dfrac{80}{-8}$ 10. $\dfrac{-56}{-8}$

11. $-60 \div 10$ 12. $32 \div 8$ 13. $-0.54 \div -0.9$ 14. $1.4 \div -0.07$

15. $\dfrac{3}{7} \div -\dfrac{6}{7}$ 16. $-\dfrac{4}{5} \div -\dfrac{8}{15}$ 17. $\dfrac{7}{8} \div -14$ 18. $-\dfrac{2}{3} \div -2$

19. $-25 \div 1\dfrac{1}{4}$ 20. $-\dfrac{5}{9} \div -\dfrac{10}{3}$ 21. $1\dfrac{1}{2} \div -\dfrac{9}{8}$ 22. $-\dfrac{4}{3} \div 2\dfrac{2}{3}$

Which of the following is not equivalent to the other three?

23.   (A) $\dfrac{-3}{2}$ (B) $\dfrac{3}{-2}$ (C) $-\left(\dfrac{-3}{-2}\right)$ (D) $-\left(\dfrac{-3}{2}\right)$

24. (A) $-\dfrac{3}{16} \div 1\dfrac{1}{2}$ (B) $(-\dfrac{1}{2})^{3}$ (C) $-\dfrac{1}{2} \div -4$ (D) $-1 \div 8$

OPEN-ENDED QUESTION

25. Complete the table at the right.
    For example, in the second row , n = 5.
    $(n + 1)(n - 1) = (5 + 1)(5 - 1) = (6)(4) = 24$.
    Write a description of how you discovered the
    pattern to fill in the remainder of the table.

n	(n + 1)(n - 1)
5	24
8	
12	
7	
10	
-99	
	8
	224
	-1

Review Chapters 1-2

1. Insert the appropriate inequality symbol, < or >.
   1.6^{6} ? 2.8^{2}

2. What symbol is in the 47th position of the following pattern?
   ABBCFEABBCFEABBCFE ...

3. Simplify $5 \cdot 2^{3}$.

4. Evaluate $3x + 4y$ for $x = 2$ and $y = 7$.

5. Estimate 49^{2}.

   (A) 250 (B) 1,600 (C) 2,500 (C) 25,000

6. Janet repairs refrigerators. She is paid $12 an hour plus a service charge of $25.
   If T represents the total cost of a repair and H the number of hours to do the
   repair, which formula below describes the way to compute the total cost?

   (A) $T = 25H + 12$ (B) $12(H + 25)$

   (C) $T = H + 12 + 25$ (D) $T = 25 + 12H$

Simplify.

7. $48 \div 6 - 3 \cdot 2 + 11$ 8. $70 - 5 \cdot 2^3 + 45 \div 9$

9. $\dfrac{20 + 4 \cdot 2}{13 - 2 \cdot 3}$ 10. $\dfrac{2}{3} \cdot (\dfrac{3}{4})^2$

Evaluate for the given values of the variables.

11. $\dfrac{4}{5} a + 7$ for $a = 25$ 12. $4a^3$ for $a = -2$

13.   Find the perimeter of the rectangle
       with width 8 cm and length 14 cm.

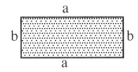

14.   The approximate value of 0.39a for a = 0.081492 is?
       (A)   0.003   (B)   0.03   (C)   0.36   (D)   3.6

15.   Mr. Rodrigues is paid a weekly salary of $125 plus a commission of
       $50 on every 45-inch projection T.V. he sells. If P represents his total
       pay for the week and N the number of televisions he sells, which formula
       below represents his earnings for the week?
       (A)   P = 125 + 45 + 50   (B)   P = 125 + 50N
       (C)   P = 50 + 125N   (D)   P = 125 + N + 50

16.   When purchasing an item, Tanya gave a clerk a $10 bill. The clerk
       gave her the item and change consisting of T dollar bills, Q quarters, and D
       dimes. Which of the following represents the cost of the item?
       (A)   10 - T - Q - D   (B)   T + Q + D
       (C)   10 - T - 0.25Q - 0.10D   (D)   D + 0.25Q + 0.10D

17.   On a multiple-choice test each correct response was worth 5 points.
       2 points were subtracted for each incorrect response.
       Which formula below represents the total score S if C represents the number of
       correct responses and W the number of incorrect ones?
       (A)   S = 5C - 2W   (B)   S = 5C + 2W
       (C)   S = 2C - 5W   (D)   S = 5 + C - 2 - W

18.   Name the integer that describes a loss of 7 points in a game.

19.   The coordinate of the point indicated by the arrow is between what two integers?

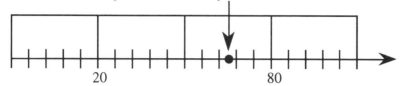

(A)   32 and 33   (B)   52 and 53   (C)   62 and 68   (D)   77 and 78

Name the coordinates of the points graphed below. (Ex. 20-21)

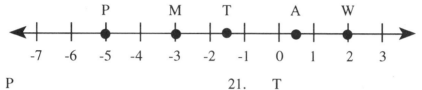

20.   P   21.   T

Insert the appropriate inequality symbol, < or >, to make a true statement.

22.   -8 ? 4   23.   -4 ? -9

Simplify.

24.   7 - 9   25.   -5 + 4 - 10 - 4   26.   -8(-4)   27.   5 · -6

28. $(-5)^3$ 29. $-7(-2)^5$ 30.   -8 ÷ -2   31. $-10 \div \frac{2}{3}$

32.   Which point could represent the product of the numbers represented by points R and V?

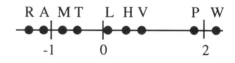

33.   If the pattern indicated at the right were continued, how many squares would be in the seventh figure?

Find the next term in each sequence.

34.   2, 9, 37, 149, ...   35.   8, 8, 16, 24, 40, ...

36.   Which of the following is not equivalent to the other three?

(A) $3(-2)^3$ (B) $6(-2)^2$ (C) $-(\frac{-48}{-2})$ (D) $-6(-2)^2$

37. At the right are three views of a die. The letters A, B, C, D, E, and F appear exactly once on the faces of this die. What letter is opposite F?

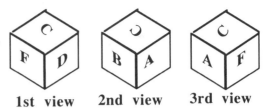

1st view   2nd view   3rd view

38. Which of the plane figures at the right cannot be folded to form a box or cube?

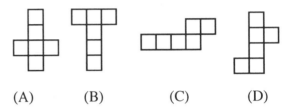

(A)   (B)   (C)   (D)

39. What is the units digit in the 85th term of the sequence $2^1, 2^2, 2^3, 2^4, 2^5, \ldots$?

40. What symbols are missing from this spiral pattern at the locations x and y?

(A)
      x   y

(B)
      x   y

(C)
      x   y

(D)
      x   y

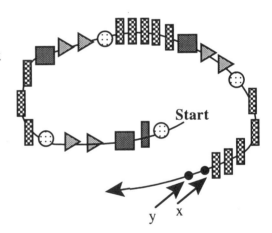

OPEN-ENDED QUESTION

41. The pattern below differs slightly from the ones you have seen so far in this text,

What is the next term in the sequence 4, 7, 13, 25, 49, ... ?

Write an explanation of how you discovered the pattern.

Also explain how to get the next term if you are given one of the terms of the sequence.

Chapter

▶ **3**

Applying Equations

3.1 Solving Equations of the Form x + b = c

OBJECTIVE   To solve equations like x + 4 = 12 or x - 5 = 10

3x + 19 = 25 is an example of an **equation**.

An equation is a mathematical sentence that contains the symbol =.

This symbol is used between two numerical or algebraic expressions.

EXAMPLE 1   Is the equation 3x + 19 = 25 true if x is replaced by 4?

Strategy   Evaluate 3 · **x**   + 19 = 25 for **x = 4**.

                      3 · **4** + 19 = 25   **Substitute 4 for x.**

                         12 + 19 = 25

                            31   = 25   **FALSE: 31 does NOT equal 25.**

Solution   So, 3x + 19 = 25 is **NOT** true if x is replaced by 4.

DISCOVERY   Can you guess what number you can replace x by in 3x + 19 = 25

                    to make the equation true?

Perhaps you guessed that when **x** is replaced by **2** in the equation 3x + 19 = 25, the equation is
then **true**. This is verified below.

$$3x + 19 = 25$$
$$3 \cdot 2 + 19 = 25 \qquad \textbf{Substitute 2 for x.}$$
$$6 + 19 = 25$$
$$25 = 25 \qquad \textbf{TRUE!}$$

The number **2** is called the **solution** of the equation 3x + 19 = 25.

2 is the value of **x** that makes 3x + 19 = 25 true.

Finding the value of x that makes 3x + 19 = 25 **TRUE** is called
                    SOLVING the EQUATION.

2 is called the **SOLUTION** of the equation 3x + 19 = 25.

It is not always easy to **guess** the solution of an equation.

For example, you might find it very difficult to **guess** the solution of the equation
139x + 243 = 1911.

In this lesson you will begin to learn strategies for solving equations.
You will start with simple equations like x - 7 = 13.

Remember, the strategy is important so that you can solve equations that are too hard to solve
by guessing.

DISCOVERY   Is 8 + 5 = 13 a true equation?

Add 4 to each side.

Is the resulting equation true?

EXAMPLE 2   The equation 8 + 5 = 13 is true.

Subtract 3 from each side of the equation.

Is the resulting equation true?

Strategy   8 + 5   =   13

8 + 5 **- 3**   =   13 **- 3**   **Subtract 3 from each side of the equation.**

13 - 3   =   10

Solution   10   =   10   **True**

Note that since you know how to add signed numbers, you can think of **subtraction** in terms of
addition! Think: 8 **subtract** 5 is the same as

8 **added to** -5.

8 - 5 = 3   **Read as 8 added to -5.**

Thus, 5 subtract 7 can be written as

5 - 7 .

-2   **Think 5 + (-7).**

You can think of an equation as a balance scale.

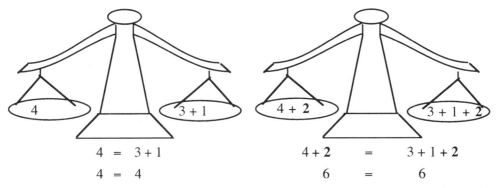

$$4 = 3 + 1$$
$$4 = 4$$

The scale is **balanced**.

$$4 + 2 = 3 + 1 + 2$$
$$6 = 6$$

Adding **2** to each side of the scale keeps it balanced.

Addition and subtraction properties of equations

If you add the same number to each side of a true equation, the resulting equation is true.
If you subtract the same number from each side of a true equation, the resulting equation is also true.

Consider the equation $n = 6$. If **n** is replaced by **6**, the equation is true.

$$6 = 6 \quad \textbf{TRUE}$$

So, **6** is a **solution** of the equation $n = 6$.

If you add the same number to each side of the equation $n = 6$,
you will get an equation whose solution is still 6!

For example, add 8 to each side of the equation $n = 6$.

$$n = 6$$
$$n + 8 = 6 + 8 \qquad \textbf{Add 8 to each side.}$$
$$n + 8 = 14$$

Show **6** is still a **solution** of this new equation.

$$n + 8 = 14 \qquad \textbf{Substitute 6 for n.}$$
$$6 + 8 = 14 \qquad \textbf{The equation is still true.}$$

Therefore, **6** is a **solution** of the new equation $n + 8 = 14$.

In Example 3 below, the Addition Property of Equations is used to solve x - 8 = 5. In this equation, notice that x is **not alone** on the left side of the = symbol, since -8 is added to it.

To **UNDO** the operation, 8 (**the opposite of -8**) is added to each side.

EXAMPLE 3   Solve x - 8 = 5. Check the solution.

Strategy

x - 8	=	5	**x is not alone on the left of the = symbol.**
x - 8 + **8**	=	5 + **8**	**8 is the opposite of -8. Add 8 to each side.**
x + 0	=	13	**-8 + 8 = 0**
x	=	13	**x is now alone on the left of the = symbol.**

Check

$$\begin{array}{c|c} x - 8 & 5 \\ \hline 13 - 8 & 5 \\ 5 & \\ 5 & = 5 \end{array}$$

Replace x by 13.

True

Solution   Thus, the solution is 13.

EXAMPLE 4   Solve a + 9 = 32

Strategy

a + 9	=	32	**a would be alone on the left of the = symbol if there were no 9.**
a + 9 - **9**	=	32 - **9**	**-9 is the opposite of 9. Add -9 to each side.**
a + 0	=	23	
a	=	23	

Solution   Thus, 23 is the solution.   **Check on your own.**

The next example applies the rules for adding signed numbers.

Recall -9 + 4 is   **For unlike signs, subtract absolute values:**   **|-9| - |4| = 5**

-5   **Give the result the same sign as the sign of the number with the larger absolute value, -9, negative.**

EXAMPLE 5   Solve -9 = -4 + x

Strategy   -9   = -4 + x   **x would be alone on the right of the = symbol**
                                         if there were no -4.

                -9 + 4 = -4 + 4 + x   **4 is the opposite of -4. Add 4 to each side.**

                   -5   = 0   + x   **-4 + 4 = 0. Use rules for adding signed**
                                         numbers with unlike signs: -9 + 4 = -5.

                   -5   =   x

Solution   Thus, -5 is the solution.   **Check on your own.**

Sometimes, it is helpful to use a calculator to solve an equation involving large numbers.

Also recall that **subtracting 119.8** from a number is the same as
          adding - 119.8 to that number.

EXAMPLE 6   Solve 119.8 + x = 25.687

Strategy   119.8   + x = 25.687   **x would be alone on the left of the**
                                                 = symbol if there were no 119.8.

                119.8 - **119.8** + x = 25.687 - **119.8**   **Subtract 119.8 from each side, or**
                                                 add the opposite of 119.8, -119.8, to
                                                 each side.

                   0   + x =   -94.113   **Use a calculator to subtract.**
                          x =   -94.113

Solution   Thus, -94.113 is the solution.   **Check on your own.**

SUMMARY

Use the equation 6 + 1 = 7 to answer Exercises 1-3.

1.   Is the equation true?

2.   What equation do you get if you add 3 to each side?

3.   Is the resulting equation true?

4.   What property of equations do Exercises 1-3 illustrate?

5.   Give a numerical example of the Subtraction Property of Equations.

Use the equation x - 7 = 16 to answer Exercises 6-12.

6.   Is x on the left or right side of the = symbol?

7.   Is x alone on that side? Explain?

8.   What can you do to each side of this equation to get x alone?

9.   Solve for x.

10.   The answer to Exercise 9 is called the _____ of the equation.

11.   How do you check your answer?

Use the equation 24 + x = 55 to answer Exercises 12-17.

12.   Is x on the left or right side of the = symbol?

13.   Is x alone on that side? Explain?

14.   What can you do to each side of this equation to get x alone?

15.   Solve for x.

CLASSROOM PRACTICE

Solve each equation.

1. $x - 8 = 3$	2. $b + 7 = 21$	3. $c - 8 = 19$
4. $x + 7 = 10$	5. $b - 10 = 8$	6. $7 + x = 5$
7. $8 = 4 + c$	8. $9 = -10 + x$	9. $-5 = -4 + t$
10. $a + 8 = -4$	11. $4 = x + 2$	12. $c - 9 = 3$
13. $6 = 15 + x$	14. $b - 13 = 8$	15. $-12 + p = 18$
16. $n - 28 = 8$	17. $3 = x + 5$	18. $x - 19 = 4$
19. $-4 + a = -9$	20. $x + 13 = -6$	21. $15 + t = 10$

Use a calculator to solve each equation.

22. $b - 2,4904 = -818$	23. $3,0087 = x + 2,459$
24. $-4.63245 + x = 7.98355$	25. $-0.000567 = x - 3.0647$

WRITTEN EXERCISES

Solve each equation.

1.	$x - 9 = 4$	2.	$b + 6 = 9$	3.	$c - 5 = 9$
4.	$x + 14 = 10$	5.	$b - 11 = 9$	6.	$9 + x = 5$
7.	$11 = 4 + c$	8.	$9 = -13 + x$	9.	$-15 = -4 + t$
10.	$a + 7 = -6$	11.	$4 = x + 12$	12.	$c - 19 = 3$
13.	$6 = 15 + x$	14.	$b - 15 = 8$	15.	$-14 + p = 28$
16.	$n - 22 = 9$	17.	$13 = x + 1\ 5$	18.	$x - 18 = 4$
19.	$-7.3 + a = -11.8$	20.	$x + 4.3 = 2.0$	21.	$2.4 + t = 11$

Use a calculator to solve each equation.

22.	$312 = t + 437$	23.	$23,419 + c = 19,803$
24.	$1,432,211 = a + 918$	25.	$0.00456 = m + 2.67583$

REVIEW

1. Which of the following formulas correctly represents the perimeter of the rectangle?

I   LW

II $L + W$

III $L + W + L + W$

IV $2L + 2W$

(A)   I only

(B)   III only

(C)   I or III

(D)   III or IV

Simplify.

2.	$5 \cdot -8$	3.	$-5 - 8$	4.	$-15 \div 3$	5.	$(-3)^5$

OPEN-ENDED QUESTION

6. Use a calculator to evaluate $\dfrac{n}{n + 1}$ for the following values of n: 10, 100, 1,000, 10,000. Suppose you continued evaluations for larger and larger values of n. Your answers appear to be getting closer and closer to what whole number? Explain why you think your answer is correct.

3.2 Solving Equations of the Form $ax = c$ or $\frac{x}{a} = c$

OBJECTIVES   To solve equations like $4x = -28$

To solve equations like $\frac{x}{7} = 4$ or $\frac{3x}{5} = 2$

You have seen that subtraction can be used to **UNDO** addition.

Likewise, addition can be used to **UNDO** subtraction.

DISCOVERY   What operation will **UNDO** division?

Multiplication of 9 by 5 can be **undone** by **dividing** by 5.

This is illustrated below.

$$\frac{\boxed{5} \cdot 9}{\boxed{5}} = \frac{45}{5} = 9 \qquad \boxed{\textbf{9 remains unchanged}}$$

So, multiplication can be **undone** by division.

EXAMPLE 1   Simplify $\frac{2 \cdot 7}{2}$.

Strategy   Multiply 2 times 7 and then divide the result by 2.

$$\frac{\boxed{2} \cdot 7}{\boxed{2}} = 7$$

Solution   **7** is the final answer.

The work above suggests a pattern for expressions like $\frac{4 \cdot 3}{4}$ or $\frac{8 \cdot 9}{8}$.

$$\frac{4 \cdot 3}{4} = 3 \qquad\qquad \frac{8 \cdot 9}{8} = 9$$

This pattern can be extended to variables.

DISCOVERY   Simplify $\frac{6x}{6}$.

EXAMPLE 2   Simplify $\frac{9a}{9}$.

Strategy $\frac{9a}{9}$ $=$ $\frac{9 \cdot a}{9}$ **9a means 9 · a.**

$=$ $\frac{\boxed{9} \cdot a}{9}$

Solution $=$ **a**   **Multiplying 9 times a and then dividing by 9 leaves a unchanged.**

Recall the Addition and Subtraction Properties of Equations.

You can add the same number to each side or subtract the same number from each side of an equation.

Let's see if you can divide each side of an equation by a non-zero number.

First, recall that **division** can be indicated by a fraction.

So, <u>45 **divided by** 9</u> can be indicated by

$$\frac{45}{9}$$

EXAMPLE 3   The equation 9 · 5 = 45 is true.

Write the equation you get by dividing each side by 9.

Is this resulting equation true?

Strategy $\frac{9 \cdot 5}{9} = \frac{45}{9}$ **Use fractions to indicate division.**

5 = 5   **Resulting equation**

Solution   The resulting equation is true.

This example suggest the following property.

Division Property of Equations

If you divide each side of a true equation by the same non-zero number, the resulting equation is true.

In the equation x + 9 = 6, 9 is added to x.

To solve the equation x + 9 = 6, you want to get x alone on the left of the = symbol.

To do this, you **undo** addition of 9 by adding -9 to each side.

A similar method can be used to solve an equation like 8x = 32, in which x is **multiplied** by 8.

DISCOVERY   Solve 8x = 32.

What is being done to x on the left side of the = symbol?

How can you **undo** this operation?

What must you do to each side of the equation to solve for x?

EXAMPLE 4   Solve 4x = 44. Check the solution.

Strategy   x is not alone on the left side of the = symbol.

x is **multiplied** by 4.

To **undo multiplication** by 4, **divide** each side by 4.

$$\frac{\boxed{4} \cdot x}{\boxed{4}} = \frac{44}{4} \qquad \textbf{Divide each side by 4.}$$

$$x = 11$$

Check

$$\begin{array}{c|c} 4x & 44 \\ 4 \cdot 11 & 44 \\ 44 & \\ 44 \stackrel{?}{=} 44 & \end{array} \qquad \begin{array}{l} \textbf{Replace x by 11.} \\ \\ \textbf{True} \end{array}$$

Solution   Thus, the solution is 11.

EXAMPLE 5   Solve -21 = -3x

Strategy $-21 = -3x$ **x is multiplied by -3.**

$$\frac{-21}{-3} = \frac{-3x}{-3} \qquad \textbf{Undo multiplication by -3 . Divide each side by -3.}$$

Solution $7 = x$ $\dfrac{\textbf{neg.}}{\textbf{neg.}} = \textbf{pos.}$

You have seen that multiplication can be **undone** by division.

Similarly, **division** can be undone by multiplication.

For example, 18 divided by 3, or $\frac{18}{3}$, can be **undone** by multiplying by 3.

$$\boxed{3} \cdot \frac{18}{\boxed{3}} = 3 \cdot 6 = 18 \qquad \boxed{\textbf{18 remains unchanged.}}$$

This suggests a pattern.

$$7 \cdot \frac{3}{7} = 3 \qquad\qquad 8 \cdot \frac{5}{8} = 5 \qquad 4 \cdot \frac{3}{4} = 3 \qquad 6 \cdot \frac{x}{6} = x$$

DISCOVERY   The equation $\frac{16}{8} = 2$ is true.

Multiply each side by 8 and write the resulting equation.

Is the resulting equation true?

This suggests the following property.

Multiplication Property of Equations

If you multiply each side of a true equation by the same number, the resulting equation is true.

DISCOVERY   Consider the equation $\frac{a}{5} = 7$.

What is being done to x on the left of the = symbol?

How can you undo this operation?

What should you do to each side of the equation to get an equation in which x is on the left side of the = symbol by itself?

Solve the equation.

EXAMPLE 6   Solve $\frac{x}{4}$ = -9. Check the solution.

Strategy   x is not alone on the left side of the equal symbol: x is **divided** by 4.

Multiply each side by 4 to **undo** division by 4.

$$\frac{x}{4} \;=\; -9 \qquad\qquad \textbf{Undo division by 4.}$$

$$\boxed{4} \cdot \frac{x}{\boxed{4}} \;=\; 4 \cdot -9 \qquad\qquad \textbf{Multiply each side by 4.}$$

$$x \;=\; -36 \qquad\qquad \textbf{(pos.)} \cdot \textbf{(neg.)} = \textbf{neg.}$$

Check

$$\frac{x}{4} \;=\; -9$$

$$\frac{-36}{4} \;\bigg|\; -9 \qquad \textbf{Substitiute -36 for x.}$$

$$-9 \;\bigg|$$

$$-9 \;=\; -9 \qquad \textbf{True}$$

Solution   Thus, -36 is the solution.

The next Example illustrates the two types of equations studied so far in this lesson.

EXAMPLE 7   Solve 35 = -7g and -4 = $\frac{m}{-6}$

$$35 \;=\; \mathbf{-7}g \qquad\qquad\qquad\qquad -4 \;=\; \frac{m}{-6}$$

$$\frac{35}{\mathbf{-7}} \;=\; \frac{\mathbf{-7}g}{\mathbf{-7}} \qquad\qquad\qquad \mathbf{-6} \cdot -4 \;=\; \mathbf{-6} \cdot \frac{m}{-6}$$

Solution $-5 = g$ **pos. ÷ neg. = neg.** $24 = m$ **neg. · neg. = pos.**

The next equation requires **undoing two** operations.

EXAMPLE 8   Solve $\frac{3x}{5}$ = -12.

Strategy $5 \cdot \frac{3x}{5} = 5 \cdot -12$ **Undo division by 5. Multiply each side by 5.**

$$3x = -60 \qquad \textbf{pos. · neg. = neg.}$$

$$\frac{3x}{3} = \frac{-60}{3} \qquad \textbf{Undo multiplication by 3. Divide each side by 3.}$$

Solution $x = -20$ **neg. ÷ pos. = neg.**

SUMMARY

Simplify each expression.

1. $7 \cdot \dfrac{5}{7}$ 2. $-6 \cdot \dfrac{x}{-6}$ 3. $\dfrac{4 \cdot -3}{4}$ 4. $\dfrac{-8k}{-8}$

Use the equation $3x = -15$ to answer Exercises 5-9.

5. What is being done to x?
6. How do you undo what is being done to x?
7. What must you do to each side of the equation to solve for x?
8. How do you write this?
9. Solve for x.

Use the equation $\dfrac{a}{-3} = 5$ to answer Exercises 10-14.

10. What is being done to a?
11. How do you undo what is being done to a?
12. What must you do to each side of the equation to solve for a?
13. How do you write this?
14. Solve for a.

Use the equation $\dfrac{5x}{7} = -10$ to answers Exercises 15-21.

15. What two operations must be undone to solve for x?
16. What must you do first to each side of the equation?
17. How do you show this?
18. What is the resulting equation?
19. What must you do each side of the resulting equation?
20. How do you show this?
21. Solve for x.

CLASSROOM PRACTICE

Solve each equation.

1. $7x = 56$ 2. $32 = 8k$ 3. $7e = 21$ 4. $48 = 16j$

5. $5x = -40$ 6. $-24 = -3k$ 7. $-3m = -21$ 8. $45 = -15t$

9. $\dfrac{a}{4} = 9$ 10. $14 = \dfrac{m}{2}$ 11. $\dfrac{y}{12} = 3$ 12. $13 = \dfrac{t}{5}$

13. $\dfrac{j}{4} = -8$ 14. $-7 = \dfrac{r}{-3}$ 15. $\dfrac{w}{-4} = 13$ 16. $-6 = \dfrac{k}{-6}$

17. $\dfrac{3y}{5} = 9$ 18. $8 = \dfrac{4t}{5}$ 19. $\dfrac{7d}{2} = 14$ 20. $10 = \dfrac{5a}{3}$

21. $\dfrac{4x}{-3} = -8$ 22. $-4 = \dfrac{-2y}{5}$ 23. $-18 = \dfrac{9r}{5}$ 24. $-32 = \dfrac{8w}{3}$

WRITTEN EXERCISES

Solve each equation.

1. $11x = 33$ 2. $63 = 9k$ 3. $46 = 23m$ 4. $9y = 54$

5. $\dfrac{f}{8} = 9$ 6. $12 = \dfrac{s}{6}$ 7. $\dfrac{b}{11} = 8$ 8. $3 = \dfrac{x}{13}$

9. $-24 = -8d$ 10. $-6m = -66$ 11. $-39 = 3y$ 12. $-7u = 98$

13. $\dfrac{g}{6} = -13$ 14. $-7 = \dfrac{r}{-7}$ 15. $\dfrac{g}{-9} = 7$ 16. $\dfrac{t}{-14} = -2$

17. $\dfrac{4k}{3} = 8$ 18. $15 = \dfrac{5a}{2}$ 19. $48 = \dfrac{3w}{2}$ 20. $\dfrac{3h}{4} = 21$

21. $-25 = \dfrac{5x}{4}$ 22. $36 = \dfrac{3t}{-2}$ 23. $\dfrac{3d}{-7} = 9$ 24. $-18 = \dfrac{-9a}{2}$

25. $36x = 8104$ 26. $-28{,}756 = 319x$

27. $\dfrac{x}{149} = -79$ 28. $-49.4 = \dfrac{t}{-23.7}$

29. $\dfrac{23d}{37} = 2135$ 30. $5654.82 = \dfrac{-3.21h}{17.4}$

REVIEW

Insert the appropriate inequality symbol, < or >.

1. $-18 \ ? \ 14$ 2. $2^3 \ ? \ 3^2$ 3. $2.1^3 \ ? \ 1.4^7$

4. What symbol is in the 40th position of the following pattern?
    PEWQ121APEWQ121APEWQ121A...

5.   Which estimate is correct for 14.1 · 0.00049?

    (A)   0.8   (B)   0.009   (C)   0.008   (D)   0.007

6.   Add -5 -7.

7.   Multiply -5 · -7.

8.   Mrs. Swaroop repairs washing machines. There is a service charge of $30 and an hourly rate of $35. If B represents the total cost of the repair bill and H the number of hours to complete a repair, which formula below describes the way to compute the total bill?

    (A) $B = 30 + 25 + H$ (B) $B = 30 + 35H$

    (C) $B = 25(H + 35)$ (D) $B = 35(25 + H)$

9.   Evaluate $\frac{3}{5}x + 17$ for $x = 15$.

10.   Evaluate $6x^3$ for $x = 2$.

OPEN-ENDED QUESTION

11.   Below is a triangular pattern of numbers. Except for the ones, each number is the sum of the two numbers diagonally above it.

      For example: in Row 7: the first 6 = sum of 1 and 5, the two numbers diagonally above 15.

      The next number, 15 = the sum of 5 and 10 diagonally above it.

				1					Row 1
			1		1				Row 2
		1		2		1			Row 3
	1		3		3		1		Row 4
1		4		6		4		1	Row 5
1	5	10		10		5	1		Row 6
1	6	15	20	15	6	1			Row 7
1	7	21	35	35	21	7	1		Row 8

What is the sum of the numbers in the 10th row?

Write an explanation of how you got your answer.

HINT: Determine the pattern formed by the sum of the numbers in each row.

3.3 Solving Equations of the Form ax + b = c

OBJECTIVE   To solve equations like 4x + 20 = 80 and 8x - 1 = 31

To solve the equation x + 7 = 12 you have to **undo one** operation, **addition**.

To solve the equation 3x = 30 you have to **undo one** operation, **multiplication**.

Consider the equation 3x + 7 = 22.

How many operations do you think will have to be **undone**?

DISCOVERY   For the equation 3x + 7 = 22, on which side of the = symbol is 3x?

Is the 3x alone on that side?

What else is on that same side of the = symbol?

What is being done to 3x?

How do you **undo** this?

What can you add to each side of the equation to get the 3x by itself on the left side of the = symbol? Do this.

Is the 3x now alone on the left side of the = symbol?

Does this resulting equation look like a type you have already learned to solve? What type?

What can you now do to each side of this equation to solve for x?

What is the final equation?

EXAMPLE 1   Solve 4x + 20 = 80. Check the solution.

Strategy

$$4x + 20 = 80$$ **To undo addition of 20,**

$$4x + 20 - \mathbf{20} = 80 - \mathbf{20}$$ **subtract 20 from each side.**

$$4x + 0 = 60$$

$$4x = 60$$ **To undo multiplication by 4,**

$$\frac{4x}{4} = \frac{60}{4}$$ **divide each side by 4, NOT -4.**

$$x = 15$$

(Check shown on next page)

Check

$$\begin{array}{rcl} 4x + 20 & = & 80 \\ 4 \cdot 15 + 20 & | & 80 \\ 60 + 20 & | & \\ 80 & = & 80 \end{array}$$ **Substitute 15 for x.**

                                                          True

Solution   Thus, the solution is 15.

EXAMPLE 2   Solve: $6x - 7 = 13$

Strategy
$$6x - 7 = 13$$ **To undo addition of -7,**
$$6x - 7 + 7 = 13 + 7$$ **add 7 to each side.**
$$6x + 0 = 20$$
$$6x = 20$$ **To undo multiplication by 6,**
$$\frac{6x}{6} = \frac{20}{6}$$ **divide each side by 6.**
$$x = 3\frac{2}{6}$$

Solution $x = 3\frac{1}{3}$ $\dfrac{2}{6} = \dfrac{\overset{1}{\cancel{2}}}{\underset{3}{\cancel{6}}} = \dfrac{1}{3}$

EXAMPLE 3   Solve: $21 = 15 + 3a$.

Strategy
$$21 = 15 + 3a$$ **3a is not alone on the right: 15 is added to 3a. Undo addition of 15.**
$$-15 + 21 = -15 + 15 + 3a$$ **Add -15 to each side.**
$$6 = 0 + 3a$$ **Use rule for adding unlike signs.**
$$6 = 3a$$
$$\frac{6}{3} = \frac{3a}{3}$$ **To undo multiplication by 3,**
$$2 = a$$ **divide each side by 3.**

Solution   Thus, the solution is 2.

EXAMPLE 4   What is the weight of one of the blocks if each pyramid weighs 2 pounds and the scale is balanced?

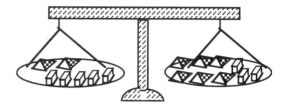

Strategy   Think of this problem as solving an equation. First take away as many pyramids as you can from each side of the balance scale.

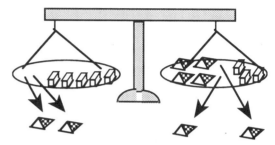

Take away **2 pyramids** from each side.

Now take away as many blocks as you can from each side.

You don't have to draw all of these diagrams. Think the process in your head.

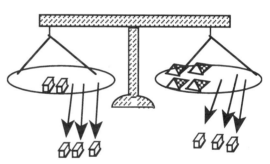

Take away **3 blocks** from each side.

The scale is left with **2** blocks on the left and **4** pyramids on the right.

Let x = the weight of each block.   The weight of each pyramid is 2 lb.

balanced

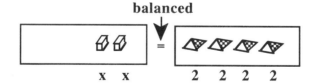

x   x   2   2   2   2

Write an equation.	$2x$	$=$	8	
Solve the equation.	$\dfrac{2x}{2}$	$=$	$\dfrac{8}{2}$	**Divide each side by 2.**
	x	$=$	4	

Solution   Thus, the weight of each block is 4 lb.

SUMMARY

To solve the equation 4y - 3 = 25:

1.   What two operations must be undone?

2.   What operation must be undone first?

3.   How is this done?

4.   What is the resulting equation?

5.   What operation must now be undone?

6.   How is this done?

7.   What is the solution?

To solve the equation 10 = 6 + 3m:

8.   What two operations must be undone?

9.   What must you do to each side of the equation to get the 3m alone on the right side of the = symbol?

10. What is the resulting equation?

11. What must you now do to each side of this resulting equation?

12. What is the solution?

13. How do you find the weight of one pyramid if one block weighs 23 lb and the scale is balanced?

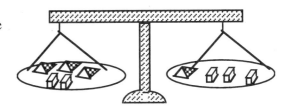

CLASSROOM PRACTICE

Solve each equation.

1.	3x - 7 = 14	2.	4x - 2 = 18	3.	5a + 3 = 23
4.	2x + 7 = 18	5.	12 = 8 + 2y	6.	14 = 4 + 5t
7.	6 + 3g = 15	8.	14 + 6y = 44	9.	4m - 20 = 28
10.	3k - 7 = 18	11.	4a + 10 = 12	12.	13 = 9 + 6b
13.	4x + 7 = 10	14.	24 = 3a - 7	15.	21 = 9 + 7g

Solve each equation. Round each solution to the nearest hundredth.

16. $435y - 218 = 781$ 17. $1,345 = 318m + 129$

18. $1,024 = 257y + 119$ 19. $3.43x - 0.09 = 318.34$

20.   Find the weight of one pyramid if one block weighs 4 lb and the scale is balanced.

21.   Find the weight of one pyramid if one block weighs 3 lb and the scale is balanced.

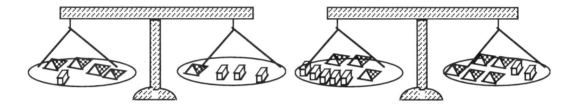

WRITTEN EXERCISES

Solve each equation.

1.	$4x - 2 = 18$	2.	$7a + 3 = 24$	3.	$36 = 4y + 8$
4.	$2x + 9 = 14$	5.	$18 = 4 + 2y$	6.	$44 = 4 + 5t$
7.	$8 + 3g = 44$	8.	$19 + 8y = 35$	9.	$10m - 30 = 20$
10.	$9k - 17 = 28$	11.	$4a + 14 = 16$	12.	$57 = 9 + 6b$
13.	$4x + 17 = 20$	14.	$34 = 5a - 7$	15.	$53 = 9 + 11g$

Solve each equation. Round each solution to the nearest hundredth.

16. $345y - 418 = 861$ 17. $2,145 = 523m + 192$

18. $1,023 = 527y + 219$ 19. $2.32x - 0.08 = 128.43$

20.   Find the weight of one pyramid if one block weighs 4 lb and the scale is balanced.

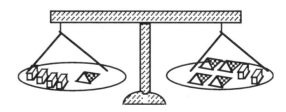

OPEN ENDED QUESTION

21. Suppose the weight of one pyramid is the same as the weight of 4 blocks. How many blocks or cubes or combinations of blocks and cubes can you add to which side (left or right) to balance the scales? Is there more than one answer? Explain how you got your answer.

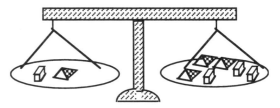

REVIEW

1. On the scale below, the reading indicated by the arrow is between

    (A)   23 and 24   (B)   26 and 28
    (C)   30 and 32   (D)   32 and 34

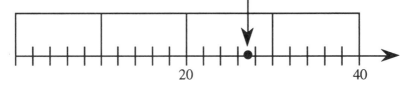

2. Three views of a die are shown at the right. Each numbers appears once on the faces of this die. What digit is opposite the 1?

1st view   2nd view   3rd view

Solve each equation.

3. $\dfrac{x}{5} = -7$ 4. $\dfrac{2a}{3} = 6$

5. What is the next number in the sequence 8, 17, 35, 71, ...

3.4 English Phrases to Algebra

OBJECTIVE   To write English phrases in mathematical form

Consider the following word problem.

The $340 selling price of a stereo is $40 more than 3 times the cost. Find the cost.

Such a problem can be solved by solving an algebraic equation.
To write the equation you have to know how to translate the English expression
40 more than 3 times the cost into a mathematical form.
This lesson will help you develop that skill.
You will learn to translate English phrases into mathematical form.

For example, **decreased by** means **made smaller by**.
So, **decreased by** calls for **subtraction**.
Similarly, **increased by** means **made greater by**.
Therefore, **increased by** calls for **addition**.

EXAMPLE 1   Write in mathematical form.

9 decreased by 2	7 increased by 6	5 decreased by x

Solution   **9 decreased by** 2   **7 increased by** 6   **5 decreased by** x
                        9 - 2   7 + 6   5 - x

Consider the phrase **6 increased by a number**.
The number might be -4, 2, 0, or any number.
If you let a letter or variable represent the number, say **n**, then

6 **increased by** a number becomes

6   +   **n.**

EXAMPLE 2   Write in mathematical form **a number decreased by 7**.

Let **x** = the number.

a **number decreased** by 7

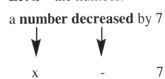

Solution   x   -   7

The word **sum** indicates that you should **add** (+).

EXAMPLE 3   Write in mathematical form **the sum of a number and 6**.

Let **y** represent the number.

the **sum** of a **number** and 6

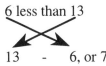

Solution   y + 6

EXAMPLE 4   Write in mathematical form **7 increased by 5 times a number**.

Let x represent the number.

7 **increased by** 5 times a number

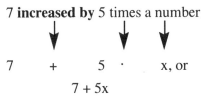

7   +   5   ·   x, or

7 + 5x

Another frequently used expression is **less than**.

For example, 6 less than 13 does **NOT** mean 6 - 13.

6 less than 13

13   -   6, or 7

Note the **switching** of the order of subtraction for the phrase **less than**.

Similarly, there is the phrase **more than**.

8 more than 3 means 3 made greater by 8.

3   +   8, or 11

EXAMPLE 5   Write in mathematical form **7 less than twice Harry's age**.

Strategy   Let **A** represent Harry's Age.

7 less than twice Harry's **Age**

7 less than **2 ·** **Harry's Age**

7 less than **2 ·** **A**

7 less than   2A   **Write 2· A as 2A**

Solution   2A   -   7

SUMMARY

What operation in arithmetic represents each of the following?

1.   increased by   2. decreased by   3. sum of

4.   How does 3 less than 7 differ from 3 decreased by 7?

5.   To write **Jane's bowling score decreased by 35** in mathematical form, you must first use a _____ to represent _____.

Match each word phrase below with its mathematical form at the right.

Word Phrase	Mathematical Form
6. x increased by 12	a. x - 20
7. 12 less than x	b. x + 12
8. the sum of x and 20	c. x + 20
9. 12 more than x	d. x - 12
10. x decreased by 20	e. 20 - x
	f. 12 - x

CLASSROOM PRACTICE

Write each word phrase in mathematical form.

1. y increased by 9
2. p decreased by 7
3. x decreased by 4
4. n increased by 11
5. the sum of 13 and w
6. the sum of b and 23
7. 5 less than k
8. 1 less than r
9. 3 more than twice x
10. 6 less than twice f
11. Bill's age increased by 12
12. Cheung's savings decreased by $200
13. $15 more than twice Hank's salary
14. 15° less than 4 times the temperature
15. The sum of 14 and twice a number
16. 3 times a number, increased by 21

WRITTEN EXERCISES

Write each word phrase in mathematical form.

1. w decreased by 7
2. p increased by 19
3. x decreased by 50
4. n increased by 31
5. the sum of b and 18
6. the sum of 19 and x
7. 14 less than k
8. 40 less than r
9. 8 less than twice x
10. 19 more than twice f
11. Tina's age increased by 9
12. Abe's savings decreased by $400
13. 25 less than twice Hank's age
14. 2° more than 4 times the temperature
15. The sum of 34 and twice a number
16. 5 times a number, decreased by 31
17. 3 times Meg's score decreased by 12
18. The sum of 14 and twice Jake's age
19. 12 lb more than twice Pat's weight
20. Ben's batting average increased by 10
21. 4 cm less than twice the width
22. 3 ft more than 4 times the length
23. 34 increased by 5 times a number
24. 3 times a number, decreased by 6

REVIEW

Solve each equation.

1. $3x - 2 = 19$
2. $21 = 4a + 13$
3. $5 + 3x = 35$
4. $x - 8 = -11$

Simplify.

5. $-7 \cdot -6$
6. $-7 - 6$
7. $(-2)^5$
8. $(-\frac{2}{3}) \cdot (-9)$

3.5 Solving Word Problems

OBJECTIVE   To solve word problems using equations

You learned in the last lesson to write word phrases in mathematical form.
You will now apply this skill to solving word problems.

A **commission** is a **bonus**, based on the amount of sales a salesperson makes during the
week. The commission is added to the salesperson's regular salary. The more you sell,
the more you earn.

DISCOVERY

Use the following word problem to answer the questions below.

The sum of Fay's salary and a $65 commission is $310.
Find Fay's regular salary.

1.   What are you asked to find in this word problem?
2.   How do you represent what you are asked to find?
3.   Use this representation to write an equation describing the first sentence of the
       word problem.
4.   Solve the equation.
5.   Check your answer.

EXAMPLE 1   9 less than 3 times Fantashia's age is 33.
                     How old is Fantashia?

Strategy   You are asked to find Fantashia's age.
                     Let F = Fantashia's age.   **Use a letter to represent
                                                           what you are asked to find.**

                     Use the first sentence to write an equation.
                     (continued on next page)

Write equation   9 less than 3 times **Fantashia**'s age is 33.

9 less than 3 times **F** is 33

9 less than 3 · F is 33

9 less than 3F is 33

3F - 9 = 33

Solve equation   3F - 9 + **9**   =   33 + **9**   **Add 9 to each side to get 3F alone.**

3F   + 0   =   42

3F   =   42

$$\frac{3F}{3} \qquad = \qquad \frac{42}{3} \qquad \textbf{Divide each side by 3.}$$

F   =   14

Check   9 less than 3 times Fantashia's age is 33

9 less than 3 times 14   33 **Replace Fantashia's age by 14.**

3· **14** - 9

42   - 9

33

33 = 33 **True**

Solution   Thus, Fantashia's age is 14.

EXAMPLE 2   The $340 selling price of a stereo is $40 more than 3 times the cost.
Find the cost of the stereo.

Strategy   You are asked to find the **C**ost of the stereo.

Let **C** = the **C**ost of the stereo.   **Use a letter to represent**
what you are asked to find.

Use the first sentence to write an equation.

340 is 40 more than 3 times Cost

340 is 40 more than 3C

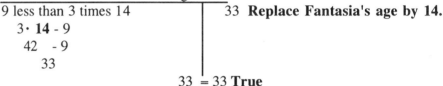

340 = 3C   +   40

Solve   340 = 3C + 40.

(continued on next page)

Solve   340   =   3C + 40

340 **- 40**   =   3C + 40 **- 40**   **Add -40 to each side.**

300   =   3C + 0

300   =   3C

$$\frac{300}{3} = \frac{3C}{3}$$ **Divide each side by 3.**

100   =   C

Solution   Thus, the cost of the stereo is $100.   **Check on your own.**

EXAMPLE 3   Write an equation you could use to solve the following word problem.
The sum of 14 and twice a number is 45.
Find the number.

Strategy   You are asked to find the number.

Let x = the number.   **Use a letter to represent what you are**
asked to find.

Use the first sentence to write an equation.

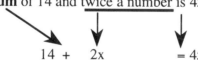

sum of 14 and <u>twice a number</u> is 45

Solution   14 +   2x   = 45

EXAMPLE 4   Write an equation you could use to solve the following problem.
Barry's weight decreased by 15 lb is 140 lb.
Find Barry's weight.

Strategy   You are asked to find Barry's weight.

Let W = Barry's weight.   **Use a letter to represent what you are**
asked to find.

Use the first sentence to write an equation.

Barry's Weight <u>**decreased by**</u> 15 lb is 140 lb

Solution   W   -   15   = 140

Let's now apply algebra to geometry.

Recall the formula for the perimeter. of a rectangle.

P = 2L + 2W

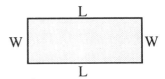

EXAMPLE 5   The length of a rectangle is 20 cm. The perimeter is 80 cm.

Write an equation to find the width.

Solve this equation to find the width of the rectangle.

Strategy   First draw a diagram of the rectangle.

Label its sides.

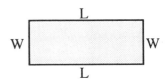

Write the formula for the perimeter.

Replace the letters by the numerical values given in the problem.

P = 80   L = 20   **Perimeter is 80 and Length is 20.**

↓   ↓

P =   2L + 2W   **Perimeter formula**

↓   ↓

80 =   2 · 20 + 2W   **Replace P by 80, L by 20.**

Equation   **80 =   40 + 2W**   **W represents what you want to find.**

Solve   80   =   40   +   2W

-40 + 80   =   -40 + 40   +   2W   **Add -40 to each side.**

40   =   0   +   2W

40   =   2W

$\dfrac{40}{2}$ = $\dfrac{2W}{2}$ **Divide each side by 2.**

20   =   W

Check   Check the solution.

(continued on next page)

$$P = 2L + 2W$$

$$80 \,\big|\, 2 \cdot 20 + 2 \cdot 20 \quad \textbf{Substitute 80 for P, 20 for L, 20 for W.}$$

$$40 + 40$$

$$80$$

$$80 = 80 \qquad \textbf{True}$$

Thus, the width is 20 cm.

Solution   This rectangle is a special type of rectangle, a square.

SUMMARY

Use the following word problem to answer exercises 1-6.

9 less than 3 times a number is 33. Find the number.

1.   The first step is to use a letter or variable to represent _____.

2.   Use this variable to next write an _____.

3.   How do you write 9 less than 3 times n?

4.   What is the equation?

5.   What are the steps in solving this equation?

6.   After you have solved the equation, how do you check your solution?

Use the following word problem to answer exercises 7-12.

The perimeter of a rectangle is 36 ft.

The width of the rectangle is 8 ft.

Find the length.

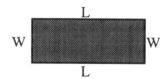

7.   What is the formula for the perimeter of a rectangle?

8.   How do you use this formula to solve the word problem above?

9.   Using the formula, 36 and 8 can replace what letters in the formula?

10.   What is the resulting equation?

11.   What two steps can be taken to solve this equation?

12.   How do you check the solution in the original problem?

Give an equation for each.

13.   6 less than twice x is 18.   14.   7 increased by 4 times n is 19

15.   9 times n, decreased by 7, is 20   16.   The sum of 4 and twice x is 18.

CLASSROOM PRACTICE

Solve each problem.

1. Jon's weight decreased by 15 lb is 117 lb. Find his weight.

2. Mona's foul shot total increased by 12 is 70. What is her total?

3. Troy added 19 comic books to his collection. If his collection now contains 120 comic books, how many did he originally have?

4. Moira's salary was decreased by $19. If her salary is now $113, what was her salary before the decrease?

5. Eleven increased by twice a number is 19. Find the number.

6. Eight less than 5 times a number is 22. Find the number.

7. The sum of 12 and 3 times a number is 42. Find the number.

8. The sum of twice a number and 24 is 60. Find the number.

9. Ten less than twice Jose's age is 64. How old is Jose?

10. 40 more than 3 times Jane's bowling score is 400. Find her score.

11. Five less than 3 times the temperature is 19. Find the temperature.

12. The $61 selling price of a camera is $5 more than 4 times the cost. Find the cost.

13. The length of a rectangle is 18 m. The perimeter is 80 m. Find the width.

14. The width of a rectangle is 16 cm. The perimeter is 100 cm. Find the length.

WRITTEN EXERCISES

Solve each problem.

1. Jason's foul shots total increased by 8 is 30. Find his total.

2. Tina's weight increased by 7 lb is 113 lb. Find her weight.

3. Tisha's salary was increased by $15. If her salary is now $110, what was her salary before the increase?

4. Jawal added 7 tapes to his collection. His collection now contains 43 tapes. How many tapes did he originally have?

5. Fourteen increased by twice a number is 40. Find the number.

6. Seven less than 6 times a number is 43. Find the number.

7. The sum of 14 and 4 times a number is 38. Find the number.

8. The sum of twice a number and 24 is 38. Find the number.

9. Four less than 3 times the temperature is 41. Find the temperature.

10. The $80 selling price of a radio is $10 more than 5 times the cost. Find the cost.

11. Eight less than twice Rashid's age is 32. How old is Rashid?

12. $30 more than 3 times Hank's salary is $480. Find his salary.

13. The width of a rectangle is 16 in. The perimeter is 72 in. Find the length.

14. The length of a rectangle is 24 cm. The perimeter is 40 cm. Find the width.

15. 119.4 more than 37 times a number is 256.78. Find the number.

16. The perimeter of a rectangle is 2456 ft. The width is 38.64 ft. Find the length.

17. Which problem below can be solved by the equation $x + 5 = 35$?

(A) Marge was paid $35 for one week's part time work as a maid. She got a $5.00 tip. How much money did she receive?

(B) Bert hiked 35 miles at 5 miles per hour. How long did he hike?

(C) Ron added 5 more stamps to his collection. If he now has 35 stamps in his collection, how many stamps did he have before adding 5 more?

(D) By noon, a motel had 35 guests registered. Five more guests registered by 6:00 P.M. How many guests were then registered?

OPEN-ENDED QUESTION

18. Consider the pattern 4, 9, 19, 39, ...
If $3x + 39$ represents the value of the sixth term of the sequence, describe in your own words how to find the value of x.
Then find x.

Review   Chapters 1-3

Solve each equation.

1.   x - 7 = 12   2.   -8 = -3 + x   3.   9 + a = 7

4.   -27 = -9k   5. $\frac{m}{-4}$ = 12   6. $\frac{3x}{4}$ = 6

7.   2x - 8 = 12   8.   24 = 12 + 3m   9.   5 + 4t = 21

       10.   39x - 276 = 621   11.   0.0456 = 3.14m - 1.236

12.   Find the weight of one pyramid if
one block weighs 3 lb and the scale
is balanced.

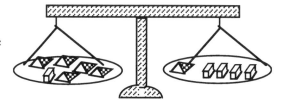

Solve each problem.

13.   8 less than 3 times Joy's age is 16.   14.   The sum of 4 and twice Harry's age
How old is Joy?   is 40. How old is Harry?

15.   5 times a number, increased by 7,   16.   The perimeter of a rectangle is 44
is 47. Find the number.   m. The width is 6 m. Find the
length.

17.   Which problem below can be solved by the equation x + 3 = 32?

(A)   Sean biked 32 miles at 3 mile per hour. How long did he bike?

(B)   Bill had $32 in his savings account. A week later he made a $3.00
deposit in his account. How much money did he have in the account after
this deposit?

(C)   A math class started with 32 students. Three more students enrolled in the
class the next day. How many students were then in the class?

(D)   Eric added 3 cars to his collection of model cars. If he then had 32 cars in
his collection, how many cars did he have before adding three more?

18. Insert the appropriate inequality symbol, < or >.

3.2^2 ? 1.9^8

19. What symbol is in the 127th position of the following pattern?

TEM$%GTEM$%GTEM$%G...

Simplify.

20. 8 - 10

21. 8 · -10

22. -7 + 5 - 8 + 12

23. $(-4)^3$

24. $-6(-2)^4$

25. $-21 \div -3$

26. $44 \div 4 - 2 \cdot 3 + 8$

27. $\dfrac{8 \cdot 5 - 4}{3 + 3 \cdot 5}$

28. Estimate 38.9^2.

(A) 90 (B) 160 (C) 900 (D) 1600

29. Monica is paid a salary of $135 a week and a commission of $15 on each large screen television she sells. If P represents her total pay for the week and N the number of televisions she sells, which formula below describes the way her pay for the week is to be computed?

(A) P = N + 135 + 15 (B) P = 135N + 15

(C) P = 135 + 15N (D) P = 15(N + 135)

30. The approximate value of 0.48 · 0.00843 is

(A) 0.003 (B) 0.004 (C) 0.03 (D) 0.04

31. On a multiple choice test, each correct answer was worth 6 points. But, 3 points were deducted for each wrong answer. Which formula below represents the total score S if C represents the number of correct answers and W the number of wrong answers?

(A) S = 6W + 3C (B) S = 6C - 3W

(C) S = 6C + 3W (D) S = 6 + C - 3 - W

32. Insert the appropriate inequality symbol, < or >, to make -9 ? 3 true.

33.   Name the integer that represents a drop of 5 degrees in temperature.

34.   Evaluate $\frac{4}{5}$ m + 24 for m = 15.

35.   On the scale below, the reading indicated by the arrow is between

(A)   38 and 40   (B)   32 and 34   (C)   28 and 30   (D)   20 and 22

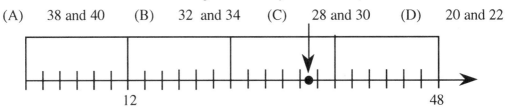

36.   Which point could represent the
        product of the numbers represented
        by points A and M?

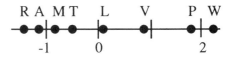

37.   Which of the following is not equivalent to the other 3?

(A)   (-8)(-4)   (B) $(-2)^5$ (C)   64 ÷ -2   (D)   - ($\frac{-64}{-2}$)

38.   If the pattern indicated at the right
        is continued, how many squares
        will be in the sixth figure?

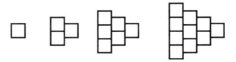

Write the next term in each sequence.

39.   5, 7, 12, 19, 31, 50, ...   40.   7, 16, 34, 70, 142, ...

41.   What is the units digit in the 33rd term of the sequence $7^1, 7^2, 7^3, 7^4, ...$

42.   Which of the plane figures at the
        right can be folded to form a box
        or cube?

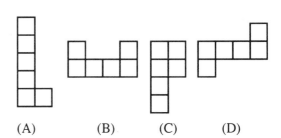

(A)   (B)   (C)   (D)

43.   At the right are three views of a
       die. Each of the letters appear only
       once on the faces of this die. What
       letter is opposite J?

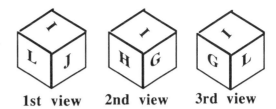

1st view   2nd view   3rd view

44.   What symbols are missing from
       this spiral pattern at the locations x
       and y?

(A)   (B)
       x   y   x   y

(C)   (D)
       x   y   x   y

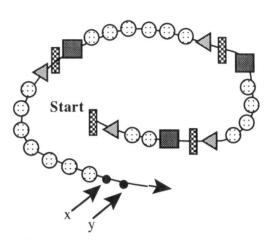

OPEN-ENDED QUESTION

45.   Recall the formula for the perimeter
       of a rectangle.

       Use grid paper like that at the right
       to construct two rectangles with the
       same perimeter as the rectangle
       shown above the grid but **NOT** the
       same length and width. Is there more
       than one answer. Explain how you got
       your answer.

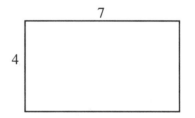

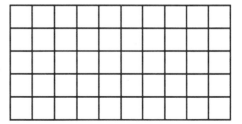

Chapter

4

Applying Algebra to Percent

4.1 Fractional Part of a Number

OBJECTIVES   To find a fractional part of a number

To find fractional part of games won if fractional part of games lost is known.

Later in this chapter you will be asked to solve problems involving **discounts.** Discounts are frequently expressed in terms of percents. However, discounts are also expressed in terms of **fractional parts.** For example, if a T.V. is advertised at $\frac{1}{3}$ off of its regular price, how much is saved. You might then be asked to compare this with a **percent** of discount. Therefore, in this lesson you will learn to work with fractional parts of a number.

In the drawing at the right there are 5 squares.

3 out of **5** of the squares are shaded.

This can be expressed as a **ratio**.

The **ratio** of the number of **shaded** squares to **total** is

$$\downarrow \qquad\qquad \downarrow \quad \downarrow$$

$$\textbf{3} \qquad : \quad \textbf{5}.$$

The **ratio 3 : 5** can also be expressed as a **fraction,** $\frac{3}{5}$.

DISCOVERY   If 4 out of 7 blocks are shaded, what fractional part of the blocks are **not** shaded?

EXAMPLE 1   If a team wins 2 out of 5 games and there are no ties, what fractional part of the games were lost?

Strategy   Think: 2 out of 5 **won.** There must be 5 - 2, or 3, games **lost.**

3 out of 5 **lost.**

Solution   Therefore, $\frac{3}{5}$ is the fractional part of games **lost.**

Once again we shall discover a mathematical pattern.

If 2 out of 5 games are won, then 3 out of 5 are lost. **(games played - wins = losses)**

So, the fraction of games lost is $\dfrac{\mathbf{5 - 2}}{\mathbf{5}} = \dfrac{3}{5}$.

This, and the following, suggest a pattern used in the next example.

4 out of 11 games lost   (no ties):   **fraction** of games **won**: $\dfrac{11 - \mathbf{4}}{11} = \dfrac{7}{11}$

3 out of 7 applications accepted: **fraction** of applications **rejected**: $\dfrac{7 - 3}{7} = \dfrac{4}{7}$

3 out of **n** applications accepted   **fraction** of applications **rejected**: $\dfrac{\mathbf{n - 3}}{\mathbf{n}}$

EXAMPLE 2   In a stereo assembly factory, an average of 5 out of every n stereos are rejected. What fractional part of the stereos are **not** rejected?

Strategy   5 out of **n** rejected.

Written as a ratio, this is   5: n   or $\dfrac{5}{\mathbf{n}}$.

Number **not** rejected is n - 5.

Solution   Fraction **not** rejected: $\dfrac{\mathbf{n - 5}}{\mathbf{n}}$.

An important arithmetic procedure is finding a fractional part of a number.

For example, finding $\dfrac{1}{5}$ **of** 10 is the same as

$$\dfrac{1}{5} \cdot 10 \quad \text{"\textbf{of}" means times.}$$

$$\dfrac{1}{5} \cdot 10 = \dfrac{1}{\cancel{5}} \cdot \cancel{10}^{2} = 2$$

Suppose a batter gets a hit $\dfrac{1}{5}$ of the times at bat.

Then to find the fractional part that represents **no-hits:**

think, hits $\dfrac{1}{5}$ of the times means **hits 1** out of 5 times.

Misses will be **4** out of 5 times, or

$$\dfrac{\mathbf{4}}{\mathbf{5}} \text{ of the times at bat.}$$

EXAMPLE 3   Roscoe, a star baseball player, gets a hit about $\frac{1}{3}$ of the time. If he batted

636 times this season, what should be his approximate total of hitless

at-bats?

Strategy   **hits:** $\frac{1}{3}$ **of the time**

hits: **1** out of 3 times

misses: **2** out of 3 times

misses: $\frac{2}{3}$ **of the time**   **(or think:** $\frac{3-1}{3}$ **)**

Now, find $\frac{2}{3}$ of 636

$$\frac{2}{3} \cdot 636$$

$$\frac{2}{\cancel{3}} \cdot \cancel{636}^{\,212}$$

$$\frac{2 \cdot 212}{1} = 424$$

Solution   Thus, 424 is his total of hitless at-bats.

Notice in the example above, 3 divided into 636 exactly.

$636 \div 3 = 212$ There was **no remainder!**

This may not always happen.

For example, suppose you want to find $\frac{2}{5}$ of 137.

$$\frac{2}{5} \cdot 137$$

But, 5 does not cancel into 137 or divide 137 exactly!

Instead, rewrite $\frac{2}{5} \cdot 137$ as

$$\frac{2}{5} \cdot \frac{137}{1} = \frac{2 \cdot 137}{5}$$

Think of this as: **2 times 137 divided by 5**.   Use a calculator.

Enter 2   enter x   enter 137   enter ÷   enter 5   enter =

Read 54.8.

Many times in mathematics there is more than one way to get the same correct answer.

For example, to find $\frac{3}{4}$ of 12:

<u>Method 1</u>

3 times 12 is 36.

36 divided by 4 is 9.

<u>Method 2</u>

12 divided by 4 is 3.

3 times 3 is 9.

<u>Method 3</u>

$$\frac{3}{4} \text{ of } 12 = \frac{3}{\cancel{4}_1} \cdot \cancel{12}^3 = 3 \cdot 3 = 9$$

<u>Method 4</u>

Use a calculator.

Enter 3   enter x   enter 12   enter ÷   enter 4   enter =

Read 9.

Frequently, stores offer customers a **discount** to encourage them to buy.

If a store advertises a $20 **discount** on a radio that regularly sells for $100, the customer

pays $100 - $20, or $80. This idea can be expressed as a formula.

Regular Price -   Discount   =   Sale Price

   $100   - $20   = $80

Stores advertise **discounts** two ways:

        (1)   in terms of percent **(taught in the next lesson)**.

        (2)   fractional part **off** the regular price.

EXAMPLE 4   A football is advertised at a special discount of $\frac{1}{3}$ off of the regular price

of $52. Find the sale srice rounded to the nearest cent.

Strategy   Find $\frac{1}{3}$ **of** 52

$$\frac{1}{3} \cdot 52 \qquad\qquad \textbf{3 does not divide 52 exactly.}$$

$$\frac{1}{3} \cdot \frac{52}{1} = \frac{52}{3}$$

$$= 17.333333 \qquad \frac{52}{3} \textbf{ means } 52 \div 3.$$

The discount rounds to $17.33   **17.333333 3 is less than 5. Round down.**

Find the sale srice. **(continued on next page)**

Regular Price - Discount   = Sale Price

        $52   - $17.33   = $34.67

Solution   Thus, the sale price is $34.67, rounded to the nearest cent.

The work for solving Example 4 can be shortened for calculator use as indicated below. First recall the rule for **Order of Operations.**

When an expression has several operations, do multiplications and **divisions first,** then additions and **subtractions.**

Think: Sale Price = Regular Price - Regular Price ÷ 3.

 Enter 52   enter -   enter 52   enter ÷ enter 3   enter =

Read 34.66667   Round to 34.67

Thus, the sale price is $34.67, the same result as in Example 4.

SUMMARY

1. Suppose 3 out of 5 people in a town use Crust Toothpaste.
   Express this as a fraction.

2. Meg makes a foul shot in basketball 3 out of 7 times this season.
   How do you find the **fraction** that describes her **misses** for the season?

3. 4 out of 9 applications for a job are accepted.
   How do you find the **fractional** part of applications **rejected**?

4. 5 out of n games are won. How do you find the fractional part of games **lost** if there are no ties?

5. What operation does the word " **of** " indicate?

6. What are three ways indicated in this lesson to find $\frac{3}{4}$ of 40?

7. How do you find $\frac{3}{4}$ of 40 using a calculator?

8. Jake scores a hit in baseball about $\frac{2}{5}$ of the time.

   If he batted 425 times this season, about how many times should he have been hitless?

9. What is meant by **discount**?

10.   What are the steps in using a calculator to find $\frac{3}{4}$ of 37?

11.   What are the steps in finding the sale price of a $55 football advertised at

       $\frac{1}{4}$ off?

CLASSROOM PRACTICE

1.   A team won 5 out of 6 games. Express this as a fraction.

2.   What fractional part of the blocks   3.   What fractional part of the blocks

       below are not shaded?   below are not shaded?

4.   If 2 out of 9 blocks are shaded, what fractional part of the blocks are not shaded?

5.   If 3 out of 10 marbles are blue, what fractional part of the marbles are not blue?

6.   If 4 out of n games are lost and there are no ties, what fractional part of the

       games are won?

7.   If 6 out of k blocks are shaded, what fractional part of the blocks are not shaded?

Find each of the following.

8. $\frac{3}{4}$ of 24   9. $\frac{2}{7}$ of 14   10. $\frac{4}{5}$ of 35

Find each of the following.

       11. $\frac{2}{7}$ of 25   12. $\frac{5}{9}$ of 17   13. $\frac{4}{13}$ of 28

14.   Hoboken High's football team played 20 games this season.

       The team won $\frac{4}{5}$ of the games played.

       How many games were lost if there were no ties?

15.   Janet works on an automobile assembly line checking for proper door alignment.
       On an average, 18 out of 20 cars are found to be acceptable.
       How many cars will she probably have to reject out of 120 cars she inspects?

16.   A skirt is advertised at a special discount of $\frac{1}{5}$ off its regular price of $25.00.
       Find the sale price.

17.   A T.V. is advertised at a special discount of $\frac{1}{3}$ off its regular price of $274. Find the sale price, rounded to the nearest cent.

WRITTEN EXERCISES

1.   A team won 7 out of 11 games. Express this as a fraction.

2.   A team won 7 out of ten games.
       What fractional part of the games played were lost if there were no ties?

3.   What fractional part of the blocks below are not shaded?

4. What fractional part of the blocks below are not shaded?

5.   If 7 out of 15 marbles are red, what fractional part of the marbles are not red?

6.   If 3 out of W games are lost and there are no ties, what fractional part of the games are won?

7.   If 3 out of B blocks are shaded, what fractional part of the blocks are not shaded?

Find each of the following.

8. $\frac{5}{6}$ of 48   9. $\frac{4}{9}$ of 27   10. $\frac{7}{8}$ of 32

Find each of the following.

11. $\frac{5}{9}$ of 33   12. $\frac{4}{11}$ of 27   13. $\frac{3}{7}$ of 45

14.   Wall Field Hockey played 15 games this season.
        The team won $\frac{3}{5}$ of the games.
        How many of the games were lost if there were no ties?

15.   A local car-rental agency has rented 24 of its 30 cars.
        What fractional part of its cars are available for renting?

16.   Mort's Sport Store advertises a football at a discount of $\frac{1}{4}$ off its regular $60 price. Find the sale price.

17.   A catcher's mitt that regularly sells for $62 is advertised at a discount of $\frac{1}{9}$ off its regular price. Find, to the nearest cent, the sale price.

OPEN-ENDED QUESTION

18.   How can you solve the following problem **without** first finding the discount and then subtracting the discount from the regular price?

A radio that regularly sells for $120 is advertised at a discount of $\frac{1}{4}$ off the regular price. Find the sale price.

Hint: If the discount is $\frac{1}{4}$ off the regular price, what fractional part must you pay? Explain how you drew this conclusion ?

REVIEW

Solve each equation.

1. $-9 = -4 + x$ 2. $\frac{x}{-4} = -8$ 3. $7 + 4m = 35$

4.   Find the weight of one pyramid if one block weighs 5 lb and the scale is balanced.

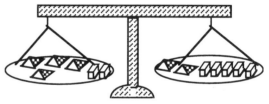

5.   The perimeter of a rectangle is 50 m. The width is 8 m. Find the length.

6.   Which problem below can be solved by the equation $x - 7 = 35$?
     (A)   7 more than a number is 35. Find the number.
     (B)   Jose had a collection of 35 records, He sold 7 of them. How many were then left in his collection?
     (C)   7 less than Raintree's age is 35. How old is he?
     (D)   Debbie swam 35 laps back and forth across a pool in 7 minutes. How many laps per minute did she swim?

4.2 Percent of a Number

OBJECTIVES   To find a given percent of a number

To solve problems involving percent

Recall that per**cent** means **hundredths**.

65%   means $\frac{65}{100}$, or 0.65   Think in terms of money: 65 **cents**.

4%   means $\frac{4}{100}$, or 0.04   Think in terms of money: 4 **cents**

125%   means $\frac{125}{100}$, or 1.25   Think in terms of money: 125 **cents**

In the last lesson you learned to find a fractional part of a number.

For example, to find $\frac{1}{5}$ **of** 35, you multiply $\frac{1}{5}$ times 35.

Thus, $\frac{1}{5}$ of 35 means $\frac{1}{5}$ · 35.

However, $\frac{1}{5}$ can be written as a decimal.

$$\frac{1}{5} = 0.20 \qquad \leftarrow \boxed{\begin{array}{r} 0.20 \\ 5\overline{)1.00} \end{array}}$$

So, $\frac{1}{5}$ **of** 35 can be thought of as

0.20 of 35 or

20 hundredths of 35 or

20%   **of** 35   **Percent means hundredths.**

So,   20% of 35 means 0.20 **of** 35.

20% of 35 means 0.20 · 35

This suggests that to find a percent of a number, you change the percent to a decimal and then multiply the number by this decimal.

Therefore, 30% of 40 means

0.30 · 40   **30% = 0. 30**

3%   of 40 means **0.03** · 40   **3% = 0. 03**

125%   of 40 means **1.25** · 40   **125% = 1. 25**

In the next lesson you will learn how to solve problems like the following:

6% of what number is 24?

4 is what percent of 5?

An easy way to solve such problems will be to rewrite each sentence as an **equation** and then solve the equation.

Therefore, in this lesson it will help to think of solving percent problems in terms of writing equations.

EXAMPLE 1   What number is 35% of 73?

Strategy   Let **n** = the number.

Use the sentence to write an **equation**.

What number is 35% of 73?

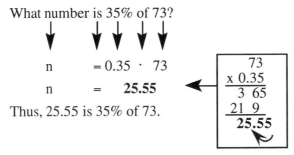

n   = 0.35 · 73

n   =   **25.55**

$$\begin{array}{r} 73 \\ \times\ 0.35 \\ \hline 3\ 65 \\ 21\ 9 \\ \hline \textbf{25.55} \end{array}$$

Solution   Thus, 25.55 is 35% of 73.

DISCOVERY   Suppose a team wins 20% of the games it plays and has no ties.

This means that if the team plays 100 games, it wins 20..

What percent of the games does the team lose?

EXAMPLE 2   Teresa usually makes 70% of her basketball foul shots.

This season she attempted 163 foul shots.

Approximately how many foul shots did she miss this season?

Strategy   70% of the shots **made** means she **made** 70 out of 100 shots.

Therefore, she **missed** <u>30 out of **100**</u> shots.

So, she **missed   30%**   of the shots.

To write an equation, first express the known data as a single sentence.

Misses are 30% of attempts   **OR**   30% of attempts are misses.

Either sentence will do. Use the first sentence to write an equation.

Let **x** = the number of **misses**.

Misses are 30% of attempts

$$x = 0.30 \cdot 163$$
$$x = 48.9$$

Solution   Thus, she missed approximately   **Round 48.9 to the nearest whole**

49 foul shots.   **number.**

EXAMPLE 3   This year, the number of seniors taking mathematics is 5% greater than it was last year. If there were 40 seniors taking math last year, how many seniors are taking math this year?

Strategy   Let **x** = this year's number.

Write an equation.

This year's number is 5% greater than last year's 40.

This year's number is 40 <u>**increased by**</u> 5% of 40.

$$x = 40 + 0.05 \cdot 40$$

(continued on next page)

Use a **calculator** to find x.

x = 40 + 0.05 · 40

 x = **Enter 40   enter +   enter 0.05   enter x   enter 40**

enter =   Read 42

Solution   Thus, 42 seniors are taking math this year.

You could have solved the problem above without using algebra to write an equation.

    1. First find 5% of 40.   0.05 · 40 = 2

    2. Then add 2 to 40.   40 + 2 = 42.

This illustrates that there are frequently many ways of approaching the solution to a problem.

The next example illustrates a strategy for solving certain types of multiple-choice problems. Using this strategy, you eliminate 3 of 4 multiple-choice answers. Then the fourth one must be the correct answer.

EXAMPLE 4   Which of the following is **NOT** a way to find 125% of a number?

    (A)   Multiply the number by 1.25.

    (B)   Divide the number by 4 and add the result to the number.

    (C)   Divide the number by 4 and multiply the result by 5.

    (D)   Multiply the number by 0.25 and multiply the result by 4.

Strategy   (A) is one way to find 125% of a number. **(125% = 1.25)**

Now rewrite 125% other ways.

$$125\% = 1.25$$

$$= 1\frac{25}{100} \qquad \textbf{Write the decimal as a fraction.}$$

$$= 1\frac{1}{4} \qquad \textbf{Reduce } \frac{\textbf{25}}{\textbf{100}} \textbf{ to lowest terms.}$$

$$= \frac{5}{4} \qquad 1\frac{1}{4} = \frac{4 \cdot 1 + 1}{4}$$

(continued on next page)

So, to find 125% of a number multiply be 1.25 **or** $\frac{5}{4}$.

Multiplying by $\frac{5}{4}$ can be done by

1. multiplying by 5 and then dividing by 4, or
2. dividing by 4 and then multiplying by 5.

Thus, (C) is a second way to find 125% of a number.

This leaves one of the two remaining choices to **NOT** be a way. Let's look at (B)

Think of **125%** as **100% + 25%**.

To find **125%** of a number,

find **100% of the number**   +   **25% of the number.**

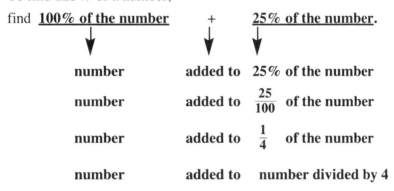

number	**added to**	**25% of the number**
number	**added to**	$\frac{25}{100}$ **of the number**
number	**added to**	$\frac{1}{4}$ **of the number**
number	**added to**	**number divided by 4**

So, (B) is a third way to find 125% of a number.

Therefore, (A), (B), and (C) are all ways to find 125% of a number.

Solution   This leaves (D) as **NOT** a way to find 125% of a number.

Notice that the example above suggests several ways to find a percent **(larger than 100%)** of a number. For example, to find 150% of a number:

(1)   Multiply the number by 1.50.

(2) $150\% = 1.50 = 1\frac{50}{100} = 1\frac{1}{2} = \frac{3}{2}$

Multiply the number by 3 and divide the result by 2.

Divide the number by 2 and multiply the result by 3.

(3) $150\% = 100\% + 50\%$

Add the number to 50% of the number.

EXAMPLE 5   A skirt that regularly sells for $25 is on sale at a discount of 30%.

Which of the procedures below could you use to find the sale price?

     I   25 - (0.30)(25)   II (25)(0.30)

     III   (25)(1.30)   IV (25)(0.70)

(A)   I only   (B)   I or IV only

(C)   IV only   (D)   II or III only

There are two ways to find the sale price.

Strategy 1   **METHOD 1:**

Step 1   Multiply $25 by 0.30 to find the **discount.**

Step 2   Subtract the **discount** from $25:   25 - **discount.**

These two methods are described by **choice I** above: **25 - (0.30)(25).**

Strategy 2   **METHOD 2:**

THINK :   a 30% **discount** means $0.30 **saved** on every dollar.

Thus, you pay **$1.00 - $.30** or

$.70 on every dollar

Now, you can find the sale price in one step. **multiply $25 by 0.70.**

This is illustrated in **choice IV** above: (25)(0.70)

Thus, the procedure for finding the sale price is **I or IV.**

Solution   So, **(B)** is the correct multiple choice response.

EXAMPLE 6   Find the total cost of a $250 stereo including a 7% sales tax.

Strategy 1   There are two ways to find the total cost.

METHOD 1:

Step 1   Find the tax: 0.07 · $250 = $17.50

Step 2   **Then find the total cost.**

Solution 1   **$250 + $17.50 = $267.50.**

METHOD 2:   **(shown on next page)**

Strategy 2   **METHOD 2:**

THINK: A 7% sales tax means you pay an additional $.07 on
                  every dollar.
                  So, you are paying $1.00 + $.07, or **$1.07** on every
                  dollar that the stereo costs.

          Now, you can find the total cost in **one step**.
                  Multiply: 250 · 1.07 = $267.50.

Solution 2   The result is the same as in **Method 1** on the previous page: **$267.50.**

EXAMPLE 7   These price tags are for the
                  same model stereo at two
                  different stores. How much
                  money is saved by buying
                  at the lower price?

Strategy   **Step 1**   Find each discount.

                            Find $\frac{1}{4}$ of $240.   Find 30% of $210.

                            $240 ÷ 4 = $60   0.30 · $210 = $63

                  Step 2   Find the sale price of each stereo.

                            $240 $210
                            -   60   -   63
                            ─────   ─────
                            $180 $147

                  Step 3   Find the amount saved by buying the less expensive stereo.

                            $180   **more expensive**
                            - 147   **less expensive**
                            ─────
                            $ 33

Solution   Thus, $33 is saved by buying the less expensive stereo.

SUMMARY

1.   How do you find 40% of 250?

How do you write each of the following percents as a decimal?

2.   4%   3. 200%

4.   How do you write the following as an equation?
        What number is 12% of 70?

5.   Tina had 20% of the answers wrong on a math test.
        How do you find the percent of answers that were correct?

6.   How do you find a number that is 5% greater than 40?

7.   How do you find a number that is 5% less than 40?

8.   You can find 125% of 40 by multiplying 40 by what decimal?

9.   You can find 125% of 40 by adding ___ to ___.

10.   Explain how to find 125% of 40 by first converting 125% to a fraction.

11.   A tennis racket that regularly sells for $75 is on sale at a discount of 20%
        What are **two different** ways to find the sale price?

12.   What are **two different** ways to solve the following problem?
        Find the total cost of a $25 video game including a 6% sales tax.

13.   How do you find out which is the better buy?

        —Discount of $\frac{1}{4}$ off regular price of $28

        —Discount of 30% on a regular price of $30

        Which is the better buy? Explain why.

CLASSROOM PRACTICE

1.   What number is 23% of 200?   2. 6% of 120 is what number?

3.   Juan usually makes 80% of his basketball foul shots.
        This season he attempted 149 foul shots. Approximately how many did he miss?

4. A test had 60 questions. Martha had 15% wrong. How many answers were right?

5. This year the number of sophomores out for football is 10% greater than last year. If there were 20 sophomores out for football last year, how many are out for football this year?

6. Last week the sophomore class sold 200 pretzels at the field hockey game. This week they sold 5% less. How many pretzels did they sell this week?

7. Which of the following is **NOT** a way to find 120% of a 30?

   (A) $30 + 0.20 \cdot 30$

   (B) $1.20 \cdot 30$

   (C)   multiply 30 by 6, divide the result by 5

   (D)   multiply 30 by 5, divide the result by 6.

8. Which of the following is a way to find 110% of 40?

   I   Multiply 40 by 10, divide the result by 11.

   II $0.11 \cdot 40$

   III Add 40 to 10% of 40

   IV $1.10 \cdot 40$

   (A)   III only   (B)   III and IV only

   (C)   II only   (D)   I and III only

9. A skate board that regularly sells for $45 is on sale at a discount of 35%. Find the sale price.

10. Find the total cost of a $70 Walkman cassette player including a sales tax of 7%.

11. A $40 jacket is advertised at $\frac{1}{4}$ off the regular price. The same brand jacket is on sale at a discount of 20% at another store. How much is saved by buying at the store with the lower sale price?

12. A sofa at the Mart is discounted by $\frac{1}{5}$ off the regular price of $350. Furniture Bargains advertises the same sofa at 40% discount on the regular $400 price. At which store is the sofa less expensive and by how much has the cost been reduced at that store?

13. A baseball team won 70% of the games and tied 5% of the games played this season. If 20 games were played, how many games were lost?

14. Of the 60 bikes at the Bicycle Rental Shop, 15% are rented. How many are left in the store?

WRITTEN EXERCISES

1. What number is 38% of 300?

2. 7% of 140 is what number?

3. Jane usually makes 70% of her basketball foul shots.
    This season she attempted 125 foul shots. Approximately how many did she miss?

4. A test had 80 questions. Rashid got 20% of the questions wrong. How many did he get right?

5. This year the amount of money raised by the sophomore class was 10% less than raised last year. Last year the sophomores raised $1200. How much did this year's class raise?

6. This year, the number of students out for Pam's basketball team is 5% greater than last year. If there were 40 girls out for basketball last year, how many are on this year's team?

7. Which of the following is **NOT** a way to find 140% of a number?
    (A)   Multiply the number by 5 and then divide the result by 7.
    (B)   Multiply the number by 0.40. Then add the result to 40.
    (C)   Multiply the number by 7 and then divide the result by 5.
    (D)   Multiply the number by 1.40.

8. Which of the following is a way to find 105% of 20?
    I $0.105 \cdot 120$
    II $20 + 0.05 \cdot 20$
    III Multiply 20 by 21 and divide the result by 20.
    IV $1.05 \cdot 20$
    (A)   II only   (B)   II or IV only
    (C)   I or IV only   (D)   II, III, or IV only

9. Find the total cost of a $30 camera including a city sales tax of 8%.

10. A compact disk that regularly sells for $19 is on sale at a discount of 25%. Find the sale price.

11. The sophomore class bought 500 hot dogs to sell at football games. 15% were sold at the first game. How many were left?

12. Harry went to bat 40 times this season. He scored a hit 10% of the time. How many of his attempts did not result in a hit?

13. Video Shack is selling a type of video game at $\frac{1}{5}$ off its regular $50.00 price. The same type of game is selling for 26% off its regular price of $62 at Bargain Videos. At which store is that type of video game less expensive and by how much has it been reduced at that store?

14. Which of the following is **NOT** equal to the other three?

   (A) $1\frac{1}{10}$ (B) $1.1 \cdot 100$ (C) $\frac{11}{10}$ (D)   110%

15. Four friends are planning to eat at a restaurant where dinners can cost between $12.00 and $17.00 per person. They plan to leave a tip of 15% of the total bill. Which of the following is closest to the final tip?

   (A) $2.00   (B) $4.00   (C) $9.00   (D) $15.00

16. The number of students in Monroe High School who contributed to the Scholarship Fund is 415. This figure is 125% of last year's. This means that

   (A)   25 more students contributed this year than last year.

   (B)   The number of Monroe High students giving to the Scholarship Fund increased from last year to this year.

   (C)   The number of contributors decreased from last year to this year.

   (D)   Monroe High raised more money this year than last year.

17. Last week Lila earned $370. As part of estimating the amount of her paycheck, she first adds and then rounds to the nearest whole number percent the deductions indicated below.

Federal Income Tax	15.0%
FICA	7.5%
Unemployment Insurance	0.25%
State Income Tax	2.5%

   Her estimate of the amount of her paycheck is between

   (A) $60 and $100   (B) $260 and $310

   (C) $320 and $380   (D) $380 and $405

18. It costs a high school Boosters Association $0.30 to buy a can of soda for sale at football games. If they are to make a 20% profit on each soda sale, which of the following computations will give the amount they should charge for each can?

   (A) $0.30 \cdot 0.20$ (B) $0.30 \div 0.20$

   (C) $0.20 \cdot 0.30 + 0.20$ (D) $0.20 \cdot 0.30 + 0.30$

19.   Mr. Burke purchased a new car for $14,000 plus a 6% sales tax. How much more would he have paid for the car if the sales tax had been 7%?

(A) $140   (B) $210   (C) $840   (D) $980

20.   A bicycle costs $85. Which of these processes could you use to find the total cost including a 7% sales tax?

I   Multiply $85 by 0.07 and add the result to $85.

II   Multiply 85 by 1.07

III   Multiply 85 by 0.93.

IV   Multiply 85 by 0.07 and subtract from 85.

(A)   I only   (B)   II only

(C)   III or IV only   (D)   I or II only

21.   A federal study found that in the park areas of a certain state, 90% of the 500 streams and 40% of the 600 lakes tested in the study were acidic enough to cause damage to some aquatic life. How many of the lakes tested were acidic enough to cause damage to some aquatic life?

(A)   600   (B)   450   (C)   360   (D)   240

OPEN-ENDED QUESTION

22.   For a sale, a store owner lowered the regular price of an item by 20%. After the sale, the store owner raised the price by 20% of its sale price. A clerk in the store reasoned that the price would now be the same as before the first sale and marked the price at the original price. Did the clerk make a mistake? Justify your answer with an example of your own.

REVIEW

1.   If the following pattern keeps repeating, what letter will be in the 114th position?
acuteacuteacute...

2.   6 less than twice Mona's age is 12. How old is Mona?

Simplify.

3.   7 - 9   4. 7 · -9   5. $(-2)^3$ 6.   64 ÷ 8 - 2 + 7 · 3

4.3 The Three Cases of Percent

OBJECTIVE   To apply the three cases of percent

In the last lesson you learned to solve problems that involve finding a percent of a number. You saw that it is possible to write an equation describing the following kind of problem.

30% of 120 is what number?

First, let **n** = the number.

30% of 120 is what **n**umber then becomes:

$$0.30 \cdot 120 = \quad \mathbf{n}$$

Two other types of percent problems are illustrated in Examples 1 and 2 below. The technique for solving these problems is basically the same as the technique used above.

EXAMPLE 1   4 is what percent of 6?

Strategy   Write the sentence as an equation.

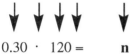

4 is what % of 6?

$$4 = \quad x \cdot 6 \qquad \textbf{Let x = the percent written as a decimal.}$$

$$4 = 6x$$

$$\frac{4}{6} = \frac{6x}{6} \qquad\qquad \textbf{Divide each side by 6.}$$

$$\frac{2}{3} = x$$

Write $\frac{2}{3}$ as a decimal.

$$x = 0.66\frac{2}{3}$$

$$\begin{array}{r} 0.66 \quad \text{or } 0.66\frac{2}{3} \\ 3\overline{)2.00} \\ \underline{1\ 8} \\ 20 \\ \underline{18} \\ 2 \end{array}$$

$0.66\frac{2}{3}$ means $66\frac{2}{3}$ %

Solution   Thus, 4 is $\mathbf{66\frac{2}{3}}$ % of 4.

EXAMPLE 2   18 is 35% of what number?

Round your answer to the nearest whole number.

Strategy   Use the first sentence to write an equation.

Let **n** = the number.

18 is 35% of what **number** ?

18 = 0.35 ·   **n**

Solve   18 = 0.35n

$$\frac{18}{0.35} = \frac{0.35n}{0.35}$$

51.428571 = n   **18 ÷ 0.35 = 51.428571**

Now round 51.428571 to the nearest whole number.

51.428571

51   **4 is less than 5. So leave the 1 unchanged in rounding.**

Solution   Thus, **51** is the number, rounded to the nearest whole number.

EXAMPLE 3   In basketball, good players make approximately 70% of their foul shots. Suppose that a good player missed 26 foul shot attempts during a season. Approximately how many foul shots did he attempt that season?

Strategy   The player missed 26 shots.

70% of the shots **made** means he made 70 out 100 shots.

Therefore, he **missed** 30 out of 100 shots, or **30%**.

To write an equation, express the given data in terms of **one** sentence.

Misses are 30% of attempts   **OR** 30% of attempts are **misses**.

Either sentence will do. Use the first sentence to write an equation.

Misses are 30% of **A**ttempts.

26   = 0.30 · **A**   **Let A = number of attempts.**

Solve the equation.   **(continued on next page)**

$$26 = 0.30A$$

$$\frac{26}{0.30} = \frac{0.30A}{0.30}$$

$$86.666667 = x$$

By calculator, 26 ÷ 0.30 = 86.666667.

Solution He attempted approximately 87 foul shots.

Round to the nearest whole number.

DISCOVERY The figure at the right shows a large rectangle divided into 5 small rectangles all the same size. One of the 5 is shaded. Write an equation to solve each of the following.

(1)   The number of shaded rectangles is what % of the number of unshaded rectangles?

(2)   The number of unshaded rectangles is what % of the total number of rectangles?

EXAMPLE 4 The figure at the right shows a large rectangle divided into 8 small rectangles all the same size. 3 of the 8 are shaded. The number of shaded rectangles is what % of the total number of rectangles?

Strategy Use the last sentence to write an equation.
Let x = the percent written as a decimal.
(continued on next page)

Shaded is <u>what %</u> of total?

↓   ↓   ↓   ↓   ↓

3   =   x   ·   8   **3 shaded, 8 total**

Solve $3 = 8x$

$\dfrac{3}{8} = \dfrac{8x}{8}$

$0.375 = x$

Now write 0.375 as a percent.

$0.375 = 37 .5\%$

Solution   Therefore, the number of shaded rectangles is 37.5% of the total number.

EXAMPLE 5   The number of shaded rectangles is what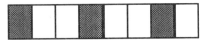
% of the number of unshaded rectangles?

Let x = the % written as a decimal.

Strategy   shaded is <u>what %</u> of unshaded?

↓   ↓   ↓   ↓   ↓

3   =   x   ·   5

Solve $3 = 5x$

$\dfrac{3}{5} = \dfrac{5x}{5}$

$0.60 = x$

$$\begin{array}{r} 0.60 \\ 5\overline{)3.00} \end{array}$$

Now write 0.60 as a percent.

$0.60 = 60\%$

Solution   Therefore, the number of shaded rectangles is 60% of the number of
unshaded ones.

EXAMPLE 6   Mr. Roth sold a T.V. and made a profit of $70.
The profit was 20% of the cost. Find the cost.

Strategy   Let c = cost.

Write the last sentence as an equation.

The profit was 20% of the cost.

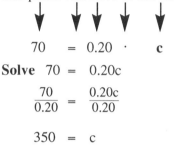

$$70 = 0.20 \cdot c$$

Solve $70 = 0.20c$

$$\frac{70}{0.20} = \frac{0.20c}{0.20}$$

$$350 = c$$

$$0.20\overline{)70.\,00} \longrightarrow 20\overline{)7000}^{\,350}$$

Solution   So, the cost of the T.V. was $350.

SUMMARY

How do you write an equation for each of the following?

1.   What is 5% of 40?   2. 3 is what % of 7?   3. 6% of what number is 12?

4.   If 60% of the sophomore class are boys, what percent are girls?

5.   If a football team won 80% of its games this season and there were no ties, what % of the games did the team lose?

6.   How do you solve the equation $4 = 5x$?
     How do you write the solution as a percent?

What equation can be written to solve each problem involving a rectangle divided into 5 rectangles of equal size?   (ex. 7-8)

7.   The number of shaded rectangles is what % of the total number of rectangles?

8.   The number of shaded rectangles is what % of the number of unshaded rectangles?

CLASSROOM PRACTICE

1. What is 6% of 40?
2. 30% of 120 is what number?
3. 48 is 60% of what number?
4. 20% of what number is 12?
5. 6 is what % of 8?
6. 5 is what % of 8?
7. 75 is 300% of what number?
8. What % of 50 is 40?
9. 20% of 80 is what number?
10. 21 is 70% of what number?

Round the answer to the nearest whole number or whole number percent.

11. 14 is 27% of what number?
12. 38 is what % of 21?
13. What is 23% of 112.34?
14. 125% of what number is 257?

15. John usually makes approximately 80% of his basketball foul shots. Suppose he missed 17 foul shots this season. Approximately how many foul shots did he attempt this season?

16. A camera store ordered 150 Minoltas. So far, 60 have been sold. What % of the 150 cameras has not yet been sold?

17. Joe sold a car and made a profit of $850. The profit was 10% of the cost. Find the cost.

18. Mona got an $8.00 raise. The raise was 5% of her salary. Find her salary.

The figure at the right shows a large rectangle divided into 9 small rectangles all the same size. Use this figure to answer exercises 19-21 below.

19. The number of unshaded rectangles is what % of the number of shaded rectangles?

20. The number of shaded rectangles is what % of the total number of rectangles?

21. The number of unshaded rectangles is what % of the total number of rectangles?

WRITTEN EXERCISES

1. What is 8% of 30?   2. 20% of 180 is what number?
3. 24 is 30% of what number?   4. 60% of what number is 36?
5. 2 is what % of 5?   6. 7 is what % of 8?
7. 40 is 200% of what number?   8. What % of 20 is 12?
9. 70% of what number is 14?   10. What number is 35% of 40?

Round the answer to the nearest whole number or whole number percent.

11. 17 is 32% of what number?   12. 51 is what % of 43?
13. What is 37% of 218.45?   14. 125% of what number is 412?

15. When bowling, Susan gets a strike approximately 30% of the time. She misses a strike 25 times in a practice session. Approximately how many times does she attempt a strike in a practice session?

16. A field hockey team won 80% of its games this season and there were no ties. The team lost 5 games. How many games did the team play?

17. Last week Jane earned $40.00 working part time. This week she earned $48.00. The increase this week is what % of last week's earnings?

18. Jan has a collection of 50 tapes and C.D.s. Of this collection, 5 are C.D.s What percent of the collection are tapes?

19. Of the 80 bicycles at the Rentabike shop, 20 are now being rented. What percent of the bikes are still available for rent?

The figure at the right shows a large rectangle divided into 7 small rectangles all the same size. Use this figure to answer exercises 20-22 below.

20. The number of unshaded rectangles is what % of the number of shaded rectangles?

21. The number of shaded rectangles is what % of the total number of rectangles?

22. The number of unshaded rectangles is what % of the total number of rectangles?

OPEN-ENDED QUESTION

23.   The Best Deal Store advertises that it will not be undersold. If you
        can find a lower regularly advertised price from another store on any item
        that Best Deal Store sells, the storewill match that lower price and also give you
        an additional reduction that is 5% of the difference of the two prices. Is the
        additional reduction significant? Present a convincing argument in support of your
        answer. Include a sample example as part of your argument.

REVIEW

1.   Insert the appropriate inequality symbol, < or >.

        1.7^7 ? 4.1^3

2.   Insert the appropriate inequality symbol, < or >, to make -10 ? -4 true.

3.   The approximate value of 0.53 · 0.00932 is

        (A)   0.004   (B)   0.005   (C)   0.04   (D)   0.05

4.   On a new quiz game, each correct answer was worth 8 points. 2 points were
        deducted for each incorrect answer. Which formula below represents the total
        score T if C represents the number of right answers and I the number of incorrect
        answers?

        (A) $T = 8 + C - 2 - I$ (B) $T = 8c + 2I$

        (C) $T = 8C - 2I$ (D) $S = 8I - 2C$

5.   Evaluate $\frac{3}{7}x + 19$ for x = 14.

6.   Which point could represent the
        product of the numbers represented
        by point T and P?

7.   What is the units digit in the 47th term of the sequence $3^1, 3^2, 3^3, 3^4, ...$?

4.4 Interpreting Data Tables

OBJECTIVES   To compare data displayed in a data table

To apply percent to interpreting a data table

Sometimes you may be asked to compare data displayed in a table or chart.
The next example shows a fairly easy comparison of this kind. Then, in the second
example, you will connect this idea to a percent application studied in the last lesson.

EXAMPLE 1   Use this table to answer the question below.

Average Weekly Incomes of Persons at Least 25 Years Old

Education Level	Men	Women
high school not completed	$332	$250
completed high school	$419	$318
1-3 years of college	$538	$432
4 or more years of college	$966	$668

According to the table, a woman who has completed 1-3 years of
college has a greater average weekly income than a man who has
completed high school but has not gone to college. How much greater
is her average weekly income?

Strategy   You are comparing salaries of :

- a **woman** with **1-3 years college** and

- a **man who completed high school but not college.**

Education Level	Men	Women
high school not completed	$332	$250
completed high school	**$419**	$318
1-3 years of college	$538	**$432**
4 or more years of college	$966	$668

$432 is how much greater than **$419**?

Subtract.   **$432 - $419 = $13**

Solution   Thus, the woman earns $13 more than the man.

EXAMPLE 2   Use the data table from Example 1 to answer the following question. The income of women with 4 or more years of college is what percent of the income of men with the same education? Round the answer to the nearest whole number percent.

Strategy   From the table, first find the income of each for 4 or more years of college.

Education Level	Men	Women
high school not completed	$432	$350
completed high school	$419	$318
1-3 years of college	$538	$432
4 or more years of college	**$966**	**$668**

The last row provides this information.

income of **women**: **$668**   income of **men**: **$966**

Let x = the percent written as a decimal and write an equation.

Income of women is what % of income of men?

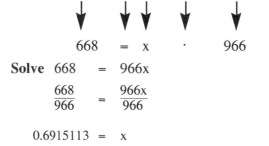

$$668 = x \cdot 966$$

Solve $668 = 966x$

$$\frac{668}{966} = \frac{966x}{966}$$

$$0.6915113 = x$$

Round 0.**69**15113 to the nearest hundredth.

        0.69

Write 0.69 as a percent.

Solution   Thus, the percent is **69%**. $0.\mathbf{69} = \mathbf{69\%}$

Sometimes data must be interpreted from an advertisement. This is illustrated in the next example.

EXAMPLE 3   Use this advertisement to answer the question below.

PIZZA CASTLE   call 893-3131

Homemade, 12-inch , Italian style, tomato pies delivered to your door,
$8.00 plus $.50 for each topping up to 3 and $.35 for each additional
topping beyond 3.

Toppings

pepperoni	ham	sausage	bacon
onions	olives	green peppers	mushrooms

A deluxe pizza costs $9.00. Its toppings are pepperoni, sausage, green peppers, olives, and mushrooms. In terms of price only, which is a better deal, a deluxe pizza or a pizza with separately priced toppings that are the same as those on a deluxe pizza? How much is saved?

Strategy   Use the advertisement to find the cost for toppings bought separately. There are **5** toppings:

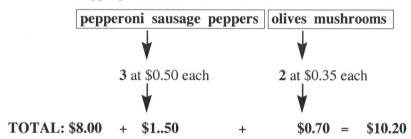

pepperoni sausage peppers	olives mushrooms
3 at $0.50 each	2 at $0.35 each

TOTAL: $8.00   + $1..50   + $0.70 = $10.20

So, the pizza would cost $10.20 if toppings are bought separately.

The saving from buying a deluxe pizza is:

cost of toppings separately   -   cost of deluxe pizza
$10.20   - $9.00

Solution   Thus, the saving is: **$1.20.**

The deluxe pizza is a better buy.

The saving can be described as a percent of the cost of the pizza with topping bought separately. This is illustrated in the next example.

EXAMPLE 4   In example 3, the saving is what percent of the cost if the toppings are bought separately? Round the answer to the nearest whole number percent.

Strategy   From Example 3: **cost of pizza toppings bought separately was $10.20 saving was $1.20**

Write an equation.

Saving is what % of cost of toppings bought separately?

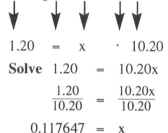

1.20   =   x   ·   10.20

Solve 1.20 = 10.20x

$$\frac{1.20}{10.20} = \frac{10.20x}{10.20}$$

0.117647 = x

Round 0.117647 to the nearest hundredth.   **7 is more than 5. Round**
            0.12   **1 up to 2.**

Write 0.12 as a percent.   0 .12 = 12%

Solution   Thus, the percent is 12%.

EXAMPLE 5   About how much more is the average income in New York City than the average income in Los Angeles?

Average Price of a New House

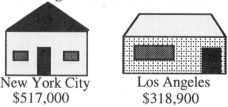

New York City   Los Angeles
$517,000 $318,900

In each city, the average home price is about 7 times the average income

Strategy   **(1)** Use the data in the figure to find the average income in each city.

Let x = New York income.   Let y = Los Angeles Income.
house price is 7 times income   house price is 7 times income
517,000   = 7 ·   x   318,900   = 7 ·   y
Solve each equation.   **(continued on next page)**

$$517,000 \quad = \quad 7x \qquad\qquad 318,900 \quad = \quad 7y$$

$$\frac{517000}{7} \quad = \quad \frac{7x}{7} \qquad\qquad \frac{318900}{7} \quad = \quad \frac{7y}{7}$$

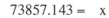

$$73857.143 = \quad x \qquad\qquad 45557.143 = \quad y$$

Round each to the nearest whole dollar.

New York City income   Los Angeles income

$73,857 $45,557

(2)   To find how much more New York income is than Los Angeles:

Subtract. $73,857   **New York income**

          -      45,557   **Los Angeles income**

                 $28,300

Solution   Thus, the New York income is about **$28,300** more than the Los Angeles income.

EXAMPLE 6   Bill spends 120 minutes a day doing homework. The percent of time he spends on each subject is given at the right. About how many minutes does he spend altogether on Spanish and Math?

Subject	%
Spanish	18%
English	20%
History	15%
Math	27%
Cooking	20%

Strategy   **(1)**   First use the table to find the percents for Spanish and Math.
Spanish: 18%
Math: 27%

Subject	%
Spanish	**18%**
English	20%
History	15%
Math	**27%**
Cooking	20%

(2)   Find the **total** for the two:
18% + 27% = **45%**

(3)   Find 45% of 120 minutes.
$$0.45 \cdot 120 = 54$$

Solution   Therefore, he spends **54** minutes on Spanish and Math together.

SUMMARY

The table at the right shows the number of
boys out for five different sports. Use the data
in this table to answer exercises 1-3.

Sport	Number of Students
Football	50
Basketball	40
Soccer	35
Wrestling	55
Track	20

1. How can you find the total number of
   boys in all five sports?

2. How can you find how many more boys are out for football than soccer?

3. How do you find what % of the number out for football is the number out for
   track?

4. A bank recommends that the average monthly take-home pay should be at
   least 5 times the average monthly mortgage payment.
   How can you find the monthly take-home pay necessary to afford a monthly
   mortgage payment of $800?

Use the table at the right to answer
exercises 5-6.

Mr. Ricardi's Budget for $300 Take-Home Pay

Expenses	Percent of Take-Home Pay
Food	20%
Rent	30%
Car	25%
Savings	15%
Entertainment	?%

5. How do you find the amount
   he budgets for food and car
   combined?

6. How do you find the amount
   he budgets for entertainment?

   HINT: The total of all the percents must be ____ ?

   Then use this total to find the percent he allows for entertainment.

Use this advertisement to answer exercises 7-8 below.

> ### VIDEO GAME SPECIAL
> video game player: $85 plus $20 for each game up to 2 and
> $15 for each additional video game beyond 2
> A Deluxe Video Game package consists of the player and 3 games and sells
> for $130.

7. How do you determine if the deluxe package is a good buy?

8. How do you find what percent the saving is of the cost if items are bought
   separately?

CLASSROOM PRACTICE

This table shows the number of students in grades 9 and 10 enrolled in foreign language courses. Use the table to answer exercises 1-10.

Language	Grade 9	Grade 10
Spanish	140	110
French	80	75
Latin	40	35
German	30	24

1. How many 10th graders take Latin?
2. How many 9th graders take French?
3. How many 9th grade foreign- language students are not in Latin?
4. How many more 10th graders study Spanish than German?
5. The number of 10th graders in German is how much less than the number of 9th graders in German?
6. The number of 9th graders in German is what percent of the number of 9th graders in Latin?
7. The number of 10th graders in German is what percent of the number of 9th graders in German?
8. Find the total number of 9th graders taking foreign languages.
9. Find the total number of 10th graders taking foreign languages.
10. The total number of 10th grade language students is what percent of the total number of 9th grade foreign language students. Round the answer to the nearest whole number percent.

Use this advertisement to answer exercises 11-12.

ICE CREAM SUPREME
24 flavors of ice cream for your favorite sundae
$1.75 plus $.35 for each topping up to 3 and $.25 for each additional topping
Toppings
strawberries, bananas, walnuts, hot fudge, hot butterscotch, cookies

---

11. Find the cost of a sundae with strawberries, walnuts, hot butterscotch, and cookies.
12. A deluxe sundae has 4 toppings and sells for $2.95. How much is saved by buying a deluxe sundae rather than ordering the toppings separately, as in Exercise 11?

13.   The amount saved by buying the deluxe sundae of Exercise 12 is what percent of the cost of ordering the toppings separately? Round your answer to the nearest whole number percent.

Use this advertisement to answer exercises 14-15.

14.   About how much more is the cost per day for the cruise than the cost for the vacation to Los Angeles?

15.   The savings by taking the Los Angeles vacation is what percent of the cost of the cruise? Round your answer to the nearest whole number percent.

COST of a ONE WEEK VACATION	
from New York to Los Angeles including plane ticket	cruise from New York to Caribbean islands
$2,800	$3,200

Use the table at the right to answer exercises 16-20.

16.   How many students received a B?

17.   How many student receive a grade of C or higher?

18.   What % of students failed?

19.   How many students received an F?

20.   What two grades account for $\frac{1}{2}$ of all grades distributed?

DISTRIBUTION OF MATHEMATICS GRADES OF 200 STUDENTS

Grade	Percent
A	16%
B	26%
C	40%
D	10%
F	?%

WRITTEN EXERCISES

The table at the right shows the weekly distribution of take home pay for two wage earners. Use this table to answer exercises 1-10.

WEEKLY EXPENSES

Expenses	Chris	Meg
Car	$45	$55
Entertainment	$25	$30
Rent	$75	$90
Savings	$15	$20
Food	$40	$55

1.   What does Meg spend on rent?

2.   What are Chris's total weekly expenses?

3.   Find Meg's total weekly expenses.

4.   How much more does Chris spend on food than entertainment?

5.   Chris's savings are what percent of Meg's savings?

6.   What percent of savings is the amount Chris spends on entertainment?

7.   Chris' s total expenses are what percent of Meg's total expenses?

8.   What are Chris's total expenses other than entertainment?

9.   The amount Chris spends on entertainment and rent is what percent of his total expenses?

10. The total of Chris's two highest expenses is what percent of his weekly income?

Use this advertisement to answer exercises 11-13.

> HUNGRY MAN'S CAFETERIA DINNER
> Choice of main course: turkey, ham, chicken: $4.75
> plus $.95 for each of the following up to 3 choices and $.75 for each
> choice beyond 3.
> salad, soup, baked potato, mashed potatoes, french fries, peas, carrots, soda,
> coffee, tea, jello, ice cream

11. Find the cost of a turkey dinner with salad, soup, baked potato, peas, soda, and ice cream.

12. A deluxe dinner offers the main course, a salad or soup, any potato, one vegetable, coffee or soda, and one desert, all for the special price of $7.95. How much can one save by taking the special rather than ordering each item separately?

13. The saving in exercise 12 is what percent of the cost of ordering each item separately, as in exercise 11?

The table at the right shows the percent of 200 sophomore girls out for sports.

SPORT	PERCENT
basketball	20%
field hockey	25%
track	10%
lacrosse	15%
softball	20%
no sport	?%

14. How many girls are out for lacrosse?

15. How many girls are not out for any sport?

16. How many girls are out for track?

17. How many more girls are out for field hockey than softball?

18. What is the total number of girls enrolled in some sport?

Some banks estimate that a person's **yearly** take-home pay should be about 6 times the person's yearly housing rent costs.

Average Yearly Cost of Renting a Bedroom Apartment

New York City: $15,000
Albuquerque: $9,000

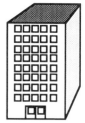

19.   The rental cost in Albuquerque is what percent of the rental cost in New York?

20.   About how much less is the average yearly income in Albuquerque than in New York?

OPEN-ENDED QUESTION

21.   Three high schools are proud of their driver-education programs. The table below shows the number of students in each school's program last year and the number of students who passed the driver's test on the first try last year.

School	number of students	students passing on first try
Forester	50	40
Clinton	90	45
Windsor West	75	55

A student at Windsor West argued that her school was the most successful in getting its students to pass the test on the first try, since 55 is greater than 40 and 45. A Forester student argued that her school's program had the best success record of the three schools. She used percent to justify her belief.

Is she right? Give a reason showing mathematically which school was best .

REVIEW

1.   4% of what number is 12?

2.   A football team won 80% of the games played this season. There were no ties. The team lost 4 games. How many games did the team play?

3.   What is the next number in the pattern 10, 21, 43, 87, ...?

4.   Solve $3x - 7 = 14$

4.5 Bar Graphs

OBJECTIVES   To interpret data displayed in a bar graph

To draw a bar graph for a given set of data

To interpret mileage charts

In the last lesson you interpreted data supplied by a **data table**. Sometimes it is more convenient to display data using a **bar graph**. This is illustrated in the examples that follow.

EXAMPLE 1   According to the bar graph, how many Juniors are taking Latin?

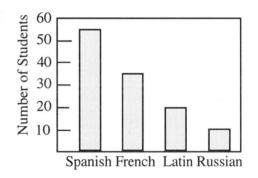

JUNIORS IN FOREIGN LANGUAGES

Strategy

In the **Latin box**, draw a dashed vertical.

From the top of the dashed vertical, draw a dashed arrow to the left: read **20**.

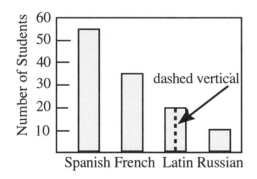

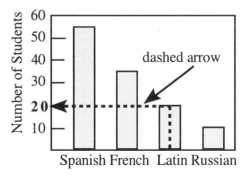

Solution   Thus, the number of Juniors in Latin is **20**.

EXAMPLE 2   The number of juniors taking French   JUNIORS IN FOREIGN LANGUAGES
is what % of all junior foreign-
language students? Round the answer
to the nearest whole number percent.

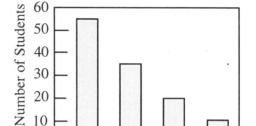

Strategy   **Think:** French is what % of **all**?

1. You need to add all numbers of
students.
So, first you must find from the table
the number of students in each
foreign language course.

2. Find from the table the number
of students in each language.

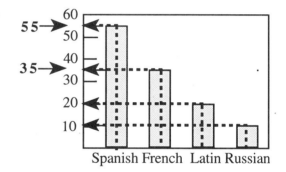

   Russian: **10**

   Latin: **20**

   French: about half-way
              between 30 and 40

   $$\frac{30 + 40}{2} = \frac{70}{2} = \mathbf{35}$$

   Spanish: about half-way
              between 50 and 60

   $$\frac{50 + 60}{2} = \frac{110}{2} = \mathbf{55}$$

3. So, the total number of students is **10** + **20** + **35** + **55** = 120.

4. Now you can write an equation involving percent.
   French is <u>what %</u> of all
   35   =   x · 120

5. **Solve.** 35   =   120x

   $$\frac{35}{120} = \frac{120x}{120}$$

   .2916666   =   x

Solution   Thus, the percent is **29%**, rounded to the nearest whole number percent.

EXAMPLE 3   Temperatures in the summer in Wyoming can vary greatly from day to night. The temperatures below were recorded for one week in July.

93, 68, 81, 79, 82, 94, 88, 85, 71, 65, 80, 87, 91, 83, 74, 80, 80, 82, 85, 80, 93

Make a bar graph showing the frequency or number of temperatures in each of an **equal** number of temperature **ranges**. Which range contains the greatest number of temperatures?

Strategy   First, write the data in numerical order:

65, 68, 71, 74, 79, 80, 80, 80, 80, 81, 82, 82, 83, 85, 85, 87, 88, 91, 93, 93, **94**. These 21 numbers can be **divided** into equal **ranges.**

Let's choose **6 equal ranges** for this problem. Find these 6 ranges.

(1)   **largest - smallest** temperature = **94 - 65 = 29**

(2)   Divide: 29 ÷ **6 = 5**, rounded to nearest whole number.

So, the 1st range will include the **5** numbers beginning with **65:**

65, 66, 67, 68, 69.

These numbers **range** from   **65** to **65 + 4,** or **65-69**

Thus, the 5 ranges are:

65-69   70-74   75-79   80-84   85-89   90-94

Find the number of items in each temperature range.

Temperature Ranges

65-69	70-74	75-79	80-84	85-89	90-94
65, 68	71, 74	79	80, 80, 80, 80, 81, 82, 82, 83	85, 85, 87, 88	91, 93, 93, 94
2	2	1	8	4	4

Number of Items in Each Temperature Range

Thus, the frequencies range from **1** to **8**.

Now you can draw the bar graph.

(continued on next page)

Use graph paper to draw the following stages of completing the bar graph.

Draw the horizontal axis for the temperature ranges. Write in the 5 ranges as shown below.

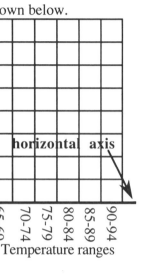

Draw the vertical axis for frequencies numbering from **1** to **8**.

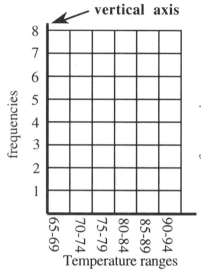

Draw the first bar in range 60-65 and **2** units high.

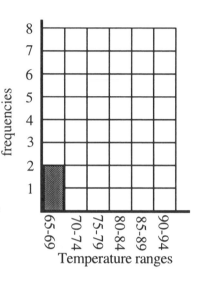

Solution   From the graph it is easy to see that the **greatest** number of temperatures fall in the **range 80-84.**

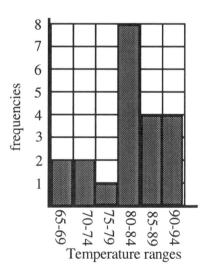

The technique for drawing the type of bar graph shown in Example 3 will be applied in Chapter 6. That chapter will introduce you to the important idea of **statistics**.

The next example shows how to interpret a **mileage chart**.

A mileage chart is read very much the same way as a bar graph.

A mileage chart is used to find distances between cities.

Such a chart is helpful in planning long-distance vacation trips.

EXAMPLE 4   Use this chart to find the driving distance from Newark to Cape May.

Mileage Between Principal Cities	Atlantic City	Bridgeton	Camden	Cape May	Cherry Hill	Easton Pa.	New York, N.Y.
Atlantic City	0	81	57	48	55	115	130
Camden	57	40	0	84	9	57	104
Newark	108	116	84	154	80	66	27
Paterson	123	131	99	165	95	63	32
Trenton	74	70	32	106	35	52	74
New Brunswick	93	99	56	128	58	45	46

Strategy   Draw a horizontal line in the row containing **Newark**.

Draw a vertical line in the column containing **Cape May**.

Mileage Between Principal Cities	Atlantic City	Bridgeton	Camden	**Cape May**	Cherry Hill	Easton Pa.	New York, N.Y.
Atlantic City	0	81	57	48	55	115	130
Camden	57	40	0	84	9	57	104
Newark	108	116	84	**154**	80	66	27
Paterson	123	131	99	165	95	63	32
Trenton	74	70	32	106	35	52	74
New Brunswick	93	99	56	128	58	45	46

The two dashed lines cross at the number **154**.

Solution   Thus, the driving distance from **Newark** to **Cape May** is 154 miles.

The next example will apply the relationship between **speed, time, and distance.**

For example, if you drive **30 mph** (miles per hour), then in **3 hours** you drive **90 miles.**

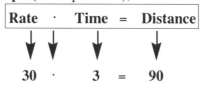

EXAMPLE 5   Using the result of Example 4 on the previous page, approximately how long would it take to drive from Newark to Cape May in traffic that averages 55 miles per hour?

Strategy   In Example 4 you saw that the driving distance from Newark to Cape May is **154** miles.

Now find the time to drive **154** miles at the rate of **55** miles per hour. Use the formula above.

Rate · Time = Distance

55 · T = 154   **Let T = the time.**

Solve 55T = 154.

$$\frac{55T}{55} = \frac{154}{55}$$

T = 2.8

Solution   So, the approximate time is **3** hours.   **Round 2.8 to 3.**

SUMMARY

Use the table at the right to answer exercises 1-3

1. How do you determine the number of accidents in 1992?

2. How do you determine in which year there were 16 accidents?

3. How do you find what % the number of accidents in 1991 was of the number of accidents in 1992?

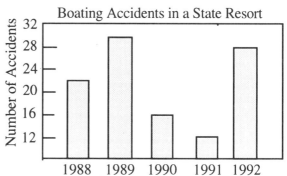

4. The grades of the 14 students in Mr. Rashid's math class for the last test were: 75, 81, 60, 96, 100, 75, 72, 60, 81, 96, 95, 80, 53, and 90.

If the data is divided into 6 equal ranges, tell how to find these 6 ranges.

5. Tell how to make a bar graph showing the frequency of grades in the data of exercise 4 above.

Use the mileage chart of example 4 of this lesson to answer exercises 6-8 below.

6. How do you find the driving distance from Camden to Easton Pa.?

7. How do you find the driving distance from Trenton to New York, N.Y.?

8. Clem drives 45 miles per hour. Explain how to find about how long it will take him to drive from Trenton to Cape May.

CLASSROOM PRACTICE

Use the chart at the right to answer exercises 1-4.

1. How much money was spent on travel?

2. How much more money was spent on wages than research?

3. What was the total amount of expenses?

4. The amount spent on travel was what percent of the amount spent on research?

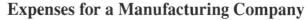
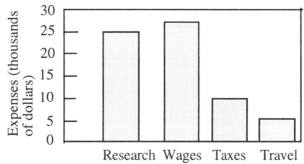

Expenses for a Manufacturing Company

At the right is a bar graph showing sales of sports equipment.

Estimate the number of balls sold for each sport.

5. soccer   6. football

7. basketball   8. volleyball

9. Name all sports for which less than 2,000,000 were sold.

10. The number of volleyballs sold was what % of the number of soccer balls sold?

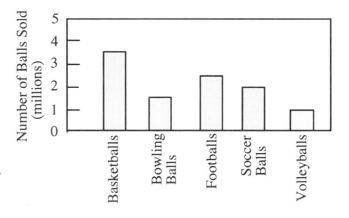

11.   Many counties in the U.S.A. are
       named after presidents. The data
       table at the right shows the number
       of counties with the same
       presidential name.
       Draw a bar graph that represents
       the same data. Use the following
       ranges for the data: 0-4, 5-9, 10-
       14, etc.

County Name	Number of Counties
Washington	32
Adams	12
Jefferson	25
Madison	20
Monroe	17

12.   The following are Natasha's bowling scores this past month.
       156, 131, 124, 115, 143, 250, 158, 131, 121, 131, 143, 152, 130, 137, 143, 124,
       137, 131, 121, 130, 152, 300, 131, 124, and 143.
       Make a bar graph showing the frequency or number of scores in each of 7
       equal ranges of scores. Which range contains the greatest number of scores?

Use the mileage chart of Example 4 to answer exercises 13 -15.

13.   Find the driving distance from Atlantic City to Easton Pa.

14.   How much further is it from Camden to Atlantic City than from Camden to N.Y.?

15.   Approximately how long would it take to drive from Paterson to Cape May
       if heavy traffic on a holiday week end makes it possible to drive at an average
       rate of 40 miles per hour?

WRITTEN EXERCISES

The bar graph at the right shows the results
of a survey of buyers of tickets to each
type of movie.
Use the bar graph to answer exercises 1-6.

1.   How many chose westerns?

2.   How many more chose science
      fiction than comedy?

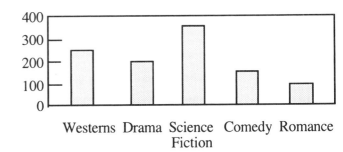

3.   Find the total number of people surveyed.

4.   How many did not choose drama?

5.   The number choosing comedy was what % of the number choosing drama?

6.   How many chose westerns or comedy?

Use the bar graph at the right to answer
Exercises 7-12.

NUMBER OF JUNIOR BOYS OUT FOR
SPORTS

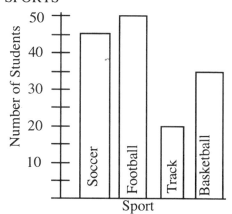

7.   How many junior boys are out for
     track?

8.   How many junior boys are out for
     soccer?

9.   The number out for basketball is how
     much less than the number out for
     football?

10. The number out for soccer is what %
     of the number out for football?

11. What is the total number of juniors
     out for sports?

12. The number out for football is what %
     of the total number of juniors out for
     all sports?

13. Draw a bar graph to   Adults Participating in Leisure-Time Activities (millions)
     display the data shown at

Activity	bicycling	softball	swimming	volleyball
Adults	55	40	47	34

     right. Use ranges 33-38,
     45-50, etc.

14. The following are test scores for a sophomore math class.

     80, 61, 92, 75, 78, 82, 85, 86, 100, 90, 93, 82, 80, 93, 61, and 80.

     Make a bar graph showing the frequency or number of test scores in each
     of 5 equal ranges of scores. Which range contains the greatest number of scores?

Use the mileage chart of example 4 to answer exercises 15-17.

15. Find the driving distance from Atlantic City to Cape May.

16. The driving distance from Paterson to Camden is how much less than from
     Paterson to Atlantic City?

17.   Joan drives 40 mph. Approximately how long will it take her to drive from New
        Brunswick to Bridgeton?

OPEN-ENDED QUESTION

18.   The four classes of a local high school
        raised the amounts shown for new
        cheerleader uniforms. Four students began
        drawing a bar graph to better display the
        data at the right. Which of the following
        four approaches is most likely the easiest
        to understand? Explain in writing why you
        think your answer is correct.

Class	Amount raised
Seniors	$245
Juniors	$213
Sophomores	$220
Freshmen	$129

(A)
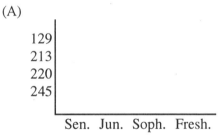

(B)
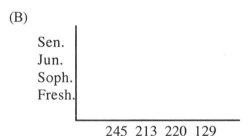

(C)
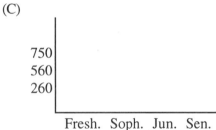

(D)
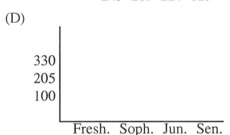

REVIEW   Chapters 1-4

1.   If 3 out of 12 blocks are shaded, what fractional part of the blocks are not shaded?

2.   If 5 out of n games are lost and there are no ties, what fractional part of the games
        are won?

3.   What is $\frac{3}{4}$ of 28?

4.    Michael usually makes 70% of his basketball foul shots.
      This season he attempted 139 foul shots.
      Approximately how many foul shots did he miss this season?

5.   This year the number of freshmen out for football is 5% greater than last year.
      If 40 freshmen were out for football last year, how many are out this year?

6.   Which of the following is **NOT** a way to find 110% of a number?
      (A)   Multiply the number by 0.10 and add the result to the number.
      (B)   Multiply the number by 10 and divide the result by 11.
      (C)   Multiply the number by 1.10.
      (D)   Multiply the number by 11 and divide the result by 10.

7.   Find the total cost of a $45 watch including a 6% sales tax.

8.   A football that regularly sells for $65 is on sale at a discount of 20%.
      Which of the procedures below could you use to find the sale price?
      I $65 \cdot 0.20$ II $65 + 0.20 \cdot 65$
      III $65 \cdot 0.80$ IV $65 - 0.20 \cdot 65$
      (A)   I and II only   (B)   II and III only
      (C)   III and IV only   (D)   III only

9.   An $80 bicycle is advertised at $\frac{1}{4}$ off the regular price. At another store, the same
      brand bike is on sale at a discount of 20% off the regular price of $90. How
      much is saved by buying at the store with the lower sale price?

10.    In basketball, good players make approximately 70% of their foul shots.
      Suppose that a good player missed 19 foul shot attempts during the season.
      Approximately how many foul shots did she attempt that season?

Use the figure at the right for exercises 11-12.

11.   The number of shaded squares is what %
      of the number of unshaded squares?

12.   The number of unshaded squares is what % of
      the total number of squares?

13.   Last week Scott earned $40 working part time. This week he earned only $36. The decrease was what % of last week's earnings?

14.   19 is 35% of what number?

15.   What are Tina's total weekly expenses?

16.   How much less does Don spend on rent than Tina?

17.   Tina's saving is what % of Don's saving?

WEEKLY EXPENSES		
Expenses	Don	Tina
Car	$60	$70
Entertainment	$40	$50
Rent	$115	$135
Savings	$25	$15
Food	$60	$80

Use this advertisement to answer exercises 18-19.

STUFF YOUR FACE DINNER MENU
Choice of main course: roast beef, ribs, chicken: $5.25
plus $1.25 for each of the following up to three choices; $1.05 for each choice beyond 3.
salad, soup, french fries, baked potatoes, onion rings, string beans, peas, soda, coffee, tea, cake, pie, ice cream

18.   A deluxe dinner offers the main course, salad or soup, any potato, one vegetable, one beverage, and ice cream, all for the special price of $9.95. How much can one save by taking the special rather than ordering each item separately?

19.   To the nearest hundredth, the saving in exercise 18 is what % of the cost of ordering each item separately?

The data table at the right shows the number of 200 sophomores taking a foreign language.

20.   How many more students take Spanish than French?

21.   How many students take no foreign language?

LANGUAGE	PERCENT
French	15%
German	10%
Spanish	60%
Latin	5%
No language	?%

The bar graph at the right shows the quiz grades of a class of General Math students.

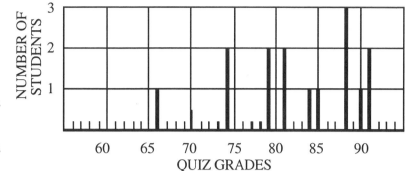

22.   How many students are in the class?

23.   How many students got an 85?

24.   The grades of Ms. Redcloud's students on the last science test were:

96, 60, 75, 81, 72, 100, 75, 96, 81, 60, 90, 59, 80, and 95.

Make a bar graph showing the frequency or number of scores in each of 6 equal ranges of scores. Which range contains the least number of scores?

25.   What is the driving distance from Camden to Elizabeth?

26.   Hank drives 35 miles per hour. How long will it take to drive from Atlantic City to Elizabeth?

Mileage Between Principal Cities	Atlantic City	Bridgeton	Camden	Cape May	Cherry Hill	Elizabeth	Jersey City
Atlantic City	0	81	57	48	55	105	119
Camden	57	40	0	84	9	81	85
Newark	108	113	84	154	80	8	6
Paterson	123	131	99	165	95	23	21
Trenton	74	70	32	106	35	48	58
New Brunswick	93	99	56	128	58	26	31

27.   Solve $7 + 3x = 28$.

28.   6 less than 3 times Marla's age is 24. How old is Marla?

29.   The perimeter of a rectangle is 48 cm. The width is 6 cm. Find the length of the rectangle.

Insert the appropriate inequality symbol, < or >, to make each true. (Ex. 30-31)

30.   -15 ? -9

31. 1.8^7 ? 2.1^5

32.   Which problem below can be solved by the equation x - 10 = 40?

(A)   Tim had $40 in his savings account. He withdrew $10. How much did he then have in savings?

(B)   Bill added 10 records to his collection. He then had 40 records. How many did he have after adding to his collection?

(C)   Myra withdrew $10 from her savings account. She then had $40 in the account. How much did she have in the account before the withdrawal?

(D)   10 more than a number is 40. Find the number.

Simplify.

33. $-7(-2)^3$ 34. $-8 + 6 - 5 + 14$ 35. $\dfrac{9 \cdot 4 - 12}{6 + 2 \cdot 3}$

36.   Estimate the value of $0.36 \cdot 0.000912$

(A)   0.0003   (B)   0.004   (C)   0.03   (D)   0.04

37.   What symbol is in the 117th position of the following pattern?

PYRAMIDPYRAMIDPYRAMID...

38.   On a multiple choice test each correct choice is worth 5 points. 2 points are deducted for each incorrect answer. Which formula below represents the total score S if R represents the number of right answers and I the number of incorrect answers?

(A) $S = 5 + R - 2 - I$ (B) $S = 5R + 2I$

(C) $S = 2I - 5R$ (D) $S = 5R - 2I$

39.   Evaluate $\dfrac{5}{6} x - 3$ for $x = 12$.

40.   Which of the following is not equivalent to the other 3?

(A)   150% of 18   (B) $-9 \cdot -3$ (C) $-\left(\dfrac{-54}{-2}\right)$ (D) $-9 \div -\dfrac{1}{3}$

Write the next term in each sequence.

41.   7, 11, 15,, 19, 23, ...   42.   8, 10, 18, 28, 46, 74, ...

43.   What is the units digit in the 35th term of the sequence $9^1, 9^2, 9^3, 9^4, ...$?

44.   Which point could represent the
       product of the numbers represented
       by points A and V?

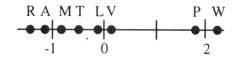

45.   Recall that a palindrome is a number that reads the same backward as forward.
       1991 is a palindrome. What is the very next larger palindrome number?

46.   On the scale below, the reading indicated by the arrow is between

       (A)   30 and 31   (B)   55 and 56   (C)   57 and 60   (D)   67 and 68

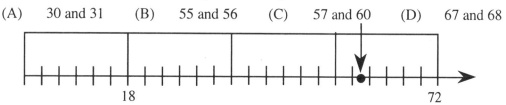

47.   Which of the plane figures below cannot be folded to form a box or cube?

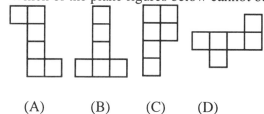

              (A)   (B)   (C)   (D)

48.   If the pattern indicated at the right
       is continued, how many squares
       will be in the seventh figure?

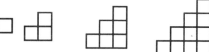

49.   Name the integer that represents a withdrawal of $250 from a checking account.

OPEN-ENDED QUESTION

50.   A store owner decided to discount every item in the store by 20%. A week later
       the owner concluded that the discount was not good enough to attract a lot of
       customers. He then discounted every item by another 10%. A clerk said that
       an original discount of 30% would have been the same as the two separate
       discounts. Is the clerk correct? Give a concrete example of why you think you are
       right.

Chapter

5

Connecting Geometry and Algebra: Like Terms, Factors, Multiples

5.1 Coordinates of Points in a Plane

OBJECTIVES   To give the coordinates of a point in a plane

To plot a point given its coordinates

In the next lesson you will formally develop the formulas for the perimeter and area of rectangles and squares. These properties will be discovered through sketches on **graph paper**. This technique calls for plotting points on graph paper, the topic of this lesson.

Recall that you can locate or graph points on a number line.

The **coordinate** of point A is -7.

The **coordinate** of point B is 6.

You need only **one** number to locate a point on a number line.

In this lesson you will now learn to locate a point on a flat surface such as a piece of paper or a sheet of graph paper. To locate such points, do you think one number would be sufficient?

DISCOVERY   How does a teacher use a **seating chart**?

If you were to describe the location of your desk in this classroom, would **one number** be sufficient?

For example, if the teacher said to you, "Sit in the fourth seat," would this be clear enough so that you could easily find your seat?

How do you find your seat in a theater or baseball stadium?

The position of a point in a flat surface or plane can be described in reference to **two number lines**. These number lines will be at **right angles to**, or **perpendicular to**, each other.

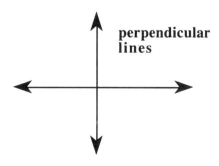

perpendicular lines

The figure at the right shows part of a
sheet of **graph paper**.
The two number lines are called the
x-axis (**horizontal number line**)
              and the
y-axis (**vertical number line**).

The point where the **axes** meet is
called the **origin**.

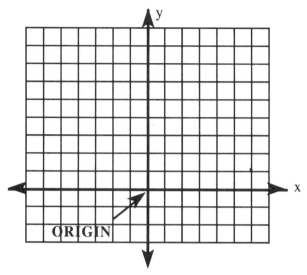

Points can be located in terms of
movement **left (negative)** or **right (positive)**.
movement **down (negative)** or **up (positive)**.

In this graph, you can get to point A
by beginning at the origin, then
moving along the **x**-axis **2** units to the
right, then **3** units **up**.

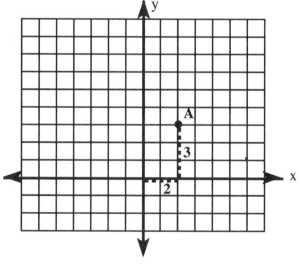

The **coordinates** of point A are
defined to be (**2,3**).
The **order** of the coordinates of the
point is very imporant.

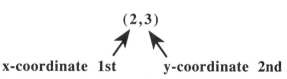

Can you guess how to graph the point B(3,2)?

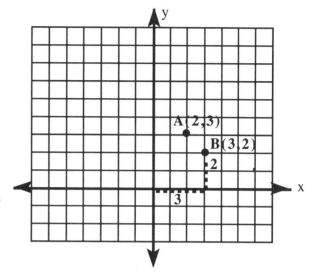

You can get to point B by beginning at the origin, then moving **3** units to the **right** along the **x**-axis and then **2** units **up**.

The coordinates of point B are defined to be **(3,2)**.

Again the **order** of the coordinates is very important.

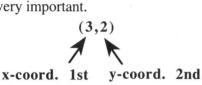

x-coord. 1st   y-coord. 2nd

A(2,3) is **NOT** the same as B(3,2).

The importance of order is better appreciated in terms of the following real-life situation. The 3rd seat in the 100th row of the Rose Bowl is **NOT** the same as the 100th seat in the 3rd row.

Thus, the symbol (2,3) is referred to as an **ordered pair**.

DISCOVERY

Write the coordinates of the point P.

HINT: Begin at the origin.

Move along the x-axis ____ units to the ____.

From here, move ____ units ____ to get to the point P.

So, the coordinates of the point P must be (,).

EXAMPLE 1   Write the coordinates of the point graphed.

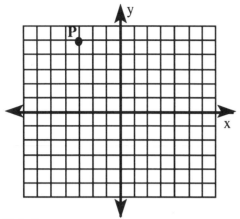

Solution

From the origin, move **left 3**, **up 5**.

(-3,5)

Solution

From the origin, move **right 5**, **down 1**.

(5,-1)

EXAMPLE 2   Give the coordinates of
points T, A, and B.

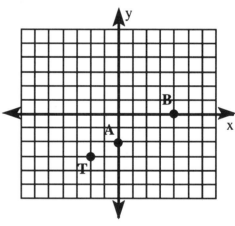

Strategy   For each point, begin at the
origin.

Solution   T: move left 2, down 3
T(-2,-3)

Solution   A: **no** left or right move,
down 2.
A(0,-2)

Solution   B: right 4, **no** up or down
move
B(4,0)

You have seen how to name the coordinates of a point already graphed.

In the next example you will be given the coordinates of a point.

Then you will see how to graph this point.

EXAMPLE 3   Graph the points S(-2,0) and G(3,-2).

Strategy

For S, begin at the origin.

Move **left 2** along the x-axis.

Do not move up or down.

Put a dot at the point.

Label the point S(-2,0).

Strategy

For G, begin at the origin.

Move **right 3** along the x-axis.

Then move **down 2**.

Put a dot at the point.

Label the point G(3,-2).

Solution

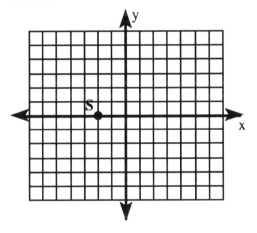

Solution

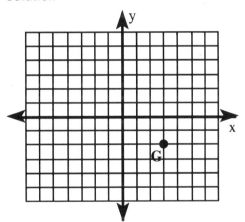

SUMMARY

Tell how to graph each of the following points.

1.	A(-4,-2)	2.	B(5,-3)	3.	C(-8,1)	4.	D(1,5)
5.	E(-4,0)	6.	F(0,-6)	7.	G(0,10)	8.	H(3,0)

Tell how to write the coordinates of the points graphed below.

9.	P	10.	Q
11.	R	12.	S
13.	T	14.	U
15.	V	16.	W

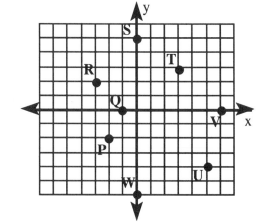

CLASSROOM PRACTICE

Write the coordinates of the points graphed.

1.	A	2.	B	3.	C
4.	D	5.	E	6.	F
7.	G	8.	H	9.	I
10.	J	11.	K	12.	L

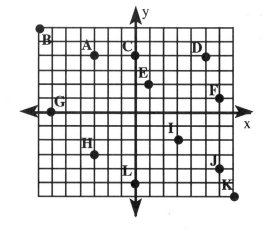

Graph the points with given coordinates.

13.	P(6,1)	14.	Q(-4,3)	15.	R(-2,-5)	16.	S(-8,0)
17.	T(0,-9)	18.	U(6,0)	19.	V(-12,0)	20.	W(-8,-3)

WRITTEN EXERCISES

Graph the points with given coordinates.

1.	P(7,2)	2.	Q(-5,1)	3.	R(-3,-5)	4.	S(-12,0)
5.	T(0,-8)	6.	U(0,11)	7.	V(-9,-8)	8.	W(7,-3)

Write the coordinates of the points graphed.

9.   A   10.   B   11.   C
12. D   13.   E   14.   F
15. G   16.   H   17.   I
18. J   19.   K   20.   L

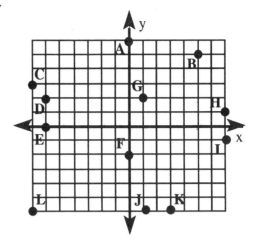

OPEN-ENDED QUESTION

21.   Given: A(2,3), B(8,3), C(8,9)

       Graph these points. Find the coordinates of a fourth point D such that if a four-sided figure is formed, the figure will be a square.

REVIEW

1.   The fare for each taxi ride consists of a $3.00 initial charge and a charge of $1.20 per half-mile. At that rate, find the cost of a taxi ride of six miles.

2.   When Mrs. Chavez goes food shopping, she keeps in her head a running total of the prices of items she puts in her shopping cart. These prices are: $3.65, $11.98, $.43, $6.34, $2.99, $2.99, $.23, $6.49, $2.78, $14.29. Estimate the total of those prices. The total is between
      (A) $30 and $40   (B) $40 and $50
      (C) $50 and $60   (D) $60 and $70

3.   The formula for changing temperature from Celsius to Fahrenheit is $F = \frac{9}{5}C + 32$.

      If the temperature of an object is 60° C, what is its temperature in degrees Fahrenheit?

4.   Solve 3x - 9 = 36.

5.2 Perimeter and Area of a Rectangle

OBJECTIVES   To find the perimeter of a rectangle

To find the area of a rectangle

To draw a rectangle with a given perimeter

You have seen that the perimeter of a rectangle is given by the formula $P = 2L + 2W$. The formula is easy to justify visually using coordinates studied in the last lesson.

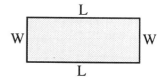

DISCOVERY   Graph the points A (0,0), B(8,0), C(8,4), D(0,4).

Draw the 4-sided figure formed by connecting the 4 points:

A to B, B to C, C to D, and D to A.

By counting blocks you should see that the length of the side from A to B is 8 units. Find the lengths of the other three sides.

Find the perimeter of this rectangle.

EXAMPLE 1   Graph points A(2,4), B(8,4), C(8,9), and D(2,9). Connect the four points to form a four-sided figure. Find the perimeter of the rectangle.

Strategy   Graph A, B, C, and D.

Connect A to B, B to C, C to D, and D to A.

The figure is a rectangle.

It is referred to as

rectangle ABCD.

Find the lengths of the 4 sides.

(continued on next page)

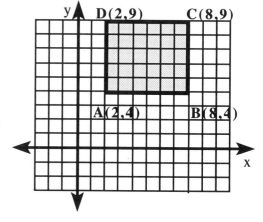

Count the units from D to C: **6**   Count the units from B to C: **5**

Count the units from A to B: **6**   Count the units from A to D: **5**

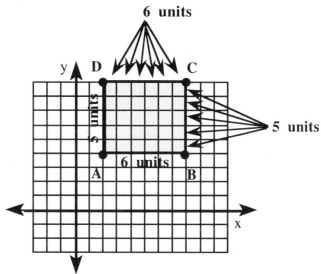

Now find the perimeter.

Find the sum of the 4 lengths.

P = 6 + 6 + 5 + 5 = 22

Solution   Thus, the perimeter of rectangle **ABCD** is 22.

The example above illustrates once again the formula you have already used in earlier chapters for the perimeter of a rectangle.

P = 2**L**   + 2**W**

P = 2 · **6** + 2 · **5**

P =   12   +   10

P =   22

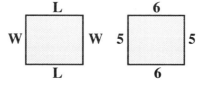

A practical application of perimeter is finding the cost of building a fence around a house. The cost for a given height of fencing is determined by the number of feet of fencing needed: the **perimeter** of the rectangle enclosed by the fence.

EXAMPLE 2   Mr. Gonzales plans to install a fence around his
property that measures 80 ft by 60 ft.
The fence contractor estimates that a 4 ft high
fence will cost $30 a linear foot to build and install,
including the gate and posts. Find the cost of the
fence.

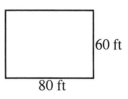

Strategy   The cost of $30 per foot is already based on the
height being 4 ft. The height will have nothing to
do with computing the cost of the fence.

1.   Find the total **length** of the fence.
The total length of the fence will be the **perimeter**
of the rectangle shown at the right.

P = 2L   + 2W
P = 2 · **80** + 2 · **60**
P =   160   + 120
P =   280

2.   Find the cost of 280 ft of fencing at $30 per foot.

Multiply. 280 · $30 = $8400.

Solution   Thus, the cost of the fence will be $8400.

DISCOVERY   Deidra has a small entrance or foyer by her front
door. She wants to cover the 5 ft by 6 ft space with
square tiles 1 ft by 1 ft. How many tiles will she
need?

Form a **mathematical model** of this problem by
using graph paper. The rectangle in the graph of
Example 1 represents a **mathematical model** of this
problem. The number of blocks in this rectangle
represents the number of tiles she will need.

EXAMPLE 3   Plot the points A(3,2), B(11,2), C(11,9), and D(3,9).

Connect the points to form a rectangle.

Find the number of little blocks or squares contained in this rectangle.

Strategy   The bottom row has **8** blocks. There are

7 rows of these **8** blocks.

$$7 \cdot 8 \ = \ 56$$

Solution   Therefore, there are **56** blocks or squares contained in this rectangle.

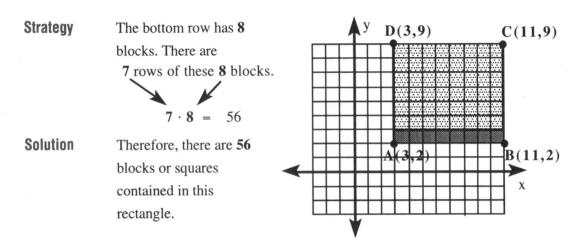

The **area** of the rectangle above is the **total** number of blocks in the interior:

$$A = 7 \cdot 8 = 56.$$

The **perimeter** of the rectangle is the total distance around the outside:

$$P = 2 \cdot 7 \ + \ 2 \cdot 8$$
$$= \ 14 \ + \ 16 \ = \ 30$$

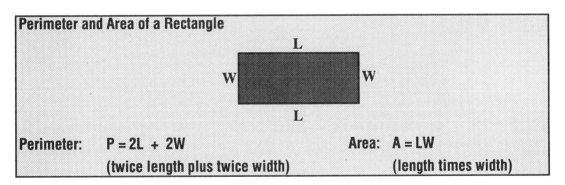

Perimeter and Area of a Rectangle

Perimeter: **P = 2L + 2W**
(twice length plus twice width)

Area: A = LW
(length times width)

Perimeter is measured in units of length: inches, miles, centimeters, meters, etc.

Area is measured in **square** units: inches^2, miles^2, centimeters^2, meters^2, etc.

Inches^2 is read as **square inches**. Meters^2 is read as **square meters**.

When working with equations you may omit units of measurement, such as cm or ft.

But the final answers must indicate the units of measurement.

This is illustrated in the next example.

EXAMPLE 4   The length of a rectangle is 10 ft and the width is 3 ft.
Find the perimeter and the area.

Strategy   Draw a sketch.

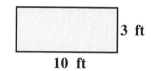

3 ft

10 ft

perimeter				**area**		
P	=	2L	+ 2W	A	=	LW
P	=	2·10	+ 2·3	A	=	10·3
P	=	20	+ 6	A	=	30
P	=		26			

Solution   The **perimeter** is **26 ft**.   The **area is 30 ft^2**.

Include the units of measurement in the final answer.

An important application involves computing the cost of installing wall-to-wall carpet.
The cost is usually computed in terms of **square yards** of area.
Therefore, you find the length and width of a carpet in terms of **yards (yd)**, **NOT** feet.
To do this recall that there are **3 ft** to **1 yd**. The procedure is illustrated in the next example.

EXAMPLE 5   Carpet costs $13.95 a square yard. Find the cost of wall to wall carpeting
for a room that measures 15 ft by 21 ft. Include a 6% sales tax.

Strategy 1.   Draw a diagram showing the carpet
measurements in yards.

Use **3 ft = 1 yd.**

So, $15 \text{ ft} = \frac{15}{3} = 5 \text{ yd}$

        $21 \text{ ft} = \frac{21}{3} = 7 \text{ yd}$

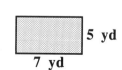

5 yd

7 yd

(continued on next page)

2.   Use A = LW to find the area.

   A = 5 · 7 = 35

So, the area is **35 yd^2** (**35 square yards**)

3.   Now find the cost of **35 yd^2** if carpet costs $13.95 for **1** yd^2.

If you know the cost of **1** yd^2, then to find the cost of **35** yd^2,

multiply: **35 · $13.95 = $488.25.**

4.   Finally, find the cost including a 6% sales tax.

Recall the short cut.

Instead of finding 6% of $488.25 and then adding to $488.25,

multiply the cost by **1.06.**

1.06 · $488.25 = $517.545

Round the result to the nearest cent.

Solution   Thus, the cost rounded to the nearest cent is $517.55.

EXAMPLE 6   The length of a rectangle is 12 cm and the perimeter is 32 cm.

Find the area.

Strategy   **1.**   Draw a diagram.

Use the perimeter formula with

P = 32 and **L = 12.**

P   =   2L   +   2W

32   =   2· 12   +   2W

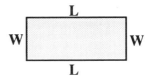

2.   Solve 32 = 24 + 2W.

32 - **24** = 24 - **24** + 2W   **Subtract 24 from each side.**

   8   =   0   + 2W

   8   =   2W

$\dfrac{8}{2}$ = $\dfrac{2W}{2}$ **Divide each side by 2.**

   4   =   W

(continued on next page)

3. Find the area using L = 12 and W = 4.

Use the area formula with **L = 12** and **W = 4**.

$$A = \textbf{LW}$$

$$A = \textbf{12} \cdot \textbf{4}$$

Solution $$A = 48$$

Thus, the area is **48 cm^2**.   **Indicate units of measurement in the answer.**

DISCOVERY   Suppose the perimeter of a rectangle is 40 in.

Find a possible length and width. Is there more than one answer?

EXAMPLE 7   Use graph paper to draw a rectangle with perimeter 30 units.
Label the side lengths.

Strategy   To draw the rectangle, you need to know the length and the width.
You are not given either. But you are given the perimeter.
Choose a number for the length.. It could be 10, or 12, or 13, or even

a number containing a fraction, $14\frac{1}{4}$.

Choose L = 11. Now find W.
Use the perimeter formula with
P = 30 and **L = 11**.

$$\textbf{P} = \textbf{2L} + \textbf{2W}$$

$$\textbf{30} = \textbf{2} \cdot \textbf{11} + \textbf{2W}$$

Solve 30 = 22 + 2W.

$$30 - 22 = 22 - 22 + 2W$$ **Subtract 22 from each side.**

$$8 = 0 + 2W$$

$$8 = 2W$$

$$\frac{8}{2} = \frac{2W}{2}$$ **Divide each side by 2.**

$$\textbf{4} = \textbf{W}$$

(continued on next page)

Draw the arectangle on graph paper.

Solution 1   **Solution 2**

A rectangle with dimensions **4** and **11**

can be drawn anywhere on graph paper.

Notice the two versions shown below.

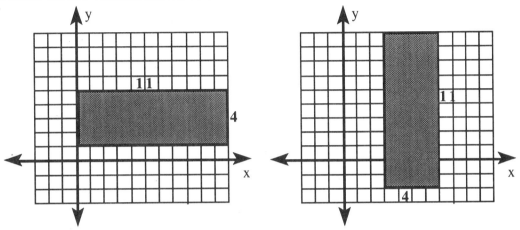

SUMMARY

1.   What is the difference between perimeter and area?

2.   How do you find the perimeter of a rectangle? What is the formula?

3.   How do you find the area of a rectangle? What is the formula?

4.   What are the steps in finding the perimeter of rectangle ABCD given
     A(1,1), B(9,1), C(9,5), and D(1,5)

5.   What are the steps in finding the area of rectangle ABCD of Exercise 4?

6.   How do you find the cost of a fence for a rectangular yard given the following
     information?
     The property measures 30 ft by 20 ft and the cost is $25 a linear foot.

The length of a rectangle is 14 m (meters) and the width is 6 m.

How do you find each of the following?

7.   perimeter of ABCD

8.   area of ABCD

9.   How do you convert 24 ft to yards?

10.   What are the steps in computing the cost, including a 6% sales tax, of carpeting a room measuring 18 ft by 24 ft at $25 per yd^2?

11.   If you know the width of a rectangle is 3 cm and the perimeter is 20 cm, how do you find the area of the rectangle?

12.   A rectangle has a perimeter of 40 units. What are the steps for drawing such a rectangle on graph paper? Is more than one answer possible?

CLASSROOM PRACTICE

For Exercises 1-4, find the perimeter and area of rectangle ABCD given the coordinates of A, B, C, and D.

1.   A(2,2), B(7,2), C(7,5), D(2,5)   2. A(11,2), B(17,2), C(17,7), D(11,7)
3.   A(2,7), B(11,7), C(11,13), D(2,13)   4. A(8,8), B(17,8), C(17,13), D(8,13)

5.   L = 7 in, W = 4 in, perimeter =?
6.   L = 14 ft, W = 6 ft, perimeter = ?
7.   L = 16 cm, W = 3 cm, area = ?
8.   L = 8 yd, W = 5 yd, area = ?

Find the **area** of each rectangle. (exercises 9-12)
9.   The length of a rectangle is 14 m. The perimeter is 40 m.
10.   The width of a rectangle is 12 km. The perimeter is 56 km.
11.   The length of a rectangle is 18 yd. The perimeter is 42 yd.
12.   The width of a rectangle is 14 in. The perimeter is 60 in.

For Exercises 13-14, round each answer to the nearest cent.

13.   Carpeting costs $29.75 per yd^2. Find the cost of carpeting a room measuring 18 ft by 24 ft.

14.   Carpeting costs $19.75 per yd^2. Find the cost of carpeting a room measuring 9 ft by 12 ft.

15.   Use graph paper to draw a rectangle with perimeter 14 units.
       Label the side lengths.

16.   Use graph paper to draw a rectangle with perimeter 16 units.
       Label the side lengths.

17.   Mr. Abrams plans to install a rectangular fence around his property that measures
       50 ft by 60 ft. The fencing contractor estimates that a 6 ft high fence will cost $35
       a linear foot to build. find the cost of the fence.

18.   Ms. Quarles plans to install a rectangular fence around her property that
       measures 60 ft by 60 ft. The fencing contractor estimates that a 5 ft high fence
       will cost $26 a linear foot to build. Find the cost of the fence.

WRITTEN EXERCISES

For Exercises 1-4, find the perimeter and area of rectangle ABCD given the coordinates
of A, B, C, and D.

1.   A(1,1), B(8,1), C(8,4), D(1,4)   2. A(0,2), B(12,2), C(12,9), (0,9)

3.   A(-3,1), B(8,1), C(8,6), D(-3,6)   4. A(4,-1), B(10,-1), C(10,7), D(4,7)

5.   L = 9 in, W = 6 in, perimeter =?
6.   L = 13 ft, W = 5 ft, perimeter = ?
7.   L = 17 cm, W = 6 cm, area = ?
8.   L = 7 yd, W = 6 yd, area = ?

Find the **area** of each rectangle. (exercises 9-12)

9.   The length of a rectangle is 16 m. The perimeter is 50 m.

10.   The width of a rectangle is 13 km. The perimeter is 54 km.

11.   The length of a rectangle is 19 yd. The perimeter is 52 yd.

12.   The width of a rectangle is 22 in. The perimeter is 90 in.

For Exercises 13-14, round each answer to the nearest cent.

13.   Carpeting costs \$39.65 per yd^2. Find the cost of carpeting a room measuring 24 ft by 21 ft.

14.   Carpeting costs \$21.75 per yd^2. Find the cost of carpeting a room measuring 15 ft by 18 ft.

15.   Use graph paper to draw a rectangle with perimeter 18 units. Label the side lengths.

16.   Use graph paper to draw a rectangle with perimeter 22 units. Label the side lengths.

17.   Mr. Jamison plans to install a rectangular fence around his property that measures 120 ft by 90 ft. The fencing contractor estimates that a 6 ft high fence will cost \$40 a linear foot to build. Find the cost of the fence.

OPEN-ENDED QUESTION

18.   A rectangle has a perimeter of 20 units. Many different rectangles can have this perimeter. Suppose side lengths can only be whole numbers. Can a side length be any whole number? If not, what is the largest whole number for the length of a side? Write an explanation of why you think your conclusion is true.

REVIEW

1.   Find the weight of one pyramid if one block weighs 5 lb and the scale is balanced.

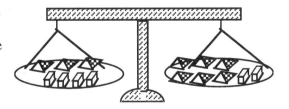

2.   Estimate 49.8^2.

(A)   250   (B)   500   (C)   2,500   (D)   25,000

3. What symbols are missing from
    this spiral pattern at the locations x
    and y?

    (A)   (B)
        x   y   x   y

    (C)   (D)
        x   y   x   y

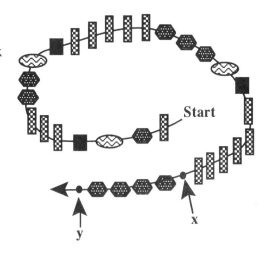

Start

y   x

4. At the right are three views of a
    die. The numbers 1, 2, 3, 4, 5, and
    6 appear exactly once on the faces
    of this die. What number is
    opposite 5?

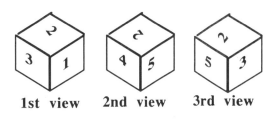

    1st view   2nd view   3rd view

5. Tyrone is paid a salary of $125 a week and a commission of 15% on all his sales
    of televisions. If P represents his total pay for the week and S the amount of sales,
    which formula below describes the way his pay for the week is computed?

    (A) $P = 125 + P$ (B) $P = 125 + 15S$
    (C) $P = 0.15S$ (D) $P = 125 + 0.15S$

6. Which of the plane
    figures at the right
    cannot be folded to
    form a box or cube?

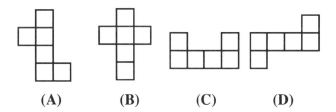

        (A)   (B)   (C)   (D)

7. The number of unshaded squares is
    what % of the total number of
    squares?

5.3 The Distributive Property

OBJECTIVE   To apply the Distributive Property

It is always helpful to make **connections** between algebra, arithmetic, and geometry. You will now use the geometric idea of **area** to discover an important property of arithmetic and algebra.

Recall the formula for the area of a rectangle: $A = LW$

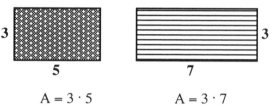

$$A = 3 \cdot 5 \qquad\qquad A = 3 \cdot 7$$

If the two rectangles are slid together, they form one large rectangle.

The large rectangles has the same area as the sum of the two separate areas of the original rectangles.

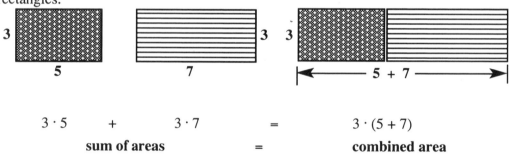

$$3 \cdot 5 \quad + \quad 3 \cdot 7 \quad = \quad 3 \cdot (5 + 7)$$

sum of areas   =   combined area

Let's check the arithmetic to make sure that the two sums are indeed equal.

Check
$$\begin{array}{c|c} 3 \cdot 5 + 3 \cdot 7 & 3 \cdot (5 + 7) \\ \hline 15 + 21 & 3 \cdot 12 \\ 36 \quad = \quad 36 & \textbf{TRUE} \end{array}$$

DISCOVERY   You have just seen that the expression

$3 \cdot (5 + 7)$ is the same as $3 \cdot 5 + 3 \cdot 7$.

This suggests a pattern for a property of arithmetic.

$$3 \cdot (5 + 7) = 3 \cdot 5 + 3 \cdot 7$$

So, you can rewrite $9 \cdot (2 + 4)$ as _____?

EXAMPLE 1   Rewrite $6 \cdot (2 + 4)$.

Strategy   The **6** is **distributed** to (passed out to) **both** the 2 and the 4.

$$6 \cdot (2 + 4)$$

Solution $6 \cdot 2 \; + \; 6 \cdot 4$

The results above are now stated as the **Distributive Property**.

We say that multiplication is **distributive** over **addition (also subtraction)**.

Distributive Property

For all numbers a, b, and c,

$$a \cdot (b + c) = a \cdot b + a \cdot c \text{ or } ab + ac$$

$$a \cdot (b - c) = a \cdot b - a \cdot c \text{ or } ab - ac$$

The expression $6 \cdot (2 + 4)$ contains parentheses to indicate grouping.

Recall that when parentheses are used, you may **omit** the multiplication symbol.

So, $6 \cdot (2 + 4)$ can be written as $6(2 + 4)$.   **Omit the raised dot.**

Now you will apply the Distributive Property to expressions containing variables.
When applying the Distributive Property to expressions with variables, you will need
to be able to simplify an expression like $7 \cdot 5m$.

$$7 \cdot 5m = 7 \cdot 5 \cdot m$$
$$= 35 \cdot m$$
$$= 35m$$

You need not show all these steps. You can do the computation in your head.
This is illustrated in the next example.

EXAMPLE 2   Simplify $9 \cdot 3k$.

Solution $9 \cdot 3k = 27k$

DISCOVERY   Use the Distributive Property and the results of Example 2 to simplify
9(3k + 4).

EXAMPLE 3   Use the Distributive Property to simplify 4(3y - 2).
Then evaluate the result for y = 5.

Strategy   **1.** 4(3y - 2) = 4 · 3y - 4 · 2 **Distribute 4 to both 3y and 2.**

                        =   12y - 8   **Think: 4 · 3y = 4 · 3 · y**

                                              =   **12y**

2. Now evaluate 12y - 8 for **y = 5.**

12 · **y** - 8

12 · **5** - 8   **Substitute 5 for y.**

 60   - 8   **Use Order of Operations. Multiply 1st.**

    52   **Subtract.**

Solution   So, 4(3y - 2) **simplifies** to **12y - 8**, and its value for y = 5 is **52**.

The Distributive Property can be used to do multiplications **mentally**.

EXAMPLE 4   Felicia buys 3 pairs of slacks at $19.99 each.
Use the Distributive Property to find the total cost mentally.

Strategy   The cost of 3 pairs of slacks at $19.99 each is **3 · $19.99**.
It is easier to multiply mentally by **$20.00** than **$19.99**.
Think of **$19.99** as **$20.00 - $0.01**.

3 · $19.99 = **3**($20.00 - $0.01)

          = **3 · $20.00 - 3 · $0.01**

          = $60.00 - $0.03

          = $59.97

Solution   Thus, the cost of the 3 pairs of slacks is **$59.97**.

SUMMARY

1. Explain how to use the Distributive Property to rewrite $7 \cdot (8 + 4)$.
2. What symbol can be omitted when parentheses are used as a grouping symbol for multiplication? How can you apply this to the expression in Exercise 1 above?
3. How do you simplify the expression 8(4m)?
4. What are the steps in using the Distributive Property to simplify 3(4k - 5)? What is the result of the simplification?
5. How do you evaluate the simplified result of Exercise 4 above for k = 2?

How can you use the Distributive Property to mentally find each of the following?

6. $7 \cdot 199$ 7. $5 \cdot 33$ 8. $6 \cdot 48$ 9. $3 \cdot 7\frac{1}{3}$

CLASSROOM PRACTICE

Simplify.
1.   7(8t)   2. 4(7g)   3. 6(9r)   4. 4(8b)

Use the Distributive Property to simplify each expression.
5.   6(4a + 5)   6.   9(3k + 5)   7.   4(7b + 8)
8.   4(3j - 7)   9.   9(2k - 5)   10. 8(3m - 10)

Use the Distributive Property to simplify each expression.
Then evaluate for the given value of the variable.
11. 4(2k + 5) for k = 3   12.   7(6a - 3) for a = 2
13. 4(5m - 4) for m = 9   14.   6(2b - 4) for b = 5

Use the Distributive Property to solve each problem mentally.
15. Find the cost of 6 boxes of hot dogs at $3.99 each.
16. Find the cost of 5 cans of soda at $0.63 each.
17. Multiply $7 \cdot 297$

WRITTEN EXERCISES

Simplify.

  1.   8(7j)   2. 3(12b)   3. 9(4m)   4. $8 \cdot 4\frac{1}{2}$

Use the Distributive Property to simplify each expression.

  5.   6(5a + 4)   6.   3(9k + 5)   7.   7(8b + 4)

  8.   9(3j - 7)   9.   7(6k - 5)   10.   10(2m - 9)

Use the Distributive Property to simplify each expression.

Then evaluate for the given value of the variable.

11.   8(3k + 5) for k = 3   12.   6(7a - 3) for a = 3

13.   5(4m - 2) for m = 6   14.   7(3b - 1) for b = 5

        15.   39(1213j + 245) for j = 72   16.   113(28t + 53) for t = 19

Use the Distributive Property to solve each problem mentally.

17.   Find the cost of 6 boxes of hamburgers at $4.99 each.

18.   Find the cost of 6 cans of soda at $0.63 each.

19.   Multiply 8 · 97

OPEN-ENDED QUESTION

20.   Does the Distributive Property work for division over addition? Make up a
       concrete example.

REVIEW

  1.   Evaluate $(-a)^3$ for a = -1

  2.   Solve 2a - 8 = 12

Simplify.

  3.   -8 + 5 - 6 + 2   4. $\frac{-18}{-9}$ 5. $4^3 + 9 \cdot 5 - 24 \div 8$

5.4 Like Terms

OBJECTIVE   To simplify an algebraic expression by combining like terms

The expression 7b + 5a - 2 has three **terms**: 7b, 5a, and -2.

In the **term 7**b, **7** is the **coefficient** of b.

A **coefficient** is a number multiplied by a variable (letter).

In the **term 5**a, **5** is the coefficient of the variable a.

The expression 7m + 7m has two terms exactly alike.

The terms 7m and 7m are **like** terms.

The expression 4x + 7x + 8x has three terms that differ only in their coefficients,

4, 7, and 8. The terms 4x, 7x, and 8x are **like** terms.

The expression 5y + 4k + 3 has three terms. These terms are **unlike** terms.

DEFINITION: Like Terms

Like terms are terms that are: exactly the same

or differ only in their coefficients.

The Distributive Property can be applied to simplifying expressions with like terms.

The expression 3x + 4x has two like terms.

The Distributive Property can be used to simplify 3x + 4x as will be seen on the next

page.

First recall that **4· 3** is the same as **3 · 4**.

Multiplication can be done in any order.

Multiplication is **commutative**.

Thus, $3x = 3 \cdot x = x \cdot 3$.

$\qquad 4x = 4 \cdot x = x \cdot 4$

Now you can simplify an expression like $3x + 4x$.

$$3x + 4x \quad = \quad 3 \cdot x + 4 \cdot x$$

$$= \quad x \cdot 3 + x \cdot 4 \qquad \textbf{Multiplication is commutative.}$$

$$\textbf{Note, x is distributed to both 3 and 4.}$$

$$= \quad x(3 + 4) \qquad \textbf{Distributive Property}$$

$$= \quad x \cdot 7$$

$$= \quad 7 \cdot x \qquad \textbf{Multiplication is commutative.}$$

$$\textbf{3x + 4x} \quad = \quad \textbf{7x}$$

You need not go through all the steps above!

Like terms can be **combined**. $\textbf{3x + 4x = 7x}$

EXAMPLE 1   Simplify $9x + 5x + 2x$.

Strategy   Combine like terms.

Solution $9x + 5x + 2x = 16x$

EXAMPLE 2   Simplify $5a + 3b + 7$.

Strategy   The terms 5a, 3b, and 7 are **unlike** terms.

Unlike terms cannot be combined.

Solution   Therefore, $5a + 3b + 7$ cannot be simplified.

To simplify an expression like $3x + 5 + x + 9$, first rearrange the terms so that like terms are grouped together. Also recall that $a = \textbf{1}a$.

EXAMPLE 3   Simplify $3x + 5 + x + 9$.

Strategy $3x + 5 + 1x + 9$ $x = \textbf{1}x$.

$(3x + 1x) + (5 + 9)$ **Rearrange to group like terms together.**

Solution $\quad 4x \quad + \quad 14$ **Combine like terms.**

Like terms can be combined when the coefficients are signed numbers.

For example, $-7x + 3x = -7 \cdot x + 3 \cdot x$

$$= (-7 + 3)\, x$$

$$= \quad -4x$$

However, you need not rewrite the expression this way.

Merely combine mentally the coefficients of the like terms.

EXAMPLE 4   Simplify $-7a + 2a$.

	$-7a + 2a$	**Like terms**
Solution	$-5a$	**Combine the coefficients: $-7 + 2 = -5$**

EXAMPLE 5   Simplify $-4b - 8b$.

	$-4b - 8b$	**Like terms**
Solution	$-12b$	**Combine the coefficients: $-4 - 8 = -4 + (-8) = -12$**

In the next example you will need to apply the idea that $-a = -1a$.

EXAMPLE 6   Simplify $5x - 4 - 6x - 3$.

Strategy	$5x - 4 - 6x - 3$	
	$5x - 6x \;\; -4 - 3$	**Rearrange to group like terms together.**
	$-1x \quad\quad -7$	**Combine like coefficients: $5 - 6 = -1$ $-4 - 3 = -7$**
Solution	$-x - 7$	**$-1x = -x$**

To simplify an expression like $3x + 2(4x - 5) - 13x$, you will first have to apply the Distributive Property and then combine like terms.

This is illustrated in the next example.

EXAMPLE 7   Simplify $3x + 2(4x - 5) - 13x$.

Strategy $3x + 2(4x - 5) - 13x$

$3x + \boxed{2 \cdot 4x - 2 \cdot 5} - 13x$ **Distribute the 2 to 4x and 5.**

$3x + \ 8x \ - 10 \ - 13x$

$\underline{3x + 8x} - 13x - 10$ **Rearrange to group like terms together.**

$11x \ - 13x - 10$ **Combine like coefficients: 3 + 8 = 11**

Solution $-2x \ - 10$ **Combine like coefficients: 11 - 13 = -2**

SUMMARY

1.   What are the terms in the expression $7x + 2m + 2$?
2.   What is the coefficient of w in $2a + 4w - 19$?
3.   What are the like terms in the expression $4a - 3 - 7a$?
4.   What is the coefficient of the term a in the expression $3a + 5 + a$?
5.   What are the steps in simplifying $6x + 2 + x - 4$?
6.   Explain the steps in simplifying $4x + 3(2x - 5) - 9x$?

CLASSROOM PRACTICE

Simplify if possible.

1. $3x + 4x$ 2. $8k - 2k$ 3. $5b + b$ 4. $m + 7m$
5. $-3x + 8x$ 6. $-4y - 3y$ 7. $2y - 9g$ 8. $7x - 12x$

9. $7x + 3x + 2x$ 10. $3a + 4 + 6b$ 11. $4y + 5 + 6y$
12. $3a + a + 4a$ 13. $m + 3m + 4m$ 14. $3k + 5k + k$
15. $4x + 5 - 6x - 2$ 16. $2b - 8 - 6b + 9$ 17. $3a - 6 - 4a + 2$

18. $5 + 3(2a + 6) + 7a$ 19. $1 + 4(2a - 3) + 4$
20. $7 + 2(3t - 4) - 7t$ 21. $4h + 3(5h - 4) - 5$

WRITTEN EXERCISES

Simplify if possible.

1. $5x + 8x$ 2. $7k - 3k$ 3. $9b + b$ 4. $m + 11m$

5. $-4x + 9x$ 6. $-5y - 2y$ 7. $8y - 9g$ 8. $7x - 8x$

9. $8x + 7x + 3x$ 10. $2a + 6 + 8b$ 11. $y + 4 + 6y$

12. $5a + a + 8a$ 13. $m + 2m + 6m$ 14. $11k + 4k + k$

15. $5x + 4 - 9x - 3$ 16. $7b - 5 - 10b + 6$ 17. $6a - 8 - 7a + 3$

18. $4 + 2(3a + 8) + 8a$ 19. $1 + 5(2a - 6) + 5$

20. $11 + 2(4t - 6) - 9t$ 21. $3h + 3(6h - 2) - 9$

OPEN-ENDED QUESTION

22. The length of a rectangle is 4 ft more than twice the width. The perimeter is 62 ft. Write an explanation of how you would find the length of the rectangle. Include in your explanation how the solution applies the ideas of the Distributive Property and combining like terms.

REVIEW

1. Solve $2x - 8 = 20$.

2. The length of a rectangle is 12 cm. The perimeter is 32 cm. Find the width.

3. Find the perimeter and area of rectangle ABCD for A(3,1), B(10,1), C(10,6) and D(3,6).

4. An $80 bicycle is advertised at $\frac{1}{5}$ off the regular price. At another store, the same brand bike is on sale at a discount of 25% off the regular price of $84. How much is saved by buying at the store with the lower sale price?

5. Find $\frac{3}{4}$ of 32.

5.5 Equations with Like Terms

OBJECTIVES   To solve equations that contain like terms

To solve equations that contain parentheses

To solve problems that involve equations with like terms or parentheses

---

DISCOVERY   The equation $2x + 4 + x = 19$ contains two like terms.

If you combine the like terms you will get an equation which is a type you know how to solve. Solve the equation.

EXAMPLE 1   Solve $3x + 7 + x = 23$.

Strategy	$3x + 7 + 1x$	$=$	23	**Rewrite x as 1x.**
	$3x + 1x + 7$	$=$	23	**Group like terms together.**
	$4x + 7$	$=$	23	**Combine like terms.**
	$4x + 7 - 7$	$=$	$23 - 7$	**Subtract 7 from each side.**
	$4x + 0$	$=$	16	
	$4x$	$=$	16	
	$\dfrac{4x}{4}$	$=$	$\dfrac{16}{4}$	**Divide each side by 4.**
Solution	x	$=$	4	

You need not write out all the steps in Example 1.

You can shorten your work as follows.

Solve: $3x + 7 + x$	$= 23$	
$3x + 7 + 1x$	$= 23$	**Rewrite x as 1x.**
$4x + 7$	$= 23$	**Combine like terms.**
$4x$	$= 16$	**Subtract 7 from each side.**
x	$= 4$	**Divide each side by 4.**

This shortened form of the work will be used in the remainder of the text.

The equation 7 + 2(5x + 2) = 31 contains parentheses.

In this case, use the Distributive Property to remove parentheses.

Combine like terms.

Solve the resulting equation.

This is illustrated in the next example.

EXAMPLE 2   Solve 7 + 2(5x + 2) = 31.

Strategy

7 + **2**(5x + 2) = 31	
7 + **2** · 5x + **2** · 2 = 31	**Apply the Distributive Property.**
7 + 10x + 4 = 31	
10x + 11 = 31	**Combine like terms: 7 + 4 = 11.**
10x = 20	**Subtract 11 from each side.**
Solution x = 2	**Divide each side by 10.**

Notice in the example above we have used the shortened form of the work.

You have already worked with **data tables**. Sometimes equations with parentheses are used in connection with a data table. This is illustrated in Example 3 below.

EXAMPLE 3   Complete the data table at the right.

m	m + 3(2m - 4)
5	
	2

Strategy   **Step 1**   To complete the first row, **evaluate** m + 3(2m - 4) for **m = 5**.

$$m + 3(2m - 4)$$

$$5 + 3(2 \cdot 5 - 4) \qquad \textbf{Substitute 5 for m.}$$

$$5 + 3(10 - 4)$$

$$5 + 3 (6)$$

$$5 + 18$$

$$\textbf{23}$$

Step 2   To complete the second row, find m.

Solve the equation m + 3(2m - 4) = 2.

(continued on next page)

$$1m + 3(2m - 4) = 2 \qquad \textbf{m = 1m}$$
$$1m + 3 \cdot 2m - 3 \cdot 4 = 2 \qquad \textbf{Distribute the 3.}$$
$$1m + 6m - 12 = 2$$
$$7m - 12 = 2 \qquad \textbf{Combine like terms.}$$
$$7m = 14 \qquad \textbf{Add 12 to each side.}$$
$$m = 2 \qquad \textbf{Divide each side by 7.}$$

Solution   Thus, the completed table is:

m	m + 3(2m - 4)
5	23
2	2

m = 2 →

Now let's apply equations with like terms or parentheses.

A business application of percent involves percent of profit based on the cost of an item sold by a merchant.

The following formula will be applied in the next example.

cost + profit = selling price

EXAMPLE 4   A store manager lists the selling price of a television at $168.
The profit is 20% of the cost. How much did the television cost the merchant?

Strategy   Use the formula above.

cost	+	profit	=	selling price
cost	+	20% of cost	=	selling price
c	+	20% of c	=	168	**Let c = the cost.**
c	+	0.20 · c	=	168
1c	+	0.20c	=	168	**c = 1c**
		1.20c	=	168	**Combine like terms:**
					1c + 0.20c = 1.20c
		c	=	$\dfrac{168}{1..20}$	**Divide each side by 1.20.**
		c	=	168 ÷ 1.20
		c	=	140

Solution   Thus, the television cost the merchant $140.

The next example applies equations with parentheses to geometry.

First note that for the rectangle ABCD at the right, the length of the shaded side is referred to as **AB**.

AB does **NOT** mean A times B.
AB (or BA) refers to the **length** of the side of the rectangle joining points A and B.

The other three side lengths are BC, CD, and AD.

EXAMPLE 5   The perimeter of the rectangle is 26.
Find AB (the length of the side joining the points A and B).

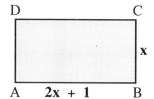

Strategy   Write an equation for the perimeter and solve for x.
Then use this value of x to find AB.

P	=	2L	+ 2W

1. Equation $26 = 2(2x + 1) + 2(x)$

2. Solve $26 = 2 \cdot 2x + 2 \cdot 1 + 2x$ **Distribute the 2 to 2x and 1.**

$26 = 4x + 2 + 2x$

$26 = 6x + 2$ **Combine like terms: $4x + 2x = 6x$**

$24 = 6x$ **Subtract 2 from each side.**

$4 = x$ **Divide each side by 6.**

This is **NOT** the answer to the problem.

Use **AB = 2x + 1** to find AB.

3. Find AB $AB = 2x + 1$

$AB = 2 \cdot 4 + 1$ **Substitute 4 for x in 2x + 1 to find AB.**

$AB = 8 + 1$

Solution   Thus, AB = **9**.

SUMMARY

What are the steps in solving each equation?

1. $3x + 5 + x = 17$ 2. $8 + 3(2x - 1) = 35$

3. How do you complete row 1 of this data table?
4. How do you complete row 2 of this data table?

x	$3(2x + 1) + x$
2	
	31

Use the following word problem to answer Exercises 5-8.

A camera is sold for $280. The profit was 40% of the cost. How much did it cost the owner of the camera store?

5. If you let **c** represent the cost of the camera, what equation should you write to solve the problem?
6. How should you rewrite **c** in the equation?
7. Are there any like terms in the equation?
8. Describe how to finish solving the equation.

Use the following word problem to answer Exercises 9-11.

The perimeter of the rectangle at the right is 26. Find the length.

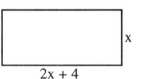

2x + 4

9. How do you write an equation to solve this problem?
10. Explain how the Distributive Property is used.
11. After you have solved the equation for x, have you then solved the problem? Why?

CLASSROOM PRACTICE

Solve each equation.

1. $3x + 7 + x = 23$ 2. $4a + 8 + 2a = 32$ 3. $42 = m + 24 + 5m$
4. $37 = x + 10 + 8x$ 5. $5b - 4 + 3b = 36$ 6. $47 = 6t - 16 + t$
7. $3(x - 2) = 12$ 8. $4 (5 + x) = 48$ 9. $24 = 8(a - 3)$
10. $4x + 2(3x + 2) = 34$ 11. $2a + 3(2a + 5) = 31$
12. $5a + 3(2a + 1) = 25$ 13. $3x + 2(4x - 5) = 23$

Complete each data table.

14.

x	4(2x - 1) + x
4	
	41

15.

x	3(2x + 5) + 4
3	
	43

16.   The perimeter of ABCD is 26. Find AB.

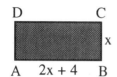

17.   The perimeter of PQRS is 36. Find RS.

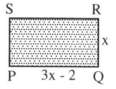

18.   The selling price of a stereo is $260. The profit is 30% of the cost. Find the cost.

19.   The owner of a furniture store marks the sale price of a couch at $545. He knows his profit is 35% of the cost. Find the cost rounded to the nearest cent.

WRITTEN EXERCISES

Solve each equation.

1. $4x + 8 + x = 28$

2. $5a + 8 + 2a = 43$

3. $52 = y + 24 + 3y$

4. $37 = m + 1 + 8m$

5. $6b - 4 + b = 45$

6. $50 = 5t - 16 + t$

7. $4(x - 2) = 36$

8. $6(4 + x) = 66$

9. $16 = 8(a - 4)$

10. $3x + 2(4x + 1) = 35$

11. $3a + 5(4a - 1) = 41$

12. $4a + 2(3a + 1) = 32$

13. $6x + 4(3x - 5) = 16$

Complete each data table.

14.

x	2(3x - 2) + 5
4	
	31

15.

x	4(2x - 3) + 8
2	
	28

16.   The perimeter of ABCD is 38.   17.   The perimeter of PQRS is 70.
       Find AB.   Find PQ.

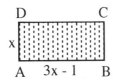

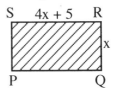

18.   Tyrone plans to make a profit of 30% of the cost on a 15-speed mountain bike,
       If the sale price of the bike is $273, what must have been his cost?

    19.   The owner of a Tape City store marks the sale price of compact disk at
                               $29. He knows his profit is 25% of the cost. Find the cost rounded to
                               the nearest cent.

20.   A number increased by 40% of that number is 28. Find the number.

OPEN-ENDED QUESTION

21.   Describe in detail how to solve the problem below.
       Indicate where the Distributive Property and combining
       like terms are used. Also explain why or why not the
       solution of the equation is the solution of the problem.
       The perimeter of the triangle is 22. Find AC.

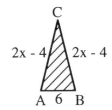

REVIEW

1.   If 3 out of n games are lost and there are no ties, what fractional part of the games
      are won ?

2.   Last week Abul earned $20 working part time. This week he earned $24.
      The increase was what % of last week's earnings?

3.   What symbol is in the 79th position of the following pattern?
      polygonpolygonpolygon...

4.   6 less than twice Harry's age is 10. How old is Harry?

5.6 Number Problems

OBJECTIVE   To solve problems involving two numbers

The following statement compares **two** ages, Selena's and Ed's.

> **Selena** is two years older than **Ed**.

How can you represent the age of each?

Notice that Selena's age is given in terms of Ed's age, not vice versa.

The cue is the word **_than_**..

If you know Ed's age, you can find Selena's age.

You do two things:

1. Use **x** for the quantity <u>**after**</u> the word **_than_**..

        Selena is two years older than Ed.

                Let x represent Ed's age.

2. Represent the other quantity in terms of **x**.

    Selena's age: 2 years older than **Ed**

                    2 older than **x**

                    x   +   2

Thus, the representations of their ages are:

            Ed's age: x

            Selena's age: x + 2

EXAMPLE 1   The larger of two numbers is 6 less than 7 times the smaller.
            Represent the numbers.

Strategy   What quantities are being compared?

            Larger is compared with **smaller**.

            Which of these comes **after** the word **than**?   **(continued on next page)**

The word **smaller** comes **after** the word **than**.

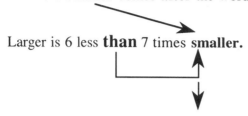

Larger is 6 less **than** 7 times **smaller.**

Let **x** represent the **smaller.**

So, the representations of the two numbers being compared are:

Solution   Let **x** = smaller.   6 less than 7 times **smaller**

7x - 6 = larger number.   6 less than 7**x**

                                                 7x   -   6

EXAMPLE 2   The length of a rectangle is 2 cm less than 3 times the width.

The perimeter is 44 cm. Find the length and the width of the rectangle.

Strategy   The first sentence gives the relationship between the **length** and **width**.

1.   Use that sentence to write representations for the **length** and **width**.

The **width** comes **after** the word **than**.

length is 2 less **than** 3 times **width**

Let **x** represent the **width.**

                                      2 less than 3 times **width**

Let 3x - 2 represent the length.   2 less than 3**x**

                                      3x   -   2

2.   Draw a diagram. Use the perimeter formula to write an equation.

(continued on next page)

Use   P = 2L   + 2W

44 = 2(3x - 2)   + 2(x)

44 = 2 · 3x - 2 · 2 + 2x

3.   44 = 6x - 4   + 2x   **Solve.**

44 = 8x - 4   **Combine like terms.**

48 = 8x   **Add 4 to each side.**

6 = x   **Divide each side by 8.**

4.   Use the representations to find the length and the width.

width: **x = 6**

length: 3x - 2

3 · **6** - 2   **Substitute 6 for x.**

18 - 2

16

Solution   Thus, the width is 6 cm and the length is 16 cm.

Sometimes two numbers are **compared** without the use of the word **than**.

Consider the following statement.

The larger of two numbers is 3 times the smaller.

What quantities are being compared?

The **larger** of two numbers is 3 times the **smaller**.

The **larger** is compared with the **smaller**:

How can you write representations of the two numbers?

The **larger** is 3 times the **smaller**.

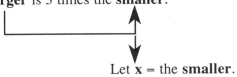

Let **x** = the **smaller**.

Then **3x** = the **larger**.   **Larger is 3 times smaller.**

Larger is 3 times x.

EXAMPLE 3   Julie's salary is 4 times Liz's salary. Together they earn $320.
Find the salary of each girl.

Strategy   What are the two quantities that are compared and must be represented?
The first sentence makes the comparison.

Julie's salary is 4 times **Liz's** salary.

You need **representations** for **Julie's** salary and **Liz's** salary.

Julie's salary is 4 times **Liz's** salary.

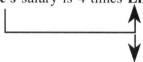

1.   Let **x = Liz's salary.**

Then **4x** = Julie's salary. **Julie's is 4 times Liz's.**

Julie's is 4 times x.

2.   Use the second sentence to write an equation.

Together they earn $320.

x + 4x = 320   **Liz's salary plus Julie's salary is $320.**

(TOGETHER tells you to ADD.)

3.   Solve the equation.

1x + 4x = 320   **x = 1x**

5x = 320   **Combine like terms.**

x = 64   **Divide each side by 5:** $\dfrac{320}{5} = 64.$

Use the representations to find the salary of each.

Liz's salary: **x = 64**

Julie's salary: **4x**

4 · **64** **Substitute 64 for x.**

256

Solution 4.   Thus, the two salaries are: Liz's = $64

Julie's = $256

Check: $256 is 4 times $64 **and** $64 + $256 = $320

EXAMPLE 4   The players on a basketball team scored 72 points in one game.
They made four times as many field goals as they did free throws.
Each field goal is worth two points and each free throw is worth one
point. How many field goals did the players on that team make during
the game?

Strategy   **1.**   First write representations for the number of field goals and the number
of free throws.

Let   x = **free throws**.   4 times as many **field goals** as **free throws**

4x = **field goals**

2.   Write an equation for the total number of points.

2 points for field goal   **1** point for free throw

field goal points   +   free throw points   =   total points

2(4x)   +   **1**(x)   =   72

8x   +   1x   =   72

3. Solve.   9x   =   72

x   =   8

4.   But, x = 8 is **NOT** the answer to the problem.

Use the **representation** to find the number of field goals.

Number of field goals: **4x**

4 · **8** = 32   **Substitute 8 for x.**

Solution   Thus, the number of field goals is 32.

SUMMARY

Use the following phrase to answer exercises 1-3.

The first of two numbers is 5 more than twice the second.

1.   What two quantities are being compared?

2.   Which is the basis of comparison, the one you call x?

3.   Give algebraic representations of the two quantities.

Use the following problem to answer exercises 4-11.

The length of a rectangle is 3 times the width.

The perimeter is 40. Find the length and the width.

4.   What are the two quantities that must be algebraically represented?

5.   Which is the basis of comparison? Which one do you call x?

6.   How can you then represent the second quantity?

7.   What formula can you then use to write an equation?

8.   What is the equation?

9.   What are the steps in solving the equation?

10. Once you have found x, how do you then find the length and width?

11. How can you **check** the problem? Is the length 3 times the width? Is the perimeter 40?

CLASSROOM PRACTICE

Solve each problem.

1.   The length of a rectangle is 2 ft more than 3 times the width. The perimeter is 28 ft. Find the length and the width.

2.   The length of a rectangle is 3 m less than 5 times the width. The perimeter is 18 m. Find the length and the width.

3.   The length of a rectangle is twice the width. The perimeter is 42 cm. Find the length and the width.

4.   The length of a rectangle is 6 times the width. The perimeter is 56 yd. Find the length and the width.

5.   Ned's age is 3 more than twice Rita's age. The sum of their ages is 24. Find each of their ages.

6.   Tom's income is 3 times that of Kevin. Together they earn $600. Find the income of each.

7.   The players on a basketball team scored 90 points in one game. They made 4 times as many field goals as they did free throws.. Each field goal is worth 2 points and each free throw is worth 1 point. How many field goals did the players score during the game?

8.   Martha has $105 worth of cassette tapes and disks. She has twice as many

cassettes as disks. Cassettes cost $10.00 each and disks cost $15.00 each. How many cassettes does she have in her collection?

WRITTEN EXERCISES

Solve each problem.

1. The length of a rectangle is 6 m more than 4 times the width. The perimeter is 72 m. Find the length and the width.

2. The length of a rectangle is 2 in. less than 3 times the width. The perimeter is 68 in. Find the length and the width.

3. The length of a rectangle is twice the width. The perimeter is 54 cm. Find the length and the width.

4. The length of a rectangle is 8 times the width. The perimeter is 36 yd. Find the length and the width.

5. Noah's age is 10 more than twice Tina's age. The sum of their ages is 34. Find each of their ages.

6. Bill's income is 4 times that of Ryan. Together they earn $540. Find the income of each.

7. The players on a basketball team scored 84 points in one game. They made 3 times as many field goals as they did free throws. Each field goal is worth 2 points and each free throw is worth one point. Which of the following equations cannot be used to find the number of field goals the players on that team made during the game?

    (A) $2(3x) + x = 84$ (B) $x + 6x = 84$
    (C) $3 + x = 84$ (D) $7x = 84$

8. A sports shop has $570 worth of men's shirts and shorts. There are 3 times as many shorts as shirts. Shirts sell at $12 each and shorts sell at $15 each. How many shorts are there?

9. A 30 in. board is separated into two pieces. The longer piece is 8 in. longer than the shorter one. Find the length of each piece.

10. The second of two numbers is 8 less than twice the first.

Their sum is 19. Find the two numbers.

11.   James has saved $560 in two years. He saved 3 times as much during the first year as during the second year. How much did he save each year?

12.   Hisako has 2 records fewer than 3 times the number Natasha has. Together they have 42 records. How many records does Hisako have?

13.   The length of a rectangle is 3 m more than 5 times the width. The perimeter is 126 m. Find the length and the width.

14.   The width of a rectangle is 2 ft more than twice the length. The perimeter is 28 ft. Find the length and the width.

OPEN-ENDED QUESTION

15.   The length of a rectangle is 2 cm less than 3 times the width. The perimeter is 44 cm. Write a detailed explanation of how to find the length. Include how you decide which side length to call x. Also explain how you got the equation and what was necessary to do after solving the equation.

REVIEW

The data table at the right shows how many students out of 200 sophomores are enrolled in foreign languages.

LANGUAGE	PERCENT
French	10%
German	5%
Spanish	55%
Latin	5%
No language	?%

1.   How many sophomores take German?

2.   How many more sophomores take Spanish than French?

3.   How many sophomores take a foreign language?

4.   Which of the following is not equivalent to the other 3?

   (A)   125% of 8   (B) $8 \div \frac{4}{5}$ (C) $4 - 7 + 13$ (D) 5^2

5.   What is the next term in the sequence 9, 19, 39, 79, ...?

6.   Evaluate $\frac{4}{5} x + 18$ for $x = 15$.

5.7 Factors and Multiples

OBJECTIVES   To solve problems about multiples

To solve problems about factors

Many problems in arithmetic and algebra involve determining whether a number is an **exact multiple** of another. This is illustrated by the following practical illustration. Suppose you have a Sound Track gift certificate for $30. Tapes cost $5.00 each. How many can you buy?

30 is divisible exactly by 5.

30 is said to be a **multiple** of 5.

You can buy 6 tapes.

$$\frac{6}{5\overline{)30}}$$

Suppose instead that tapes cost $7.00 each. How many can you buy for $30?

But you can't buy $4\frac{2}{7}$ tapes.

Therefore, the most you can buy is **4** tapes.

$$\begin{array}{r} 4 \\ 7\overline{)30} \\ \underline{28} \\ 2 \end{array} \quad 4\frac{2}{7}$$

30 is **NOT** a multiple of 7.

30 is **NOT** divisible exactly by 7.

Sometimes a problem like the one above requires you to **raise** the answer if the division is **NOT** exact. This is illustrated in Example 1 below.

EXAMPLE 1   A medium-size school bus can transport no more than 32 students as passengers. If each bus makes only one trip, what is the smallest number of busses needed to transport 419 students to a football game?

Strategy   Does 32 divide into 419 exactly?

$419 \div 32 = 13.09375$

But you can't have a decimal part of a bus!

Solution   13 busses would not be enough.

Therefore, 13 + 1, or **14**, busses are needed.

For the **product** $5 \cdot 4$ the numbers 5 and 4 are called **factors**.

Recall that **factors** are numbers that are **multiplied**.

Sometimes, you can write a number as a product of factors in several ways.

For example, 40 can be **factored** as $20 \cdot 2$ or

$$10 \cdot 4 \text{ or}$$
$$4 \cdot 5 \cdot 2 \text{ or}$$
$$2 \cdot 2 \cdot 5 \cdot 2.$$

In the last case, neither of the factors, 2 and 5, can be factored further.

This is true because the only factors of 2 are 2 and 1. The only factors of 5 are 5 and 1.

The numbers 2 and 5 are called **prime** numbers.

A **prime number** is a whole number greater than 1 whose only factors are 1 and itself.

You can find factors by dividing.

For example, 12 is a factor of 36 since 12 divides into 36 exactly:

$36 \div 12 = 3$. There is **NO REMAINDER.** 36 is a **multiple** of 12.

An important property of factors is illustrated by the following.

12 is a factor of 36 **ONLY** if any factor of 12 is **ALSO** a factor of 36.

> 2 is a factor of 12 **and** 2 is also a factor of 36.
>
> 3 is a factor of 12 **and** 3 is also a factor of 36.
>
> 4 is a factor of 12 **and** 4 is also a factor of 36.
>
> 6 is a factor of 12 **and** 6 is also a factor of 36.
>
> 12 is a factor of 12 **and** 12 is also a factor of 36.

EXAMPLE 2   12 is not a factor of 80 because

(A)   80 is not a prime number   (B)   12 is not a prime number.

(C)   8 is not a factor of 80.   (D)   6 is not a factor of 80

Strategy   (A) is irrelevant. Non-primes like 80 do have factors.

(B) is irrelevant. Not all factors are prime. 12, not prime, is a factor of 36

(C) is incorrect. 8 **is** a factor of 80.

(D) 6 is a factor of 12. However, 6 is **NOT** a factor of 80.

Solution   Therefore, the correct choice is **(D)**.

12 is **NOT** a factor of 80 because 6, a factor of 12, is **NOT** a factor of 80.

The ideas of **multiple** and **factor** are applied in solving packaging problems in warehouses.

Suppose that a warehouse manager stocks baseballs in boxes of 8 or 12.
The total number of baseballs depends upon the number of boxes of 8 and the number of boxes of 12. Some examples are illustrated below.

$$\text{5 boxes of } \mathbf{8} \text{ and 2 boxes of } \mathbf{12}$$
$$5 \cdot \mathbf{8} \ + \ 2 \cdot \mathbf{12} = \mathbf{64}$$

$$\text{3 boxes of } \mathbf{8} \text{ and 7 boxes of } \mathbf{12}$$
$$3 \cdot \mathbf{8} \ + \ 7 \cdot \mathbf{12} = \mathbf{108}$$

$$\mathbf{a} \text{ boxes of } \mathbf{8} \text{ and } \mathbf{b} \text{ boxes of } \mathbf{12}$$
$$\mathbf{a} \cdot \mathbf{8} \ + \ \mathbf{b} \cdot \mathbf{12} = \mathbf{total}$$

or $\mathbf{8a + 12b} \quad = \mathbf{total}$

This suggests that if baseballs are packed in boxes of **8** or **12**, then the total number can be represented by: $\mathbf{8a + 12b} \qquad = \mathbf{total}$

$$\mathbf{multiple \ of \ 8 + \ multiple \ of \ 12 = total}$$

Before we apply this to a problem notice the following pattern.

For $5 \cdot \mathbf{8} \ + \ 2 \cdot \mathbf{12} = \mathbf{64}$, any factor of **8** and **12** is also a factor of **64**.

For example, 2 is a factor of 8 and 12.   2 is also a factor of 64! $64 \div 2 = 32$

For example, 4 is a factor of 8 and 12.   4 is also a factor of 64! $64 \div 4 = 16$

For $3 \cdot \mathbf{8} \ + \ 7 \cdot \mathbf{12} = \mathbf{108}$, any factor of **8** and **12** is also a factor of **108**.

For example, 2 is a factor of 8 and 12.   2 is also a factor of 108! $108 \div 2 = 54$

For example, 4 is a factor of 8 and 12.   4 is also a factor of 108! $108 \div 4 = 27$

Likewise, for $\mathbf{8a + 12b} \quad = \mathbf{total}$, any factor of **8** and **12** is also a factor of **total**.

EXAMPLE 3   Show the total 6a + 12b = 20 can never be true for any whole number values of a and b.

Strategy   To be true, any factor of 6 and 12 must also be a factor of 20.
2 is a factor of 6 and 12. **2** is also a factor of 20.

3 is a factor of 6 and 12. But 3 is **NOT** a factor of 20. 20 ÷ 3 = 6.666

Solution   So, 6a + 12b = 20 **cannot** be true for whole number values of a and b since there is a factor of 6 and 12, **3**, that is **NOT** a factor of 20.

EXAMPLE 4   A warehouse manager's computer showed that there were 282 baseballs in stock. They were all in full boxes of 9 or 18. He claimed that the computer's count was wrong. The manager was correct because 282 is not divisible by what number?

Strategy   First represent the total as shown above on the previous page.
Let **9a** represent a **multiple** of 9. Let **18b** represent a **multiple** of 18
Then the total number of baseballs in stock is

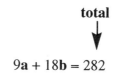

total

$$9a + 18b = 282$$

Any **factor** of **9** and **18** must also be a factor of 282.
3 is a factor of 9 and 18. 3 is also a factor of 282.   282 ÷ 3 = 94
9 is a factor of 9 and 18. But 9 is **NOT** a factor of 282. 282 ÷ 9 = 31.333
(282 is NOT divisible by 9).

Solution   Therefore, the manager was correct because there is a factor of 9 and 18, **9,** that is **NOT** a factor of 282.

Factors can be used to tell us something about the values of x or y to make an equation true. Consider the equation 2x + 9y = 24.

Suppose that x and y must be whole numbers to make the equation true.

Does the equation tell us something that we can predict about the value of x?

This is illustrated in the next example.

Note, by the way, that   **3 is a factor of 15**   means the same as saying

                                 15 is a multiple of 3.

Similarly,   **3 is a factor of x**   means the same as saying

                                 x is a multiple of 3.

EXAMPLE 5   A student trying to solve a problem in algebra came up with the equation 2x + 9y = 24. The problem called for x and y to be whole numbers.

The student told her teacher that the equation tells you something about the value of x. In fact,

(A)   x must be divisible by 2.   (B)   x must be a multiple of 3.

(C)   x must be even.   (D)   x must be a multiple of 9.

Strategy   First note that the multiple choices all involve the value of **x.**

Let's get the **x term** by itself on the left side of the equation.

2x + 9y =   24

2x   =   24 - 9y   **Subtract 9y from each side.**

                                               2x is now alone on the left.

As in Example 4, any factor of **24** and **9** must be a factor of **2x.**

3 is a factor of **24** and **9**.

So, **3** must be a factor of 2x.

Now, 2x = **2 · x.**

3 is **NOT** a factor of **2**. Therefore, **3** must be a factor of **x.**

Solution   Thus, x must be a **multiple** of **3**. (B)

Notice the similarity of the solutions of Examples 4 and 5. Both involved factoring and looking for the same factor on both sides of the equation.

The idea of multiples and factors can be extended to undoing errors in calculations with a calculator.

Suppose, for example, you hit the multiplication key instead of the division key on a calculator.

What should you do with the answer to undo the error?

Let's first try an easy illustration of the idea.

Suppose you want to divide 12 by 4. You should get **3** as an answer.

Instead you make the mistake of **multiplying** 12 by 4.

You get $12 \cdot 4 = 48$.

You try to **undo** this by dividing 48 by 4.

You get $48 \div 4 = 12$. This is **NOT** 3.

You must now divide 12 by 4 as you were asked to do in the beginning!

$12 \div 4 = \textbf{3}$.

So, if you mistakenly **multiply**, instead of **divide**, a number by 4, you can get the right answer by **dividing** by 4 **twice!**

EXAMPLE 6   Kathy mistakenly multiplied by 15 instead of dividing by 15 while using her calculator. If the **in**correct answer displayed on the calculator is 90, what is the correct answer.

Strategy   She first has to **UNDO** multiplication of 90 by 15.

Multiplication is **UNDONE** by division.

So, first divide 90 by 15: $90 \div 15 = 6$.

But this is **NOT** the correct answer.

6 is the number she began with.

She was supposed to have **divided** 6 by 15.

$6 \div 15 = 0.4$.

Solution   Therefore, the correct answer is 0.4.

The concept of multiples is illustrated in the next example which involves separating a collection of workers into two groups.

EXAMPLE 7   An engineering firm encourages its research people to work together in groups of 5 on Fridays. On other days they work together in groups of 2 or 4. However, when all workers are present, there is always one person left over to sum up previous group decisions. Which of the following could be the number of research people altogether ?

(A)   16   (B)   21   (C)   11   (D)   6

Strategy   Determine which of the multiple-choice answers are multiples of 5, 4, and 2 with 1 left over each time.

That is, look for the multiple-choice answer which when divided by 5 or 4 or 2 always leaves a remainder of **1**.

For example, first try 16.

$16 \div 5 = 3$ with a remainder of **1.**

But, $16 \div 2 = 8$ with a remainder of **0, NOT 1.**

Now try 21.

$21 \div 5 = 4$ with a remainder of **1.**

$21 \div 2 = 10$ with a remainder of **1.**

$21 \div 4 = 5$ with a remainder of **1.**

All three divisions result in a remainder of 1 left over.

None of the others have this result. For example,

$11 \div 5 = 2$ with a remainder of **1**

$11 \div 2 = 5$ with a remainder of **1**

$11 \div 4 = 2$ with a remainder of **3, NOT 1.**

$6 \div 4 = 1$ with a remainder of **2, NOT 1.**

Thus, 21 is the only possible number of research people altogether.

21 is the only number of the choices that is a multiple of 5, 2, and 4 with **1** left over.

Solution   The choice is (B).

EXAMPLE 8   As cars come off an assembly line, inspectors check them. Inspector
                  1 checks the 10th car and every 10th one after that. Inspector 2 checks the
                  15th car and every 15th one after that for the quality of paint finish. Thus a
                  particular automobile could be inspected as many as two times. If 90 cars are
                  produced one day, how many of them will have been inspected twice?

Strategy   Cars inspected by Inspector 1.   Cars inspected by Inspector 2
                  Multiples of 10:   Multiples of 15:
                  10, $10 \cdot 2$, $10 \cdot 3$, $10 \cdot 4$, etc.   15, $15 \cdot 2$, $15 \cdot 3$, $15 \cdot 4$, etc.
                  10, 20, **30**, 40, etc   15, **30,** 45, etc.

                  Thus, both inspectors will have checked the **30th** car and every 30 cars after it.

Solution   If 90 cars are produced then the number of cars inspected twice will be
                  $90 \div 30 = 3$.

In Example 8 above you wrote out multiples of 10 and 15.
The number **30** was the first multiple of **both 10 and 15.**
So, **30** is the **least** multiple **common** to both 10 and 15.
30 is called the **least common multiple (LCM)** of 10 and 15.

EXAMPLE 9   Find the least common multiple of 6 and 8.

Strategy   Begin writing **multiples** of 6 and 8. Look for the first one that is
                  the **same** for or **common to** both 6 and 8.
                  Multiples of 6   Multiples of 8
                  6, $6 \cdot 2$, $6 \cdot 3$, $6 \cdot 4$, $6 \cdot 5$, etc.   8, $8 \cdot 2$, $8 \cdot 3$, $8 \cdot 4$, $8 \cdot 5$, etc.
                  6, 12, 18, **24,** 30, etc.   8, 16, **24**, 32, 40, etc.

Solution   Thus, the least common multiple of 6 and 8 is **24**.

SUMMARY

1.   Is the number 7 prime? Why?

2.   What factors of 12 are not factors of 30?

3.   Complete the following statement.

      If 12 is a factor of 30, then every factor of 12 must be _____.

      How does this illustrate that 12 is not a factor of 30?

4.   A school bus can transport at most 30 students. How do you determine the least number of busses needed to transport 179 students to a field hockey game?

5.   How do you determine if $4a + 8b = 30$ is true for any whole number values of a and b?

6.   Consider the equation $3x + 5y = 25$. If x and y are whole numbers, how do you find out what x must be a multiple of?

7.   Suppose you used a calculator to subtract 24 from a number. By mistake, you hit the add key instead of the subtract key and got an answer of 78. How can you find the correct answer?

8.   How do you find the least common multiple of two numbers?

CLASSROOM PRACTICE

1.   A publisher ships books in cartons which can contain at most 12 books. What is the least number of cartons needed to ship 290 books?

2.   Tables in a cafeteria can seat up to 6 people. What is the smallest number of tables needed to seat 125 students for a sophomore dance?

3.   Which of the following reasons would make a true statement?

      15 is not a factor of 50 because _____

      (A)   4 is not a factor of 50.   (B)   3 is not a factor of 50.
      (C) $15 \div 50$ is not an integer.   (D)   50 is not a prime number.

4.   14 is not a factor of 40 because __ is not a factor of 40.

5.   The computer of a sporting goods warehouse manager' showed there were 236 footballs in stock. They were all in boxes of 9 or 12. He claimed that the computer was wrong because 236 was not divisible by a certain number. What number could this be?

6.   School sweatshirts of the same size and color are packed in boxes of 4, 8, and 20. The inventory shows that there is supposed to be a total of 150. A clerk indicated that there must be an error, since 150 is not a multiple of ____.

7.   Suppose that x and y represent whole numbers. Then, for the equation $3x + 2y = 24$,. what do you know about the value of y?
      (A)   y must be a multiple of 2.   (B)   y must be a multiple of 3.
      (C)   y must be an even number.   (D)   y must be divisible by 24.

8.   While solving a problem, a group of students determined that a and b must be whole numbers to make the equation $11a + 3b = 66$ true. One student concluded that the fact that only whole number values can make the equation true means that the value of b
      (A)   must be divisible by 3   (B)   must be odd.
      (C)   must be divisible by 11.   (D)   must be a multiple of 3

9.   Tyrone mistakenly divided by 14 instead of multiplying by 14. If the incorrect answer displayed on the calculator was 3, what is the correct answer?

10.   Janet was supposed to subtract 146 from a number.
      By mistake, she added 146 and got 358. What is the correct answer?

11.   A class of interns at a hospital meetssd four days a week to share ideas.
      On Mondays they work in groups of 4. On other days they break up into groups of 6 or 9. When all the interns are present, there are always 2 interns left over to compare results of the different groups. Which of the following could be the total number of interns?
      (A)   26   (B)   38   (C)   20   (D)   50

12.   As cars come off an assembly line, inspectors check them for quality of door
        fittings. Bill checks the 3rd car and every 3rd one after that and Wanda checks the
        8th car and every 8th one after that. If 72 cars are produced one day, how many
        of them will have been inspected twice?

Find the least common multiple for each set of numbers.

13.   4 and 10   14.   8 and 10   15.   3, 6, and 8

WRITTEN EXERCISES

1.   12 is not a factor of 90 because

        (A)   90 is not a prime number.   (B)   12 is not a prime number.

        (C)   4 is not a factor of 90.   (D)   6 is not a factor of 90.

2.   16 is not a factor of 60 because

        (A)   5 is not a factor of 16.   (B)   Both numbers are even.

        (C)   2 is not a factor of 60.   (D)   8 is not a factor of 60.

3.   Boxes of cereal are packaged in cartons of at most 8 to a carton. What is the least
        number of cartons needed to ship 43 boxes of cereal?

4.   A clerk at Sound Store is doing an inventory of the number of blank cassettes
        available for a big upcoming sale. The cassettes are all packed in full boxes of 8
        or 12. He told his boss that the total count was 262. His boss said there must be
        an error in the count.
        There was an error because 262 is not divisible by
        (A)   8   (B)   4   (C)   12   (D)   2

5.   Ten ounce drinking cups are packed in boxes of 6, 12, and 33. If a computer
        inventory shows that there are 1,252 cups altogether, then there must be a
        computer error since 1,252 is not divisible by
        (A)   3   (B)   4   (C)   6   (D)   12

6.   Suppose that a and b can represent only whole numbers. Then, what do you know about the value of b in the equation $6a + 5b = 21$?

(A)   b must be a multiple of 5.   (B)   b must be a multiple of 6.

(C)   b must be divisible by 3.   (D)   b must be a factor of 21.

7.   While solving a problem a group of students determined that a and b must be whole numbers to make the equation $7a + 5b = 63$ true. One student concluded that the fact that only whole number values can make the equation true means that the value of b

(A)   must be odd.   (B)   must be a prime.

(C)   must be divisible by 5.   (D)   must be a multiple of 7.

8.   Jose mistakenly divided by 12 instead of multiplying by 12. If the incorrect answer displayed on the calculator was 24, what is the correct answer?

(A)   6   (B)   48   (C)   3,456   (D) none of these answers

9.   Rudy was supposed to subtract 119 from a number.
By mistake, he added 119 and got 247. What is the correct answer?

(A)   9   (B)   19   (C)   128   (D)   366

10.   On some days, a history teacher has the students in his class work in groups of 3, on other days in groups of 5 or 6. However, when all students are present, there is always one student left over after the groups are formed. Which of the following could be the number of students in that class?

(A)   37   (B)   31   (C)   28   (D)   25

11.   Boxes of salt-water taffy are checked for proper weight by three different inspectors. Hank checks the 3rd box and every 3rd one after that. Twana checks the 6th one and every 6th one after that. Bill checks the 10th one and every 10th one after that. If 240 boxes of taffy are turned out in 5 hours, how many will have been checked three times?

Find the least common multiple of each set of numbers.

12.   6 and 10   13.   8 and 12   14.   4, 6, and 8

OPEN-ENDED QUESTION

15.   A warehouse manager glanced at her computer and told a group of visiting high-school students that there were 8,456 cans of juice in her warehouse inventory. Moreover, she said that all these cans were packed in boxes of 12 or 30 of the same size can. One student argued that this tally could not possibly be correct. Explain why this student was correct.

REVIEW   CHAPTERS 1-5

1.   Find the perimeter and area of the rectangle for A(3,5), B(10,5), C(10, 11), and D(3, 11).

2.   Find the area of a rectangle with length 8 cm and perimeter 40 cm.

3.   Carpeting costs $25.95 a square yard. Find the cost, to the nearest cent, of carpeting a room measuring 15 ft by 18 ft.

4.   Use graph paper to draw a rectangle with perimeter 24 units.

5.   Mr. Gonzalez plans to build a 5 ft high fence around a rectangular lot that measures 60 ft by 80 ft. The fencing contractor charges $36.00 a linear foot. Find the cost of the fence.

Simplify.

6. $4(3k)$

7. $3(5x + 8)$

8. $4(2m - 6)$

9. $-4(-2)^3$

10. $-7 + 5 - 9 + 12$

11. $\dfrac{4 \cdot 9 + 8}{19 - 2 \cdot 4}$

12. $3x + 4 + x + 12$

13. $-4m - 5m$

14. $4x + 3(2x - 5) - 11x$

Solve.

15. $18 = 12 + 3x$

16. $4x + 7 + x = 42$

17. $8 + 3(2x - 5) = 23$

18.   A store manager lists the selling price of a T.V. at $252. If he plans on a profit of 40% of the cost, what must the T.V. have cost him?

19.   Complete the data table.

n	n + 3(n - 4) + 7
3	
	15

20.   The length of a rectangle is 4 ft less than twice the width.
       The perimeter is 28 ft. Find the length and the width.

21.   The larger of two numbers is 3 times the smaller. The sum of the two numbers is
       32. Find the numbers.

22.   The players on a basketball team scored 88 points in one game.
       They made five times as many field goals as they did free throws. Each
       field goal is worth two points and each free throw is worth one point.
       How many field goals did the team players make during the game?

23.   A school bus can carry at most 42 students. If each bus makes only one trip,
       find the least number of busses needed to transport 250 sophomores to a
       class picnic at the end of the school year.

24.   15 is not a factor of 80 because

       (A)   80 is not an odd number.   (B)   5 is not a factor of 80.

       (C)   3 is not a factor of 80.   (D)   2 is a factor of 80 but not of 15.

25.   Cassette tapes are stored in boxes of 8 or 12. A weekly inventory indicates that
       the total number of cassettes in stock is supposed to be 320. Why is this not
       possible?

26.   Find the least common multiple of 5 and 8.

27.   Suppose that m and n represent whole numbers.
       Then for the equation $7m + 3n = 15$, what must be true about the value of m?

       (A)   m must be divisible by 7.   (B)   m must be divisible by 3.

       (C)   m must be a multiple of 5.   (D)   m must be odd, since 3 and 15 are
                                                    both odd.

28.   Jenny mistakenly multiplied by 5 instead of dividing by 5 while using her
       calculator. If the incorrect answer displayed on the calculator is 275,
       what is the correct answer?

29.   Mr. Johnson encourages his class to work together in small groups of 3
       on Wednesdays. On other days they work together in groups of 4 or 6.
       When all students are present, there are always 2 students left over to

write up group conclusions. Which of the following could be the number of students in the class?

(A)   13   (B)   14   (C)   25   (D)   30

30. As cars come off the assembly line, inspectors spot-check them. Ricci checks the 3rd car and every 3rd one after that. Donna checks the 8th car and every 8th one after that. If 72 cars are produced in one day, how many of them will have been inspected twice?

31. Find the weight of one pyramid if one block weighs 7 lb and the scale is balanced.

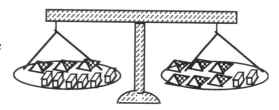

32. There are 4 different symbols appearing in the spiral . If they are labeled R, S, T, and U in the order in which they first appear, (beginning at start and going clockwise), what letters represent the missing figures in the spiral?

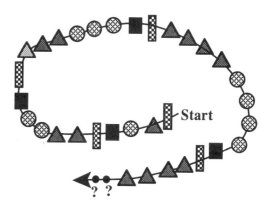

(A)   RR   (B)   TS   (C)   ST   (D)   TU

33. At the right are three views of a die. The numbers 1, 2, 3, 4, 5, and 6 appear exactly once on the faces of this die. What number is opposite 4?

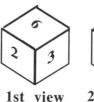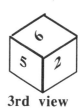

1st view   2nd view   3rd view

34.   Find the area of a circle with radius 7 cm.

Use $A = 3.14r^2$.

35.   Dana usually makes 65% of her basketball foul shots. This season she attempted 125 foul shots. Approximately, how many did she miss?

36.   Which of the following is **NOT** a way to find 120% of a number?

(A)   Multiply the number by 0.12.

(B)   Multiply the number by 6 and then divide the result by 5.

(C)   Add the number to the number multiplied by 0.20.

(D)   Add the number to $\frac{1}{5}$ of the number.

37.   A football that regularly sells for $75 is on sale at a discount of 30%. Which of the procedures below could you use to find the sale price?

| I | $75 \cdot 0.70$ | II | $0.30 \cdot 75$ |
| III | $75 + 0.30 \cdot 75$ | IV | $75 - 0.30 \cdot 75$ |

(A)   II only   (B)   I or IV only

(C)   III only   (D)   I or III only

38.   A $60 bicycle is advertised at $\frac{1}{3}$ off the regular price. At another store, the same brand bike is on sale at 30% off of its regular price of $70. How much is saved by buying at the store with the lower price?

39.   The area of the shaded portion of the circle is what % of the unshaded area of the circle?

40.   Last week Rita earned $50 working part-time. This week she earned only $40. The decrease was what % of last week's earnings?

Insert the appropriate inequality symbol, < or >, to make each true. (Ex. 41-42)

41.   -40 ? 5   42. 2.9^5 ? 1.7^{10}

43. What are Don's total expenses?

44. Don's entertainment expense is what % of Tina's entertainment expense?

45. Don's total expenses are how much less than Tina's expenses?

WEEKLY EXPENSES		
Expenses	Don	Tina
Car	$80	$90
Entertainment	$30	$50
Rent	$125	$150
Savings	$35	$45
Food	$70	$90

NUMBER OF SOPHOMORE GIRLS OUT FOR SPORTS

46. What is the total number of girls out for sports?

47. The number of girls out for softball is what % of the number out for field hockey?

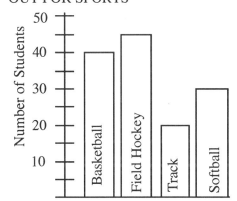

48. What is the driving distance from Camden to Elizabeth?

49. Jon drives 55 miles per hour. Approximately how long will it take him to drive from Newark to Bridgeton?

Mileage Between Principal Cities	Atlantic City	Bridgeton	Camden	Cape May	Cherry Hill	Elizabeth	Jersey City
Atlantic City	0	81	57	48	55	105	119
Camden	57	40	0	84	9	81	85
Newark	108	113	84	154	80	8	6
Paterson	123	131	99	165	95	23	21
Trenton	74	70	32	106	35	48	58
New Brunswick	93	99	56	128	58	26	31

50. Estimate the value of 0.49 · 0.00003978.

    (A) 0.00003   (B) 0.00002   (C) 0.000016   (D) 0.0002

51. What symbol is in the 113th position of the following pattern?

squaresquaresquare...

52. What is the next term of the sequence 14, 30, 62, 126, 254, ... ?

53. What is the units digit in the 45th term of the sequence $3^1, 3^2, 3^3, 3^4, ...$

54. Which problem below can be used to solve the equation $x + 2x - 4 = 11$.

   (A) 4 less than twice a number is 11. Find the number.

   (B) The larger of two numbers is 4 more than twice the smaller. The sum of the numbers is 11. Find the numbers.

   (C) The smaller of two numbers is 4 less than the larger. The sum of the numbers is 11. Find the numbers.

   (D) The larger of two numbers is 4 less than twice the smaller. The sum of the numbers is 11. Find the numbers.

55. Evaluate $\frac{4}{5} x - 7$ for $x = 15$.

56. On a multiple-choice test each correct choice is worth 6 points. But, 2 points are deducted for each wrong answer. Which formula below represents the total score T if C represents the number of correct answers and W the number of wrong answers?

   (A) $T = 6C + 2W$ (B) $T = 2W - 6C$

   (C) $T = 6C - 2W$ (D) $T = 6 + C - 2 - W$

OPEN-ENDED QUESTION

57. The perimeter of a rectangle is 24 units. How many different rectangles can be drawn with this perimeter if the dimensions are whole numbers? Form a data table showing all possible lengths, widths, and areas.

   Also use graph paper to draw some of the rectangles.

   Which length and width produces a rectangle with the largest area?

Length	Width	Area

6

Connecting Algebra to Geometry and Statistics

6.1 Segments and Distance

OBJECTIVES   To find the distance between two points on a number line

To find the length of the smallest subdivision marked off between two integers on a number line

To identify and name segments and lines

Notice that the **coordinate** of A is -4.

The absolute value of -4, written as |**-4**|, is 4.

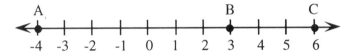

The **line** goes on forever in both directions. That's why it is indicated by two arrowheads. The line is named by **any two points** on the line.

Symbols for the line are $\overleftrightarrow{AB}$, $\overleftrightarrow{BA}$, $\overleftrightarrow{AC}$, $\overleftrightarrow{CA}$, etc.

DISCOVERY   Think of the set of points consisting of B and C and all points with coordinates **between** 3 and 6. How can you graph this set of points?

Don't forget to include points corresponding to fractions like $4\frac{1}{2}$.

The set of points consisting of P and Q and all points with coordinates between 1 and 5 is graphed at the right.

This set of points is called a **segment**.

A **segment** is a part of a line. P and Q are the endpoints of the **segment**.

The symbol for the **line** containing P and Q is $\overleftrightarrow{PQ}$.

The symbol for the **part of the line** above that is called a "segment" is $\overline{PQ}$.

Notice the difference: the **line** symbol contains **two arrowheads**.

the **segment** symbol contains **no arrowheads**.

DEFINITION

Segment AB is the set of points consisting of A, B, and all points between A and B.
A and B are the **endpoints** of the segment.

Either $\overline{AB}$ or $\overline{BA}$ can be used to name the segment.

EXAMPLE 1   Identify each figure below.

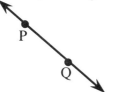

Solution

The **line** containing P and Q is symbolized by $\overleftrightarrow{PQ}$ or $\overleftrightarrow{QP}$.

The **segment** with endpoints G and H is symbolized by $\overline{GH}$ or $\overline{HG}$.

$\overline{AB}$ refers to the **segment**, the actual set of points forming the segment.

The **length** of the segment is **4**.
The **length** of the segment is symbolized by AB.
(There is **NO** bar over the letters.)
AB is the **distance** between the **endpoints** A and B of the segment.

$\overline{AB}$ is the **segment**.
AB is the **length** of the segment.

The difference between $\overline{AB}$ and AB can be compared with the difference between **Mary** and Mary's **weight** in the following sentence.

        Mary has a **weight** of 128 pounds.

        Mary is a person.   Her **weight** is 128 ponds.

Similarly, $\overline{AB}$ is a **segment**.   **AB** is 4, the **length** of the segment.

EXAMPLE 2   Given: a segment with endpoints R and S and length 7.

Write a symbol for the segment.   Write an equation for its length.

Solution   Symbol: $\overline{RS}$ or $\overline{SR}$ Equation: RS = 7 or SR = 7

(no bar over the letters)

AB is the **distance** between the points A and B of the segment. You can see from the figure that the distance is 4 units.

We shall define the distance between the two points A and B with coordinates 1 and 5, respectively, to be the

absolute value of the difference of their coordinates.

AB = |5 - 1| = |4| = 4   or   AB = |1 - 5| = |-4| = -(-4) = 4

DEFINITION

The **distance** between two points A and B with coordinates m and n is

|m - n| or |n - m|.

EXAMPLE 3   Find HK and AH.

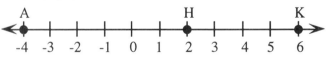

Solution   **HK** = |6 - 2| = |4| = 4

Strategy   AH = |2 - (-4)| **double negative is positive**

= |2 + 4|

= |6|

Solution   =   6

Sometimes finding the distance between two points involves subtracting fractions with unlike denominators, such as $7\frac{1}{2}$ and $3\frac{2}{5}$.

To do this subtraction, you will have to write each expression so that the denominators are **like** or **common**. It is simpler if the common denominator is the **least common denominator** **(LCD)**.

The **LCD** of $\frac{1}{2}$ and $\frac{2}{5}$ is the **least common multiple (LCM)** of the denominators 2 and 5.

EXAMPLE 4   Find ST for the given coordinates of S and T. $n = 7\frac{1}{2}, m = 3\frac{2}{5}$

$$ST = |\, 7\frac{1}{2} - 3\frac{2}{5}\,|$$

$$ST = 7\frac{1}{2} - 3\frac{2}{5}$$

Strategy   First find the **LCM** of the denominators 2 and 5.

The LCM of 2 and 5 is **10** (the **smallest** number divisible by both 2 and 5). Rewrite the subtraction with each fraction having **10** as the common denominator.

$$7\frac{1}{2} \;=\; 7\frac{1 \cdot 5}{2 \cdot 5} \;=\; 7\frac{5}{10}$$

$$-\,3\frac{2}{5} \;=\; -3\frac{2 \cdot 2}{5 \cdot 2} \;=\; -3\frac{4}{10}$$

$$\rule{1cm}{0.4pt} \qquad \rule{1.5cm}{0.4pt} \qquad 4\frac{1}{10}$$

Think: $2 \cdot ? = 10$. Multiply num. and den. of $\frac{1}{2}$ by 5.

Think: $5 \cdot ? = 10$. Multiply num. and den. of $\frac{2}{5}$ by 2.

Solution   Thus, ST $= 4\frac{1}{10}$

EXAMPLE 5   What is the smallest subdivision between the two integers 4 and 6?

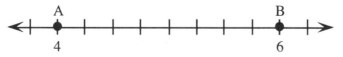

(solution on next page)

Strategy   The distance from
                 A to B is 6 - 4 = 2.
                 The distance **2** is
                 divided into **8** equal
                 subdivisions.

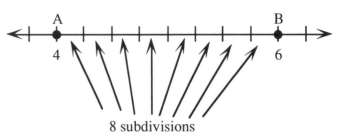

8 subdivisions

Solution   The length of each subdivision is $2 \div 8 = \frac{1}{4} = 0.25$.

SUMMARY

1. How does the symbol for the segment joining the points F and H differ from the symbol for the line joining those two points?

2. What is the difference between the symbols PQ and $\overline{PQ}$?

3. How do you find PQ?

4. How do you find the length of the smallest subdivision between the two integers 2 and 5?

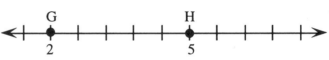

5. To find PQ, does the order of subtraction of the coordinates of P and Q matter? Why?

CLASSROOM PRACTICE

Given: F and Y are two points on a line. (Exercises 1-2)

1. Write a symbol for the segment with endpoints F and Y.

2. Write a symbol for the line containing F and Y.

3. Which of the following represents the length of a segment?

    (A) $\overline{TU}$ (B) TU   (C) $\overleftrightarrow{TU}$

Find PQ for the given coordinates of P and Q.

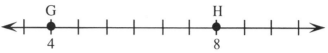

4.   P: 4, Q: 11   5.   P: 2,   Q: 18

6.   P: -5, Q: 9   7.   P: -6, Q: 12

8.   What is the length
      of the smallest
      subdivision between
      G and H?

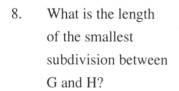

WRITTEN EXERCISES

Write a symbol for each of the following.

1.   2.   3.

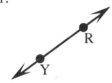   

                                                    Distance between T and J

Write a symbol for each of the following.

4.   the segment with endpoints F and Q

5.   the line containing the points D and M

6.   the length of the segment with endpoints U and E

Use the number line at the
right to find each length.

7.   HJ   8.   GK   9.   JG   10.   GI

11.   DG   12.   EH   13.   AJ   14.   BG

15.   AK   16.   CH   17.   BF   18.   CK

Find BG for the given coordinates of B and G.

19.   B: $4\frac{1}{2}$,   G: $7\frac{1}{8}$ 20.   B: $-2\frac{1}{2}$,   G: $4\frac{1}{3}$ 21.   B: $4\frac{3}{4}$,   G: 7

22.   Find the length of the
      smallest subdivision
      between M and N.

OPEN-ENDED QUESTION

23.   Given: PQ = 6 and the coordinate of P is -5.
      Find the coordinate of point Q. Is more than one answer possible?
      Explain why or why not.

REVIEW

Find the next term in each sequence.

1.   7, 9, 12, 16, 21, 27, ...   2.   4, 4, 8, 12, 20, 32, ...

3.   Which of the four 3-dimensional figures is a possible result of folding the pattern
     shown on the far left?

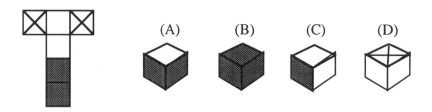

4.   A store manager lists the selling price of a stereo at $234. If he plans on a
     profit of 30% of the cost, what must the stereo have cost him?

5.   Find the perimeter and area of the rectangle ABCD for A(2,3), B(10, 3)
     C(10,12), and D(2,12).

6.   Find the area of a rectangle with length 12 ft and perimeter 30 ft

7.   Carpeting costs $35.95 a square yard. Find the cost of carpeting a room
     measuring 18 ft by 21 ft.

6.2 The Segment Addition Property

OBJECTIVE   To apply the Segment Addition Property

DISCOVERY

This diagram is a portion of a road map
showing three roads. If you were to bicycle
from Julep to Montville, there would be 3
possible bicycling routes. What would be
the shortest bicycling distance?

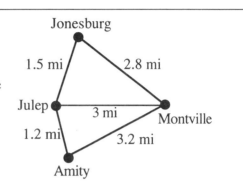

EXAMPLE 1   Use the figure above to find the three different bicycling distances from
Julep to Montville. Which is the shortest?

Strategy   Distance from Julep to Montville via Jonesburg: $1.5 + 2.8 = 4.3$
Distance from Julep to Montville via Amity: $1.2 + 3.2 = 4.4$
Distance from Julep to Montville via **one road**:   3

Solution   Thus, the shortest distance is the straight line segment distance of **3** miles.

The results above suggest a way to determine the **shortest distance** between two points
A and B. Can you guess what this is?

EXAMPLE 2   Draw two points A and B. Draw several paths between them.
What is the **shortest distance** between the two points.

Strategy   Draw the two points A and B and several
paths between them. Notice that the
shortest distance between them is the

Solution   segment $\overline{AB}$.

The results of Example 2 suggest the following important property.

SHORTEST DISTANCE PROPERTY

The shortest path between two points A and B is the segment, $\overline{AB}$.

EXAMPLE 3   Find AC, CB, and
AB.
Find AC + CB.
Draw a conclusion.

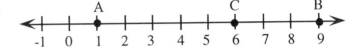

Strategy $AC = |6 - 1| = |5| = 5$

                     $CB = |9 - 6| = |3| = 3$

                     $AB = |9 - 1| = |8| = 8$

                     AC + CB   AB

                      5 + 3   8

Solution   So,   AC + CB =   AB

Notice in Example 3 that C is a point in $\overline{AB}$ and C is **between** A and B.

The results of Example 3 suggest the following property.

SEGMENT ADDITION PROPERTY

If C is **between** A and B, then AC + CB = AB.

EXAMPLE 4   PQ = 5, QR = 7, PR = ?

Strategy   Use the Segment Addition Property

                     PQ + QR =   PR

                      5 + 7 =   12

Solution   So, PR   = 12

EXAMPLE 5   FM = 18, RM = 7.
                  Find FR.

Strategy   Copy the figure and label its parts.

                  Let FR = x.
                  Write an equation using the Segment
                  Addition Property. Solve the equation.

                  FR + RM = FM
                  x   + 7   = 18
                  x   = 11   **Subtract 7 from each side.**
Solution   Thus, FR = 11.

The next example **connects** the geometric idea of segment addition with the algebraic
idea of equations with **like terms**.

EXAMPLE 6   AC = x + 4, CB = 2x + 3, AB = 22.
                  Find CB.

Strategy   **1.** Write an equation using the Segment Addition Property.
                       Solve the equation.

                       AC   +   CB   =   AB
                       1x + 4 + 2x + 3 = 22   **x = 1x**
                             3x + 7 =   22   **Combine like terms.**
                             3x   =   15   **Subtract 7 from each side.**
                             x   =   5   **Divide each side by 3.**

               2. x = 5 is **NOT** the answer to the problem.
                       Use   CB = 2**x** + 3 to find AC.
                              CB = 2 · **5** + 3   **Substitute 5 for x in 2x + 3.**
                              CB = 10   + 3
Solution   Thus, CB = 13

The Segment Addition Property can be used to model a real life problem as shown in Example 7 below.

EXAMPLE 7   Abul is typing a manuscript measuring $8\frac{1}{2}$ in by 11 in.

Specifications call for a print area with a maximum width of 6 inches. If the typing is to be centered, what must be the width of each side margin?

Strategy   **1.** Draw a diagram of the manuscript page.

Let x represent the width of the margin.

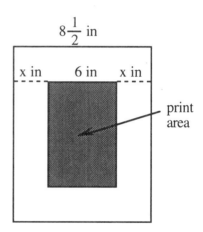

The problem can be modeled by a Segment Addition Property drawing.

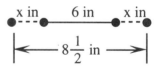

2. Use the Segment Addition Property to write an equation. Solve the equation.

$1x + 6 + 1x \quad = \quad 8\frac{1}{2}$ **x = 1x**

$2x + 6 \quad\quad = \quad 8\frac{1}{2}$ **Combine like terms.**

$2x \quad\quad\quad = \quad 2\frac{1}{2}$ **Subtract 6 from each side.**

$x \quad\quad\quad = \quad 1\frac{1}{4}$ $2\frac{1}{2} \div 2 = \frac{5}{2} \cdot \frac{1}{2} = \frac{5}{4} = 1\frac{1}{4}$

3. Check: margin width + print width + magin width = page width

$1\frac{1}{4}$ in   +   6 in   + $1\frac{1}{4}$ in   = $8\frac{1}{2}$ in **TRUE!**

Solution   Thus, the width of each margin is $1\frac{1}{4}$ in.

SUMMARY

1.   What is the shortest distance between two points?
2.   What does the Segment Addition Property say?

Explain how to solve each problem.

3.   AC = 7, CB = 9, AB = ?
4.   AB = 18, CB = 5, AC = ?

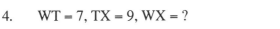

Use the information below to answer exercises 5-7.
FR = x + 6, RM = 2x + 1, FM = 13.

5.   To find FR, what equation must you first write?
6.   The solution of this equation is x = 2. Is this the value of FR? Why?
7.   How do you now find FR?

8. $\overline{QR}$ is centered on $\overline{PS}$.
     PS = $14\frac{1}{2}$ units, QR = 6 units.

     How do you find PQ and RS?

CLASSROOM PRACTICE

1.   VN = 7, NJ = 9, VJ = ?
2.   NJ = 9, VJ = 14, VN = ?
3.   VJ = 17, VN = 6, NJ = ?

4.   WT = 7, TX = 9, WX = ?
5.   WT = 8, WX = 12, TX = ?
6.   WX = 6, WT = 2, TX = ?

7.   AC = 4x, CB = 5x, AB = 27.
     Find CB.

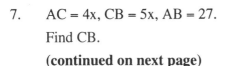

(continued on next page)

8. AC = x, CB = 4x, AB = 35.
    Find CB.

9. AC = x + 5, CB = 2x + 10, AB = 39.
    Find CB.

10. AC = 3x - 6, CB = x + 9, AB = 18.
    Find AC.

11. AC = 2x - 3, CB = x + 8, AB = 20.
    Find AC.

12. Jasmine is typing a manuscript on paper measuring $8\frac{1}{2}$ in. by 11 in.
    Specifications call for a print area with a maximum width of 7 in.
    If the typing is to be centered, what must be the width of each side margin?

13. The figure at the right shows a photo measuring 5" by 7"
    centered on a white background board measuring $7\frac{1}{2}$ " by 9".
    How far from the top of the board must the picture be
    positioned? How far from the vertical sides of the board must
    the picture be positioned?

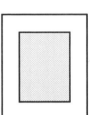

WRITTEN EXERCISES

1. RE = 5, EC = 13, RC = ?
2. RC = 21, EC = 7, RE = ?
3. RC = 33, RE = 15, EC = ?

4. TW = 19, WK = 16, TK = ?
5. TK = 23, WK = 15, TW = ?
6. TK = 9, TW = $3\frac{1}{4}$, WK = ?
7. TW = $3\frac{1}{2}$, WK = $2\frac{5}{6}$, TK = ?

8. GH = 3x, HK = 5x, GK = 32.
    Find HK.

9. GH = 5x, HK = 2x, GK = 21.

    Find GH.

10. AC = x + 4, CB = 2x + 7, AB = 32.
    Find CB.

11. AC = 4x + 3, CB = x - 1, AB = 17.
    Find CB.

12. AC = 3x - 4, CB = x + 8, AB = 24.
    Find CB.

13. AC = 2x + 3, CB = 3x - 4, AB = 24.
    Find AC.

14. A brochure measures $6\frac{1}{2}$ in wide by 8 in long. The advertisement space has a
    maximum width of 5 in. If the advertisement is to be centered, what must be the
    width of each side?

15. The figure at the right represents a room measuring
    16' by 20' with a 14' by 17' carpet centered in the
    room. How far is the carpet from
    (a) each vertical edge?
    (b) each horizontal edge?

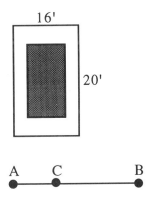

16. AB = 14, AC is 30% of AB.
    Find AC.

17. AC = 4, CB= 5.
    AC is what % of CB?

18. AB = 8, AC = 2.
    CB is what % of AB?

OPEN-ENDED QUESTION

19. The homes of Marge, Jane, José, and Mona are along the same road. Jane's house
    is between the houses of Marge and José. Mona's house is halfway between those
    of Jane and José. Jane lives 6 miles from Marge. José's house is 14 miles from
    Marge's. How far is Mona's house from José's? Is there more than one answer?

REVIEW

1. You are playing a game in which you move a chip on a number line. Where you move the chip is determined by the cards you draw from a pack. Each card has an integer printed on it. Your chip is now at the position shown below.

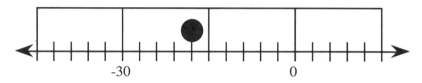

On each turn, you move your chip to the location equal to the sum of the coordinate of your current location and the number on the card you draw. Suppose you draw cards with the following sequence of numbers: -2, 6, -7, -12, and -4. What is the coordinate of your chip after you complete the sequence of moves?

2. If the pattern shown in the four figures below continues, how many blocks will be in the eighth figure?

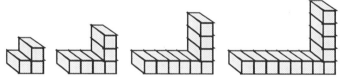

Simplify.

3. $5(2m - 6)$ 4. $-3(-2)^5$ 5. $-8 + 4 - 6 + 2$

6. Complete the data table.

x	2(3x - 5) + x
4	
	32

7. The length of a rectangle is 3 cm less than twice the width. The perimeter of the rectangle is 24 cm. Find the length.

8. Use graph paper to draw a rectangle with perimeter 18 units.

9. Evaluate $\frac{2}{3}x - 7$ for $x = 15$.

6.3 Ratio

OBJECTIVES   To write algebraic representations of numbers in a given ratio

To solve problems about ratio

Recall that a fraction can be used to make comparisons.
At the right, 3 out of 7 squares are shaded.

You say that $\frac{3}{7}$ of the squares are **shaded**.

7 squares

3 squares shaded

4 squares unshaded

Comparing the **shaded** squares with the **unshaded** ones,

you say that the number of **shaded** squares is $\frac{3}{4}$ of the

unshaded squares.

$$\frac{3}{4} = \frac{\text{shaded}}{\text{unshaded}}$$

A **ratio** is a comparison of two numbers using a fraction.

Thus, you can say that the ratio of **shaded** squares to **unshaded** squares above is $\frac{3}{4}$.

Another way to indicate a ratio is with the use of a **colon**.

The ratio of **shaded** squares to **unshaded** squares is **3:4**.

EXAMPLE 1   Express the **ratio** of the shaded region of the
circle to the area of the unshaded region of the
circle in two ways.

Strategy   Compare shaded area with unshaded area.

Use a colon   4 : 6

or

Use a fraction $\frac{4}{6}$

The fraction can be written in lowest terms as $\frac{2}{3}$.

4 equal parts shaded

6 equal parts unshaded

Solution   Therefore, the ratio can be written as 4 : 6 or $\frac{2}{3}$.

Let's now apply the idea of ratio in **connection** with the Segment Addition Property.

EXAMPLE 2   RE = 7, RC = 10

Find EC : RC.

Strategy   You know RE = 7. You need EC to find

the ratio.

Use the Segment Addition Property.

RE + EC = RC

7 + x = 10   **Let x = EC.**

   x = 3

So, **EC** = 3.

Now find **EC** : **RC**.

              ↓   ↓

              3 :   10

Solution   Thus, EC : RC = 3 : 10.

For each of the two figures below the two shaded areas can be compared in several ways.

1.   The ratio of the 1st shaded area to
     the 2nd is 2 : 3.

2.   The 1st area is $\frac{2}{3}$ of the 2nd.

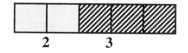

1.   The ratio of the 1st shaded area to
     the 2nd is 4 : 6.

2.   The 1st area is $\frac{4}{6}$ of the 2nd,

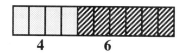

or again $\frac{2}{3}$ of the 2nd.

You have just seen that if two numbers are in the ratio 2 : 3, the numbers could be

                        2 and 3 or

                        4 and 6.

Other possibilities are   6 and 9

                        8 and 12   or any **multiple**, say **m**, of 2 and 3

                   2m   and   **3m**

EXAMPLE 3   AB : BC = 2 : 3, AC = 40
                  Find BC.

Strategy   **1.** Write representations for AB and BC.

                  AB : BC = 2 : 3

                  Let AB = 2x, BC = 3x

              2. Use the Segment Addition Property to write an equation. Solve it.

                  AB + BC = AC

                  2x + 3x = 40   **Substitute 2x for AB, 3x for BC, 40 for AC.**

                     5x   = 40

                      x   = 8   **Divide each side by 5.**

              3. Use   BC = 3**x** to find BC.

                  BC = 3 · **8**

Solution   Thus, BC = 24.

Suppose, one number is $\frac{4}{5}$ of another, or

the ratio of two numbers is 4 : 5. Then the numbers can be represented algebraically as

                  4m and **5m**.

This idea is applied in the next example.

EXAMPLE 4   The width of a rectangle is $\frac{4}{5}$ of the length. The perimeter of the

                  rectangle is 36 ft. Find the length.

Strategy   **1.** Draw a diagram.
              2. Use the width is $\frac{4}{5}$ of the length to write

                  representations for the length and the
                  width.

                     width is $\frac{4}{5}$ of the length

                  width = 4m   length = 5m

              3. Write an equation for the perimeter.
              (continued on next page)

Formula for rectangle perimeter

$$\mathbf{P} = 2\mathbf{L} + 2\mathbf{W}$$

$$\mathbf{36} = 2 \cdot \mathbf{5m} + 2 \cdot \mathbf{4m}$$

W = 4m

4. 36 = 10m + 8m   **Solve.**   L = 5m

36 =   18m   **Combine like terms.**

2 =   m   **Divide each side by 18.**

5. Use   length = 5**m** to find the length.

length = 5 · **2** = 10

Solution   Thus, the length is 10 ft.

If three numbers are in the ratio 3 : 4 : 5, they can be represented algebraically as

3x, 4x, and 5x.

The next example shows you how this may be applied in solving a problem.

EXAMPLE 5   Three partners in a small company, Janet, Martin, and Beth, share its profits in the ratio 3 : 4 : 5, respectively. The company's profits this year amount to $36,000. What is Martin's share?

Strategy   **1.**   First represent algebraically the share of each.

Janet's share   = 3x   Janet : Martin : Beth

Martin's share   = 4x   3 : 4 : 5

Beth's share   = 5x   3x   4x   5x

2.   Write an equation. Solve it.

Total profits are 36000

3x + 4x + 5x = 36000   **Add three profits to get 36000.**

12x = 36000

x = 3000   **Divide each side by 12.**

Use the **representation** to find Martin's share.

Martin's share: **4x**

4 · **3000**   **Substitute 3000 for x in 4x.**

Solution   **3.**   Thus, Martin's share is $12,000.

SUMMARY

1. Two numbers are in the ratio 5 : 7. How can you write the ratio two different ways?

2. Write the ratio of the number of unshaded squares to the number of shaded squares two ways.

    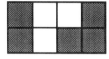

3. Write the ratio of thenumber of shaded squares to the total number of squares two ways.

4. MT = 7, TW = 4.
    How do you find MT : MW?

5. MW = 14, TW = 5.
    How do you find MT : MW?

Use the following data to answer Exercises 6-8.
AB : BC = 3 : 7, AC = 20. To find BC:

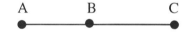

6. How do you represent AB and BC ?

7. How do you use the Segment Addition Property to write an equation?

8. After you have solved the equation, how do you then actually find BC?

Use the following word problem to answer Exercises 9-11.

The width of a rectangle is $\frac{5}{6}$ of the length.

The perimeter of the rectangle is 66 in. Find the length.

9. How do you represent the length and the width?

10. What equation do you write to solve the problem?

11. How do you find the length once you have solved the equation?

12. Three numbers are in the ratio 4 : 4 : 5.
    How do you write algebraic representations of the three numbers?

CLASSROOM PRACTICE

1. RE : EC = 3 : 4, RC = 35.
   Find EC.

   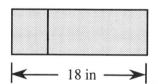

2. RE : EC = 2 : 1, RC = 24.
   Find RE.

3. EC = $\frac{2}{3}$ of RE, RC = 30.
   Find EC.

4. RE is $\frac{5}{4}$ of EC, RC = 27.
   Find EC.

5. The width of a rectangle is $\frac{2}{3}$ of the length. The perimeter of the rectangle is 80 m.
   Find the length.

6. The width of a rectangle is $\frac{5}{6}$ of the length. The perimeter of the rectangle is 44 m.
   Find the width.

7. The width of a rectangle is $\frac{4}{7}$ of the length. The perimeter of the rectangle is 88 cm.
   Find the length.

8. The figure at the right shows an 18 inch board.
   It is cut into two pieces with lengths in the ratio 2 : 7.
   Find the length of the shorter piece.

   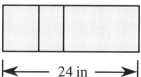

9. A 16-inch board is cut into two pieces with lengths in the ratio 3 : 5. Find the length of the longer piece.

10. The general partners in a small company, Martin, Johnson, and Calvi, share its profits in the ratio 2 : 3 : 4, respectively. The company's profits this year amount to $24,300. What is Ms. Johnson's share?

11. Three numbers are in the ratio 4 : 5 : 6. The sum of the three numbers is 30.
    Find the largest number.

12. A 24-inch board is cut into three pieces with lengths in the ratio 2 : 1 : 3.
    Find the length of the middle piece.

WRITTEN EXERCISES

1. AB : BC = 5 : 7, AC = 36.
    Find BC.

    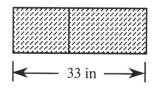

    A   B   C

2. AB : BC = 3 : 10, AC = 26.
    Find AB.

3. AB = $\frac{5}{9}$ of BC, AC = 28.

    Find BC.

4. AB = $\frac{4}{3}$ of BC, AC = 35.

    Find AB.

5. The width of a rectangle is $\frac{2}{5}$ of the length. The perimeter of the rectangle is 42 yd.
    Find the length.

6. The width of a rectangle is $\frac{4}{9}$ of the length. The perimeter of the rectangle is 52 cm.
    Find the length.

7. The length of a rectangle is $\frac{5}{3}$ of the width. The perimeter of the rectangle is 48 cm.
    Find the length.

8. The figure at the right shows a 33 inch board.
    It is cut into two pieces with lengths in the ratio
    5 : 6. Find the length of the shorter piece.

    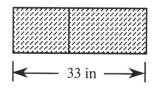

    ⟵ 33 in ⟶

9. A 26-inch board is cut into two pieces with lengths in the ratio 6 : 7. Find the
    length of the longer piece.

10. At a refreshment stand, the ratio of sales of cola, ginger ale, and iced tea was
    3 : 4 : 5. The amount of sales of the three drinks for the day was $360.
    Find the amount of sales of ginger ale.

11. Three numbers are in the ratio 4 : 5 : 3. The sum of the three numbers is 36.
    Find the largest number.

12. A 21-inch board is cut into three pieces with
    lengths in the ratio 4 : 1 : 2.
    Find the length of the middle piece.

    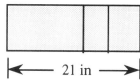

    ⟵ 21 in ⟶

13.   The lengths of the three sides of a triangle are in the
ratio 2 : 3 : 4. The perimeter of the triangle is 45 cm.
Find the length of the longest side of the triangle.

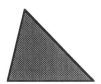

14.   The width of a rectangle is $\frac{2}{13}$ of the length. The perimeter of the rectangle is 60 ft.
Find the area of the rectangle.

OPEN-ENDED QUESTION

15.   R is a point on the segment $\overline{PQ}$. The point R divides the segment into two
segments with lengths in the ratio 2 : 5. If PQ = 49, find RQ. Is more than one
answer possible? Explain why you think you are correct.

REVIEW

1.   The players on a basketball team scored 90 points in one game. They made four
times as many field goals as free throws. Each field goal is worth two points and
each free throw is worth one point. How many field goals were scored during the
game?

2.   A school bus can carry a maximum of 51 students. If each bus makes at most one
trip, find the least number of buses needed to transport 230 sophomores to a girls'
championship basketball game.

3.   12 is not a factor of 30 because
(A)   2 is not a factor of 80.   (B)   5 is not a factor of 12.
(C)   10 is a factor of 80 but not of 12.   (D)   4 is not a factor of 30.

4.   Medium sized blue caps are stored in boxes of 6 or 10. A weekly inventory
indicates that the total number of these caps in stock is supposed to be 45.
Is this possible? Why?

5.   A team scored 40 points in its last basketball game. Today's score was 30 points.
Today's decrease is what % of last week's score?

6.4 Proportions

OBJECTIVES   To solve a proportion

To solve problems using proportions

If two ratios are equal, the resulting equation is called a **proportion**.

$$\boxed{\frac{4}{6} = \frac{2}{3}}$$ is an example of a proportion.

Note that if a proportion is true, you can **cross multiply** to get an equation with no fractions.

$$\frac{4}{6} \; = \; \frac{2}{3}$$
$$4 \cdot 3 \; = \; 6 \cdot 2$$
$$12 \; = \; 12 \; \textbf{True!}$$

PROPERTY OF PROPORTION

In a proportion, $\dfrac{a}{b} \; = \; \dfrac{c}{d}$

$$a \cdot d \; = \; b \cdot c$$

EXAMPLE 1   Solve $\dfrac{x}{5} \; = \; \dfrac{3}{7}$.

Strategy $7 \cdot x \; = \; 5 \cdot 3$ **Cross multiply.**

$7x \; = \; 15$

Solution $x \; = \; \dfrac{15}{7}$ or $2\dfrac{1}{7}$ **Divide each side by 7.**

Frequently, comparisons are used in commercials seen on television to convince the public that many people use a certain product. This helps the manufacturer of the product to increase sales. The next example illustrates an application of proportion to such a real-life situation.

EXAMPLE 2   If 1 out of 5 people buy Elley Fant brand peanuts, how many people
can be expected to buy this brand of peanuts in a city of 35,000 people?

Strategy   Let E = the number of people buying Elley Fant peanuts.

Write the **ratio** $\dfrac{\text{Elley Fant buyers}}{\text{total population}}$ two ways. Set the two ratios equal.

1 out of 5	=	how many out of 35000
1 out of 5	=	E out of 35000
$\dfrac{1}{5}$	=	$\dfrac{E}{35000}$
$1 \cdot 35000$ =	$5 \cdot E$	**Cross multiply.**
35000 =	5E	
7000 =	E	**Divide each side by 5.**

Solution   Thus, 7,000 can be expected to buy this brand.

EXAMPLE 3   If 7 out of every 10 students at Wall High are out for sports, about how
many of the 481 students of the school are out for sports?

(A)   34   (B)   340   (C)   70   (D)   700

Strategy   Let n = the number of students out for sports.

Write the ratio $\dfrac{\text{students out for sports}}{\text{total number of students}}$ two ways. Set them equal.

$\dfrac{7}{10}$	= $\dfrac{n}{481}$	**Write a proportion.**
$7 \cdot 481$	= $10 \cdot n$	**Cross multiply.**
3367	= 10n	**By calculator**
336.7	= n	

Solution   Thus the closest answer of the multiple choices is 340, **(B)**.

Proportions can be applied to practical problems that involve interpreting a road map.
For example, a scale on a road map can be used with proportions to find the distance in
miles between two cities.

This is illustrated in the next example.

EXAMPLE 4   The scale on a map is $\frac{1}{2}$ inch = 20 miles. How far apart are two cities that are measured to be 5 inches apart on that map?

Strategy   First , write $\frac{1}{2}$ inch = 20 miles as a ratio.

$$\textbf{RATIO:} \quad \frac{\frac{1}{2}}{20} \quad \frac{\text{inches}}{\text{miles}} \quad \text{inches compared with miles}$$

Let x = the number of miles between the two cities.

Write a proportion that compares inches to miles.

$$\frac{\frac{1}{2}}{20} = \frac{5}{x} \qquad \frac{\textbf{inches}}{\textbf{miles}}$$

Solve the proportion.

$$\frac{1}{2}x \quad = 100 \qquad \textbf{Cross multiply.}$$

$$2 \cdot \frac{1}{2}x \quad = \textbf{2} \cdot 100 \qquad \textbf{Multiply each side by 2.}$$

$$1x = 200$$

Solution   Thus, the two cities are 200 miles apart.

EXAMPLE 5   Wanda used $13\frac{1}{2}$ gallons of gasoline to drive 270 miles.

How many miles per gallon did she get on the trip?

Strategy   First write **miles per gallon** as a ratio.

$$\textbf{RATIO:} \quad \frac{\textbf{miles}}{\textbf{gallon}}$$

Let n = number of miles.

Write a proportion comparing miles to gallons.

270 miles per 13.5 gallons   n miles per 1 gallon $13\frac{1}{2}$ **= 13.5**

$$\frac{270}{13.5} \quad = \quad \frac{n}{1}$$

$$270 \cdot 1 \quad = \quad n \cdot 13.5 \qquad \textbf{Cross multiply.}$$

$$270 \quad = \quad 13.5n$$

$$20 \quad = \quad n \qquad \textbf{Divide each side by 13.5}$$

Solution   Thus, Wanda gets 20 miles per gallon on the trip.

Both ratios in a proportion must compare the same quantities.

You cannot write $\dfrac{\text{miles}}{\text{hours}} = \dfrac{\text{miles}}{\text{minutes}}$.

Both denominators must be the **same**: each minutes or each hours.

EXAMPLE 6   Bill jogs 3 miles in 40 minutes.

What is his average hourly speed?

Strategy   Let x = number of miles in one hour.

You are asked to find miles per **hour.**

You **CANNOT** write $\dfrac{3}{40} = \dfrac{x}{1}$

since 40 represents **minutes** and 1 represents **hours.**

TWO proportions are possible. **Each gives the same answer!**

1. **BOTH** ratios: **hours**

Write 40 minutes as $\dfrac{40}{60}$ or $\dfrac{2}{3}$ **hour**   **Change 40 minutes to hours.**

Write a proportion.

$$\dfrac{3}{\frac{2}{3}} = \dfrac{x}{1} \qquad\qquad \textbf{Compare: } \dfrac{\textbf{miles}}{\textbf{hour}}$$

$$3 \cdot 1 = \dfrac{2}{3} \cdot x \qquad\qquad \textbf{Cross multiply.}$$

$$3 = \dfrac{2}{3}x$$

$$3 \div \dfrac{2}{3} = x \qquad\qquad \textbf{Divide each side by } \dfrac{2}{3}.$$

$$4\dfrac{1}{2} = x \qquad\qquad 3 \div \dfrac{2}{3} = \dfrac{3}{1} \cdot \dfrac{3}{2} = \dfrac{9}{2} = 4\dfrac{1}{2}$$

2. **BOTH** ratios: **minutes**

$$\dfrac{3}{40} = \dfrac{x}{60} \qquad\qquad \textbf{1 hour = 60 minutes.}$$

$$3 \cdot 60 = 40 \cdot x \qquad\qquad \textbf{Cross multiply.}$$

$$180 = 40x$$

$$4\dfrac{1}{2} = x \qquad\qquad \textbf{Divide each side by 40.}$$

Solution   Thus, the average hourly speed is $4\dfrac{1}{2}$ miles per hour

Note that you get the **same** answer **both** ways: $4\dfrac{1}{2}$ **miles per hour**

SUMMARY

1. How do you solve a proportion like $\frac{4}{5} = \frac{x}{10}$?

2. What proportion do you write to solve the following problem?
    2 out of 5 sophomores are involved in a sport. How many of the 250 sophomores are involved in a sport?

Use the following problem to answer exercises 3-4.

Jerome used 20 gallons of gasoline to go 500 miles.

How many miles per gallon did he get on the trip?

3. If you let x = the number of miles, how do you then write x miles per gallon as a ratio?

4. What proportion do you write to solve the problem?

5. Danielle drove 15 miles in 20 minutes. How can you express this as a ratio in terms of miles per **hour**?

CLASSROOM PRACTICE

Solve each proportion.

1. $\frac{7}{4} = \frac{a}{3}$ 2. $\frac{x}{5} = \frac{7}{15}$ 3. $\frac{2}{3} = \frac{8}{m}$ 4. $\frac{5}{y} = \frac{6}{7}$

Solve each problem.

5. In Stantonville, 2 out of 5 people belong to a union.
    How many union members are there if the population is 70,000?

6. If 7 out of 8 people use Crust Toothpaste, how many use this product in a city with a population of 40,000?

7. Three out of five sophomores study Integrated Math Course II. How many study this course in a sophomore class of 300?

8. If 3 out of every 10 students at Sheepshead Bay High School take a foreign language, about how many of the 965 students of the school take a language?
    (A)   29   (B)   322   (C)   290   (D)   32

9. The scale on a map is $\frac{1}{4}$ inch = 8 miles. How far apart are two cities that measure 4 inches apart on the map?

10. The measured distance between two cities on a map is 3 inches. What is the driving distance between these two cities if the map scale is $1\frac{1}{2}$ inches to a mile?

11. Tyrone used $12\frac{1}{2}$ gallons of gasoline to drive 375 miles. How many miles per gallon did he get on the trip?

12. A fuel efficient car can get 32 miles per gallon on a trip. About how many gallons of gasoline will be needed for a 336 mile trip?

13. Martha jogs 2 miles in 20 minutes. What is her average speed in miles per hour?

14. Bernie can cycle $2\frac{1}{2}$ miles in 15 minutes. Find his average hourly speed.

WRITTEN EXERCISES

Solve each proportion.

1. $\frac{3}{x} = \frac{5}{4}$ 2. $\frac{y}{3} = \frac{4}{7}$ 3. $\frac{3}{m} = \frac{7}{8}$ 4. $6 = \frac{a}{5}$

Solve each problem.

5. A survey found that 4 out of 5 people use Cleanall Soap. How many people can be expected to use this product in a city of 40,000?

6. If 7 out of every 10 high school students take a math course, about how many students in a high school with 671 students are in a math class?
    (A)   470   (B)   100   (C)   10   (D)   4,700

7. An advertisement claims that in a recent poll, three out of four dentists recommended brushing with a certain brand of toothpaste. If there were 92 dentists polled, how many of them recommended this brand of toothpaste?

8. 6 oranges cost $.99. How much do ten oranges cost?

9. Three cans of vegetables cost $.96. Find the cost of 9 cans.

10. A truck uses 8 liters of gasoline to go 120 km. How much gasoline will the truck use to go 300 km?

11. The scale on a map is $\frac{1}{2}$ inch = 10 miles. How far apart are two cities that measure 5 inches apart on the map?

12.   The measured distance between two cities on a map is 10 inches. What is the driving distance between these two cities if the map scale is $1\frac{1}{4}$ inches to a mile?

13.   The scale on a map is $\frac{1}{4}$ inch = 3 miles. Find the distance between two cities that are measured to be 7 inches apart on that map.

14.   The measured distance between two towns on a map is 9 inches. How many miles apart are the two towns if the map scale is $1\frac{1}{2}$ inches = 12 miles.

15.   Calvin used $12\frac{1}{2}$ gallons of gasoline to drive 200 miles. How many miles per gallon did he get on the trip?

16.   A car traveled 12 miles in 15 minutes. Find its average speed in miles per hour for the trip.

17.   Monica swims 4 laps in 15 minutes. Find her average speed in laps per hour.

18.   Hank jogs 3 miles in 50 minutes. What is his average hourly speed?

19.   For 60 cents, a vending machine dispenses a small bag of peanuts. The bag weighs one and one-eighth ounces. At that rate, the cost of one pound of those peanuts would be between
       (A) $2.25 and $2.80   (B) $4.15 and $4.90
       (C) $6.25 and $6,75   (D) $8.30 and $8.75
       HINT: Think: ratio of cost to weight in **ounces.** There are 16 ounces in a pound.

20.   Write a proportion to solve the following problem.
       A can containing 80 identical nails weighs 125 grams.
       When there are only 60 nails in the can the combined weight is 95 grams.
       Find the weight of the can when it is empty.
       HINT: Think of ratio of number of **nails** to weight of **nails.**
                    Let w = weight of the empty **can.**
                    Then the weight of 80 **nails** is 125 - x. **(combined weight minus nail weight)**
                    The weight of 60 **nails** is _____?
                    Now write a proportion.

OPEN-ENDED QUESTION

21.   John is planning a trip between two cities that measure 6 inches apart on a map

with a scale of $\frac{1}{2}$ inch = 20 miles. His car averages 30 miles to a gallon.

If gasoline costs $1.12 a gallon, how much should he budget for gas for the round trip?

Also explain how solving this problem involves combining two types of problems taught in this lesson. Outline the steps in solving the problem so that another student would be able to understand the solution.

REVIEW

1.   Suppose that x and y represent whole numbers.

Then for the equation 5x + 2y = 12, what must be true about the value of x?

(A)   x must be a multiple of 12.   (B)   x must be divisible by 5.

(C)   x must be a multiple of 2.   (D)   12 must be a factor of x.

2.   RS = $2\frac{3}{4}$, ST = $5\frac{1}{2}$.

Find RT.

3.   Tina mistakenly added 43 instead of subtracting 43 while using her calculator. The incorrect answer displayed on the calculator is 312. What is the correct answer?

4.   Donna usually makes 70% of her basketball foul shots.
      Last week she missed 5 foul shots. About how many foul shots must she have made?

5.   Which of the following is **NOT** a way to find 125% of a number?

(A)   Add the number to $\frac{1}{4}$ of itself.   (B)   Multiply the number by 0.25.

(C)   Multiply the number by 1.25.   (D)   Multiply the number by

5,   divide the result by 4.

6.5 Applying Averages

OBJECTIVES   To find the average or mean of a set of numbers

To find the coordinate of the midpoint of a segment

To solve problems about averages

DISCOVERY   Suppose your test scores for two math tests this month were 80 and 100.

Find your average for the two tests.

How could you find the average of four test grades?

To find the average of four test grades: 90, 80, 100, and 90, you:

1. Add the scores: $90 + 80 + 100 + 90 = 360$

2. Divide the sum by the **number** of tests, **4.** $\dfrac{360}{4} = 90$

So, the **average** of the four scores is $\dfrac{90 + 80 + 100 + 90}{4} = \dfrac{360}{4} = 90.$

DEFINITION: AVERAGE

To find the average of a set of numbers (values):

    (1)   Add the values.

    (2)   Divide the sum by **n**, the total **number** of values.

$$\text{average} = \frac{\text{sum of the numbers}}{n}$$

An **average** is also called a **mean**.

The rest of this lesson will illustrate many applications of the idea of **average** or **mean**.

You will also see a **connection** to geometry in finding the midpoint of a segment.

The idea of **mean** will be extended in the next lesson to interpreting data.

EXAMPLE 1   Martin's test scores are as follows: three 95's and one 75.
Find the **mean** score for the four tests.

Strategy   **1.** Find the sum of the test grades: $95 + 95 + 95 + 75 = 360$

2. Mean or average $= \dfrac{\text{sum}}{\text{n}} = \dfrac{360}{4} = 90$

Solution   Thus, the **mean** score for the four grades is 90.

DISCOVERY   Find AM. Find MB.

AM ? MB

What does point M do to the segment $\overline{AB}$?

For the figure at the right,

AM = 10 - 3 = **7**   MB = 17 - 10 = **7**

AM = MB

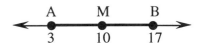

The point M is in the **MIDDLE** of $\overline{AB}$.

M is called the **MIDPOINT** of $\overline{AB}$.

DEFINITION: MIDPOINT OF A SEGMENT

M is the **midpoint** of $\overline{AB}$ if M lies on $\overline{AB}$ and AM = MB.

You have just seen that M is the **midpoint** of $\overline{AB}$.

M is **midway** between A and B.

So, 10 must be **midway** between 3 and 17.

This makes 10 the **average** of 3 and 17.

Let's verify this: $\dfrac{3 + 17}{2} = \dfrac{20}{2} = 10$!

M is the **midpoint** of $\overline{AB}$.

10 is the **average** of 3 and 17.

The result at the bottom of the previous page suggests the following formula for finding the coordinate of the midpoint of a segment.

Midpoint Formula

Given: M is the **midpoint** of $\overline{AB}$.

The coordinate of M is $x = \dfrac{x + z}{2}$.

y is the **average** of x and z.

Thus, you now see the connection between **midpoint** for geometry and **average** for arithmetic or algebra.

EXAMPLE 2   Find the coordinate of the midpoint of a segment with the given endpoints: -6 and 14.

Strategy   Use the **Midpoint Formula**.

Let x = the coordinate of the midpoint.

$$x = \frac{-6 + 14}{2} \qquad \textbf{average of -6 and 14}$$

$$x = \frac{8}{2} = 4$$

Solution   Thus, 4 is the coordinate of the midpoint of the segment.

Now let's look at some more real-life applications of finding an average.

EXAMPLE 3   John wants to have an average 90 on his math test scores.
His test grades so far are 75, 85, and 100.
What must he get on the fourth test so that his average for the four tests will be 90? **(continued on next page)**

Strategy   Let x be the grade he needs on the next test.

Write a formula for the average of his four test grades: 75, 85, 100, **x**.

$$\frac{\text{sum of test scores}}{\text{number of tests}} = \frac{75 + 85 + 100 + x}{4} = 90$$

Solve: $\dfrac{75 + 85 + 100 + x}{4} = \dfrac{90}{1}$ **Write as a proportion.**

$\dfrac{260 + x}{4} = \dfrac{90}{1}$ **Combine like terms.**

$(260 + x) \cdot 1 = 4 \cdot 90$ **Cross multiply.**

$260 + x = 360$

$x = 100$ **Subtract 260 from each side.**

Solution   Thus, John must get a grade of **100**.

Check: $\dfrac{75 + 85 + 100 + \mathbf{100}}{4} = \dfrac{360}{4} = 90$

The average of the 4 grades is now **90**.

EXAMPLE 4   This semester Jane's math test average for four tests is exactly 89. What must she get on the her fifth test to have an average of exactly 90?

Strategy   Even though she might have different scores on each test so far, the average for all four is 89. Therefore, let's assume that each score was 89 when writing an equation to solve the problem.

Let x be the grade she needs on the fifth test.
Write the formula for the average of five test grades: 89, 89, 89, 89, x.

$$\frac{\text{sum of data}}{\text{number of tests}} = \frac{89 + 89 + 89 + 89 + x}{5} = 90$$

$\dfrac{89 + 89 + 89 + 89 + x}{5} = \dfrac{90}{1}$ **Write as proportion.**

$\dfrac{356 + x}{5} = \dfrac{90}{1}$

$356 + x = 450$ **Cross multiply.**

$x = 94$

Solution   Thus, Jane must get **94** on her last test.

SUMMARY

1. How do you find the coordinate of the midpoint of a segment with endpoints 5 and 10?
2. How do you find the average of several numbers?
3. What is another name for the word "average"?
4. Bill has three test scores of 80, 90, and 90. how do you find the score on the fourth and last test to achieve a final average of 90?
5. Rowena's bowling average for her first three games is 240. How do you determine what she needs to bowl on the next game to attain an average of 250 for the four games?

CLASSROOM PRACTICE

Find the coordinate of the midpoint M of $\overline{AB}$ whose endpoints have the given coordinates.

1.	6 and 8	2.	4 and 7	3.	-8 and 2	4.	-5 and -3
5.	6 and 13	6.	-5 and -7	7.	-10 and 4	8.	9 and -13

9. Maria's daily expenses for a week were $7.50, $9.40, $17.20, $6.25, and $18.95. Find her average daily expensee for the five days.
10. Mark's bowling scores for a six-game tournament were 156, 192, 240, 210, 300, and 246. Find the mean score for the tournament.
11. Theo had an average score of 43 in five rounds of miniature golf. If he had scores of 46, 38, 39, and 44 for four of these rounds, what was his score on the other round he played?
12. Pedro's Luncheonette is open six days a week. His lunch business income for the first five days this week were $120, $110, $200, $300, and $140. What must he make the sixth day to average $200 income for the six days?
13. This semester Rowena's average for three Spanish tests is exactly 87. If all of her Spanish tests count equally, what score must she earn on her fourth test to have an average of exactly 90?

14.   Last week, the mean temperature for six days was 40 degrees. What must be the temperature on the seventh day to produce an average of exactly 45 degrees for the week?

WRITTEN EXERCISES

Find the coordinate of the midpoint M of $\overline{AB}$ whose endpoints have the given coordinates.

1.	4 and 9	2.	5 and 13	3.	0 and 15	4.	4 and 14
5.	-5 and 9	6.	4 and -6	7.	-10 and 8	8.	-7 and -13
9.	3.2 and 7.6	10.	-3.4 and -1.2	11.	-12 and 6.8	12.	$3\frac{1}{2}$ and $7\frac{1}{2}$

Solve each problem.

13.   Janet is on the swim team. She swims laps 5 days a week: 30 laps on Monday, 25 on Tuesday, 40 on Wednesday, 15 on Thursday, and 35 on Friday. What is her daily average number of laps for the week?

14.   Rinaldo has the following scores on six history tests: 80, two 70's, 90, 75, and 95. What is his average for the six tests?

15.   Dana's scores for five tests are 90, 80, 70, 90, and 85. What score must she get on the sixth test to have a final average of 80?

16.   The mean degree temperature for five days was 68. The degree temperatures were 60 on Monday, 70 on Tuesday, 80 on Wednesday, and 75 on Thursday. What was the temperature on Friday?

17.   Maureen's successful weekly foul-shot totals in basketball were 15, 25, 30, 20, and 15. How many foul shots must she score in the sixth week to have an average of 20 for the six-week period?

18.   Bill has an average of 80 on his first three English quizzes. What grade must he get on the fourth quiz to boost his average to 84?

19.   In this week's bowling tournament, Ruiz's average for the first four games is 208. What score must he make on the fifth game to have an average of exactly 200?

20.   The average of five numbers is 24. If 12 is added to each of those numbers, what is the average of the resulting five numbers?

21.   Use the following information to choose the equation that will not solve the problem.

Jack's average on four math tests is 89. What must he get on the fifth test to have an average of 90 on the five tests?

(A) $4(89) + x = 450$ (B) $356 + x = 90$

(C) $\frac{4(89)}{5} + \frac{x}{5} = 90$ (D) $\frac{4(89) + x}{5} = 90$

OPEN-ENDED QUESTION

22.   Two students asked to have their tests rescored. One student had a score of 50, which was far below the class average. The other had a score of 70 which was close to the class average. Willard believes that adding 20 points to the lower score would raise the class average more than adding 20 points to the higher score. Is Willard correct? Write a justification of your answer for someone who might disagree with you.

REVIEW

1.   The town of Mason is located on Eagle Lake. The town of Canton is west of Mason. Sinclair is east of Canton, but west of Mason. Dexter is east of Richmond, but west of Sinclair and Canton. Assuming all these towns are in the U.S.A., which town is farthest west?

2.   Eighty men and seventy women participated in a tennis tournament. Prizes were awarded to the top twenty men participants and to the top 30% of the women participants. What percent of the people who participated in that tournament were awarded prizes? Round your answer to the nearest whole number percent.

3.   Find the area of a circle with radius 9 cm. Use $A = 3.14r^2$.

4.   What is the next term of the sequence 13, 29, 61, 125, ... ?

6.6 Interpreting Data: Mean, Mode, Median, Range

OBJECTIVES   To calculate mode, median, and range

To determine the best measure of central tendency for a set of data

A student took five math tests this marking period.

His grades were as follows: 90, 20, 100, 100, 90.

His average or mean for the marking period was therefore

$$\frac{90 + 20 + 100 + 100 + 90}{5} = \frac{400}{5} = 80.$$

He felt that the 80 did not reflect the majority of his work this marking period.

His teacher agreed with him.

The one low score, 20, was an exception pulling the average down.

The mean is less than four of the five grades and is distorted by the one very low grade of 20.

For this reason some mathematicians sometimes use another method for describing a set of data.

Consider the scores above: 90, 20, 100, 100, 90.

1. Rearrange the scores in order from smallest to largest.   20, 90, 90, 100, 100.
2. What is the **middle** score?   20, 90, **90**, 100, 100

The **middle** score is **90**.

The **middle** number is called the **median**.

The **median** score of **90** seems to better represent the student's performance than the **mean** of **80**.

The above method works when the number of data is **odd**.

For example, 20, 90, **90**, 100, 100, has **5** terms and the middle term is **90**.

Can you guess what to do if the number of data is **even**?

For example, 7, 8, 8, 9, 10, 10, has an **even** number, **6**, of terms.

There is **no middle term!**

EXAMPLE 1   Mary had scores of 10, 9, 10, 8, 7, and 8 on her math quizzes.
What is her median score?

Strategy   **1.**   Arrange the scores in ascending order (from smallest to largest).

7, 8, 8, 9, 10, 10

There are **two middle** terms because the number of terms is **even**.

7, 8, **8, 9**, 10, 10

2.   Find the average of the **two middle** terms.

$$\frac{8+9}{2} = \frac{17}{2} = 8.5$$

Solution   Thus, the median score is 8.5.

DEFINITION   **MEDIAN**

The **median** of an **odd** number of data is the **middle** item when the
data are listed in numerical order.

If there is an **even** number of data, the **median** is the average of the
two middle items.

The terms **average (mean) and median** are examples of **statistical measures** used to
describe a set of data. Another measure of statistical data is the **mode**.

DEFINITION   **MODE**

The **mode** of a set of data is the item that appears most often.

There can be more than one mode.

There can also be **NO** mode if each item appears only once.

EXAMPLE 2   Peter had scores of 10, 9, 8, 7, 8, 9, 10, 8, 9, 9 on his history quizzes.
                      What is the mode of his scores?

Strategy   Group like scores. Determine the score that occurs most frequently.

7	8, 8, 8	9, 9, 9, 9	10, 10
once	3 times	4 times	twice

Solution   **9** is called the mode because it is the score that occurs most frequently.

Sometimes there is more than one mode for a set of data.

EXAMPLE 3   Tasha had scores of 92, 98, 96, 92, 100, and 96 on her science tests.
                      What is the mode of her scores?

Strategy   Group like scores. Determine the score that occurs most frequently.

92, 92	96, 96	98	100
twice	twice	once	once

Because the scores 92 and 96 both occur most frequently, there are two modes.

Solution   **92** and **96** are the modes.

Sometimes there is **NO** mode for a set of data.

EXAMPLE 4   Find the mode for the following high-degree temperatures for the week.
                      97, 91, 89, 96, 90, 93, and 94

Solution   Because each temperature occurs only once, there is **NO** mode.

Another measure of statistical data is the **range**.

DEFINITION   **RANGE**
                   The **range** of a set of data is the **difference** between the **greatest**
                   and **least** values of the data.

EXAMPLE 5   Moisha's bowling scores are 148, 196, 149, 194, 147, and 188.

What is the range of the scores?

Strategy   Choose the **highest** and **lowest** scores.

                    194   147

            Subtract: **194 - 147** = 47

Solution   The range is **47**.

Mean, median, and mode are called **measures of central tendency**. They tell something about where the data **tends** to cluster, or where the **center** of the data is located. When the **range** is small, the **mean** is more likely to be the best measure of central tendency.

EXAMPLE 6   Five people work in a store. Their weekly salaries are

$82, $78, $84, $300, and $78.

Which measure of central tendency best describes the typical wage of a worker at this store?

Strategy   Arrange the data in numerical order.

78, 78, 82, 84, 300

Mode: 78

Median: 82

Mean: $\dfrac{78 + 78 + 82 + 84 + 300}{5} = \dfrac{622}{5} = 124.4$

The mode is an **extreme low,** less than the other three, not a good measure of central tendency. All other wages are above 78, none below.

The mean is greater than 4 of the 5 data.

Notice that the range is 300 - 78 = 222, fairly large due to the extreme 300.

Therefore the mean is not a good measure of central tendency.

Solution   Thus, the median is the best of the three measures of central tendency.

All the measures, except one, are close to the median.

You have already learned how to interpret data from a bar graph.

The next example shows how to determine the best measure of central tendency when the data is presented in a bar graph.

EXAMPLE 7   The bar graph below shows the quiz grades of a class of math students. Find the mean, median, mode, and range.

Which measure of central tendency is a better indicator of the performance of the class on the test, the mean or the median?

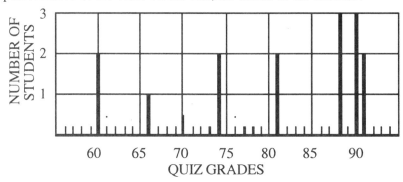

Strategy   1.   First, determine from the table the number of students for each score. For example,

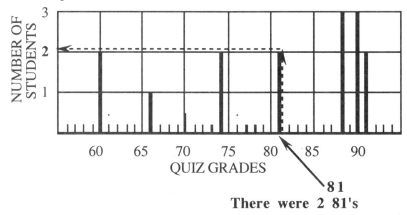

There were 2 81's

for the score **81** there were **2** students.

60: 2,   66: 1,   74: 2,   **81: 2,**   88: 3,   90: 3,   91: 2

Now write the scores in numerical order from smallest to largest.

60, 60, 66, 74, 74, 81, 81, 88, 88, 88, 90, 90, 90, 91, 91.

2. Use the data now arranged in ascending order to find the **mean**, **median**, **mode**, and **range**.

mean:

$$60 + 60 + 66 + 74 + 74 + 81 + 81 + 88 + 88 + 88 + 90 + 90 + 90 + 91 + 91 \over 15$$

$$\text{mean} = \frac{1212}{15} = 80.8$$

median: 60, 60, 66, 74, 74, 81, 81, **88**, 88, 88, 90, 90, 90, 91, 91

The median is **88**.

mode: The modes are 88 and 90.

range: **largest - smallest**

        91   -   60 = 31

Solution Thus, these are the results.

mean: 80.8   median: 88   mode: 88, 90   range: 31

The mean is greater than 5 of the data but less than 10 of the data.

The mean is **NOT** a good measure of central tendency.

The median is a better measure of central tendency.

SUMMARY

Use the following data to answer exercises 1-5: 21, 14, 16, 118, 20, 14.

Describe how to find:

1.   the mean   2. the median   3. the mode   4. the range

5.   the measure of central tendency which best represents the data

CLASSROOM PRACTICE

For the data 9, 8, 9, 8, 9, 7, 9, find each of the following.

1.   mean   2. median   3. mode   4. range

For the data 48, 47, 52, 56, 51, 58, find each of the following.

5.   mean   6. median   7. mode   8. range

For the data 77, 77, 70, 72, 72, 68, 69, find each of the following.

  9.   mean   10.   median 11.   mode   12.   range

For the data 100, 101, 98, 103, 105, find each of the following.

13.   mean   14.   median 15.   mode   16.   range

17.   Rashid's bowling scores are 240, 250, 65, 300, and 240.

        Which is the better measure of central tendency, the mean or the median?

18.   The stereo sales at an appliance store for five days were as follows:

        $600.20, $318.33, $1095.38, $439.84, and $4990.

        Decide whether the mean or the median is the better measure of central tendency.

The bar graph below shows the quiz grades of a class of General Science students.
Use this graph to answer exercises 19-24.

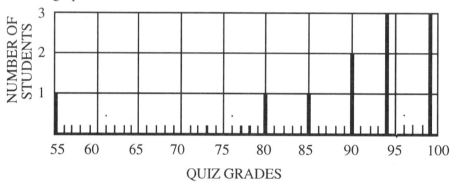

19.   How many students are in the class?

Find each of the following for the data graphed.

20.   mean   21.   median   22.   mode   23.   range

24.   Which is the best general indicator of the performance of the class—
        the mean, median, or the mode? Explain why.

WRITTEN EXERCISES

For the data 7, 8, 9, 8, 9, 7, 9, find each of the following.

  1. mean (to nearest tenth)   2. median   3. mode   4. range

For the data 48, 43, 40, 41, 48, find each of the following.

  5.   mean   6.   median   7.   mode   8.   range

For the data 99, 98, 86, 100, 98, 100, find each of the following.

  9.   mean   10.   median   11.   mode   12.   range

For the data 8, 10, 10, 9, 9, 8, 10, find each of the following.

13.   mean   14.   median   15.   mode   16.   range

17.   The manager of a deli keeps records of sales of a new type of special club sandwich. The sales for 6 days were 68, 62, 260, 78, 92, and 66. Which measure of central tendency best describes the data?

18.   Summer temperatures in Cody, Wyoming, can vary greatly from day to night The temperatures below were recorded for 3 weeks in August.

101, 68, 80, 80, 82, 102, 88, 85, 71, 65, 80, 87, 103, 83, 75, 79, 81, 81,

85, 80, 105

Which measure of central tendency best describes the data?

Use a calculator to find the mean.

The bar graph below shows the frequency of temperatures in an 11-day period of time. Use this graph to answer exercises 19-24.

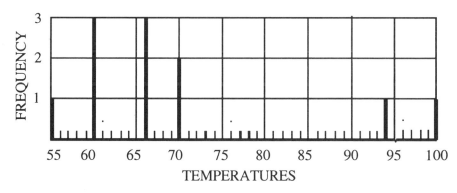

Find each of the following for the data graphed.

19.   mean   20.   median   21.   mode   22.   range

23.   Which is the best general indicator of the temperature for the time period— the mean, median, or the mode? Explain why.

24.   What is the first step in finding the median of a set of numbers?

(A)   Find the sum of the numbers.

(B)   Find the number that appears most frequently.

(C)   Write the numbers in numerical order.

(D)   Divide the sum of the numbers by the number of items.

OPEN-ENDED QUESTION

25.   The following are Natasha's bowling scores this past month.

156, 131, 124, 115, 143, 250, 158, 131, 121, 131, 143, 152, 130, 137, 143, 124, 137, 131, 121, 130, 152, 300, 131, 124, and 143.

(a)   Find the mean, the mode, and the median. (Use a calculator to find the mean.)

(b)   Make a bar graph showing the frequency or the number of scores in each of the ranges 111-120, 121-130, 131-140, 141-150, 151-160, and over 160.

(c)   Which is the best general indicator of her bowling performance—the mean, median, or mode? Explain why.

REVIEW   Chapters 1-6

Write a symbol for each of the following.

1.

G

P

2.

W

M

Distance between M and W

3.

R

L

Find PQ for the given coordinates of P and Q.

4.   P: -6,   Q: 8   5.   P: $5\frac{1}{3}$,   Q: $9\frac{1}{2}$

P   Q

6. Find the length of the smallest subdivision between points S and T.

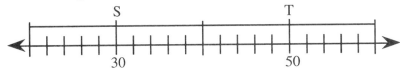

7. RS = $3\frac{1}{2}$, ST = $5\frac{1}{4}$, RT = ?

8. ST = 5, RT = 13, RS = ?

9. RS = 2x + 1, ST = 3x - 7, RT = 14, ST = ?

10. RS : ST = 5 : 7, RT = 36, ST = ?

11. RS = $\frac{4}{5}$ ST, RT = 45, RS = ?

12. The width of a rectangle is $\frac{3}{4}$ of the length. The perimeter is 42 ft.

    Find the length.

13. An 11' by 14' room has an 8' by 10' carpet centered in the room. How far is the carpet from each horizontal edge of the room?

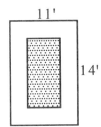

Solve each equation.

14.   2x - 7 = 9   15.   4x + 2(2x - 5) = 14   16. $\frac{x}{3} = \frac{5}{6}$

Solve each problem.

17. A survey said that 5 out of 6 people use Stickee Hair Tonic.
    How many people can be expected to use this product in a city of 30,000?

18. 6 cans of soda cost $4.80. Find the cost of 10 cans of soda.

19. A car gets 25 miles to a gallon of gas. How much gas will be needed for a trip of 450 miles?

20. The scale on a map is 3 inches = 11 miles. How many miles apart are two cities that measure 7 inches apart on the map?

21. Meta used $14\frac{1}{2}$ gallons to go 58 miles on a trip. How many miles per gallon did she get on the trip?

22.   One car traveled 18 miles in 20 minutes. Find its average speed in miles per hour.

23.   A 50-cent bag of peanuts weighs $1\frac{1}{4}$ ounces. At this rate, the cost of one pound of those peanuts would be between

(A) $6.00 and $7.00   (B) $9.50 and $10.50

(C) $8.00 and $9.00   (D) $.60 and $.70

24.   Write a proportion to solve the following problem.
       A can containing 70 identical nails weighs 120 grams.
       When there are only 60 nails in the can the combined weight is 110 grams.
       Find the weight of the can when it is empty.

25.   M is the midpoint of $\overline{AB}$. Find the coordinate of M.

26.   Mark's bowling average for four games was 170. What would he have to bowl on the fifth game to raise his mean score to 196?

27.   Tanya's successful weekly foul-shot totals in basketball were 20, 30, 35, 15, and 20. How many foul shots must she score in the sixth week to have an average of 25 for the six-week period?

The bar graph below shows Hank's recent quiz scores. Use it to answer exercises 28-32.

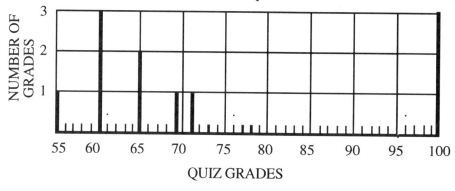

Find each of the following.

28.   mean   29.   median   30.   mode   31.   range

32.   Which measure of central tendency best represents the student's performance? Explain why.

Use the advertisement below to answer exercises 33-34.

CHOICE DINNER MENU
Main course: turkey, fried chicken, ham: $5.45
plus $1.15 for each of the following up to three choices; $.95 for each choice beyond 3.
salad, soup, french fries, baked potato, onion rings, string beans, peas, soda, coffee, tea,
cake, pie, ice cream

33.   A deluxe dinner offers the main course, a salad or soup, any potato, one
        vegetable, one beverage, and ice cream, all for the special price of $9.00.
        How much can be saved by taking the special rather than ordering each item
        separately?

34.   To the nearest whole number, the saving in exercise 33 is what %
        of the cost of ordering each item separately?

The data table at the right shows the
percents of 300 students taking a foreign
language.

LANGUAGE	PERCENT
French	20%
German	5%
Spanish	50%
Latin	5%
No language	?%

35.   How many students take no
        foreign language?

36.   How many more students take
        French than German?

37.   On the scale below, the reading indicated by the arrow is between
        (A)   28 and 29   (B)   30 and 32
        (C)   34 and 35   (D)   38 and 40

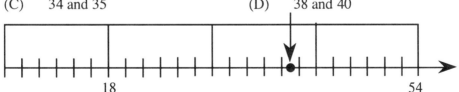

38.   Which point could represent the
        product of the numbers represented
        by points A and M?

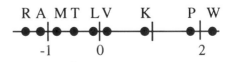

39.   Which of the plane figures below can be folded to form a box or cube?

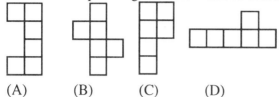

(A)   (B)   (C)   (D)

40.   If the pattern indicated at the right
        is continued, how many squares
        will be in the eighth figure?

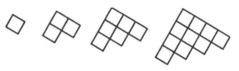

41.   Find the perimeter and area of ABCD rectangle for A(4,6), B(12,6), C(12,9),
        and D(4,9).

42.   Find the area of a rectangle with length 6 cm and perimeter 40 cm.

43.   Carpeting cost $35.75 a square yard. Find the cost, to the nearest penny,
        of carpeting a room that measures 18 ft by 21 ft.

Simplify.

44. $3x + 4(2x - 1) - 14x$ 45. $-5(-2)^3$ 46. $\dfrac{6 \cdot 2 + 4}{8 - 2 \cdot 3}$

47.   A store manager lists the selling price of a stereo at $345. If he plans on a
        profit of 20% of the cost, what must the stereo have cost him, to the
        nearest cent?

48.   Complete the data table.

n	n + 2(n - 2) + 8
4	
	22

49.   The length of a rectangle is 8 ft less than twice the width. The perimeter is 44 ft.
        Find the length of the rectangle.

50.   The players on a basketball team scored 70 points in one game. They made three
        times as many field goals as free throws. Each field goal is worth two points and
        each free throw is worth one point. How many field goals did the players make
        during the game?

51.   Suppose that x and y represent whole numbers.
        Then, for the equation 5x + 6y = 32 what must be true about the value of x?

        (A)   x must be a multiple of 6.   (B)   x must be a multiple of 5.

        (C)   x must be a multiple of 2.   (D)   32 must be divisible by x.

52. Abul mistakenly divided by 4 instead of multiplying by 4 while using his calculator. If the incorrect answer displayed by the calculator is 8, what is the correct answer?

53. What symbol is in the 113th position of the following pattern?

numbernumbernumber...

54. Find the driving distance from Raritan to Cape May.

55. Meg drives 56 miles an hour. Approximately how long will it take her to drive from Paterson to Cape May?

Mileage Between Principal Cities	Absecon	Bridgeton	Camden	Cape May	Cherry Hill	Elizabeth	Jersey City
Absecon	0	77	57	48	55	105	119
Camden	57	40	0	84	9	81	85
Newark	108	113	84	161	80	8	6
Paterson	123	131	99	165	95	23	21
Hopewell	75	70	32	106	35	48	58
Raritan	92	99	56	130	58	26	35

56. Last week the basketball team scored 80 points. This week they scored 60 points. The decrease was what percent of last week's score?

57. As cars come off the assembly line, inspectors spot-check them. Tony checks the 4th car and every 4th one after that. Mona checks the 6th car and every 6th one after that. If 90 cars are produced in one day, how many of them will have been checked twice?

58. Evaluate $\frac{5}{6}x - 12$ for $x = 24$.

59. What is the units digit in the 111th term of the sequence $2^1, 2^2, 2^3, 2^4, \ldots$?

OPEN-ENDED QUESTION

60. Use graph paper to draw a rectangle with area 24 square units and length and width restricted to whole numbers. How many answers are possible? Explain why.

Chapter

7

Angles

7.1 Rays

OBJECTIVES   To identify and name rays

To graph a ray described by an inequality

Recall: > means **is greater than.**   < means **is less than.**

$\geq$ means **is greater than or equal to.** $\leq$ means **is less than or equal to.**

Thus, $7 \geq 5$ is read as $3 \leq 6$ is read as

7 is greater than or equal to 5.   3 is less than or equal to 6.

DISCOVERY

The graph below shows points with coordinates x such that $x \leq 5$.

Are there other point with coordinates ≤ 5? How many do you think there are?

How could you show the graph of all points corresponding to $x \leq 5$?

Let's consider graphing the set of all points with coordinates such that $x \leq 4$.

First note that an **infinite** (unending) number of values of x make $x \leq 4$ true.

For example: $4 \leq 4$ $3\frac{1}{2} \leq 4$ $-5 \leq 4$ $-7 \leq 4$

The list could go on forever.

The graph of $\mathbf{x \leq 4}$ includes the point corresponding to **4** and all points to the left of this point. Therefore, the graph of $\mathbf{x \leq 4}$ is the **arrow** below.

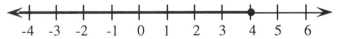

Is the geometric figure a line? Why or why not?

It is **NOT** a segment since it has only **one endpoint.**

It is **NOT** a line since it goes on forever in only **one direction**.

What do you think it might be good to name such a figure?

The geometric figure graphed at the bottom of the previous page is called a **RAY**.

RAYS

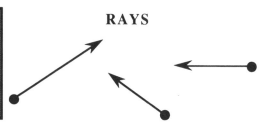

DEFINITION
A **RAY** is a part of a line that has **one** endpoint and extends forever in only one direction.

To name the ray at the right, note that the **endpoint** is at P.

Write $\overrightarrow{PQ}$. Read this as **Ray PQ**.

The ray **begins** at **P** and goes through Q.

1. The first letter names the **endpoint**.
2. The **arrow** over the letters **always** points to the **right**.

A ray can often be named in more than one way.

This ray **begins** at **A** and passes through

   E,   S,   and   T.

You can name the ray **3** ways.

$\overrightarrow{AE}$ or $\overrightarrow{AS}$ or $\overrightarrow{AT}$

EXAMPLE 1   Write three names for the ray that has endpoint Q and contains point T.

Strategy   The ray begins at Q and passes through T.

Shadow the drawing to show the ray.

Solution   Three names for the ray are: $\overrightarrow{QR}$, $\overrightarrow{QT}$, and $\overrightarrow{QS}$

It is important to be able to identify and write a name for each of the three types of geometric figures you have studied so far: line, segment, and ray.

EXAMPLE 2   Identify and write a name for each of the following.

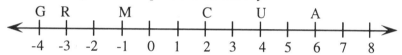

Solution   segment: $\overline{GH}$ ray: $\overrightarrow{GH}$ line: $\overleftrightarrow{GH}$

EXAMPLE 3   Copy the figure below.

Draw the ray described by the inequality x ≥ -1.

Give as many names as possible for the ray.

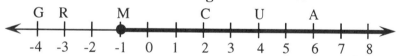

Strategy   The endpoint of the ray x ≥ -1 is **M**, the point with coordinate -1.

Put a dot at **M** and shade to the **right** since x ≥ -1.

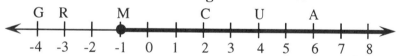

The ray begins at M and passes through points C, U, and A.

The ray can be named three ways.

$\overrightarrow{MC}$, $\overrightarrow{MU}$, or $\overrightarrow{MA}$.

Sometimes it is helpful to rewrite an inequality.

4 ≤ 7 means 4 is less than or equal to 7.

This is the same as saying   7 ≥ 4 or 7 is greater than or equal to 4.

Thus, -7 ≤ x   (-7 is less than or equal to x) can be rewritten as

x ≥ -7   (x is greater than or equal to -7)

It is easier to graph an inequality if the inequality is written with the variable first.

EXAMPLE 4   Graph the ray described by $-7 \geq x$.

Strategy   First, rewrite $-7 \geq x$ with the variable first.

$$x \leq -7$$

When drawing the graph, you need show only a rough sketch.
It is not necessary to label lots of points on the number line.
Proceed as shown below.

Solution   1. Draw a dot.

2. Label -7 below it.

3. Draw the ray pointing **left** since $x \leq -7$.

SUMMARY

1.   How does the figure for a ray differ from that of a segment or line?

2.   How does the symbol for a ray differ from that of a segment or line?

3.   How do you determine the endpoint of a ray from a symbol such as $\overrightarrow{TW}$?

4.   How can you rewrite $4 \leq 9$?

5.   How can you rewrite $-8 \geq x$ so that the variable is first?

6.   How do you draw the graph defined by $x \geq -5$?

7.   How do you draw the graph defined by $-4 \geq x$?

CLASSROOM PRACTICE

Graph the ray defined by each inequality.

1. $x \leq 2$ 2. $x \leq -1$ 3. $x \geq 6$ 4. $x \geq 0$ 5. $x \leq -4$

Identify and give a name for each of the following.

6.   7.   8.

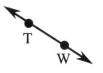

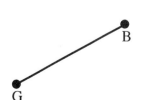

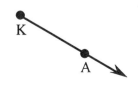

Draw the ray and write all possible names for the ray.

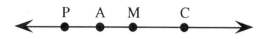

9. endpoint M: ray contains the point A

10. endpoint A: ray contains point C

11. endpoint C: ray contains point M

Copy the figure below. Draw the ray described by the inequality.

Give as many names as possible for the ray. (Exercises 12-16)

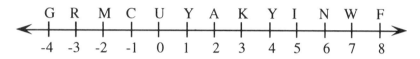

12.   x ≤ -1   13.   x ≤ -2   14.   x ≥ 5   15.   x ≥ 3   16.   x ≤ -3

WRITTEN EXERCISES

Graph the ray described by each inequality.

1.   x ≥ -8   2. x ≤ 4   3. x ≤ -2   4.   x ≥ 1   5. x ≤ -5

Identify and give the name of each of the following.

6.   7.   8.

   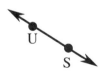   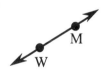

Draw the ray and write all possible names for the ray.

9.   endpoint Y: ray contains the point R

10. endpoint W: ray contains point M

11. endpoint R: ray contains point Y

Copy the figure below. Draw the ray described by the inequality.

Give as many names as possible for the ray. (Exercises 12-16)

12. $x \leq -2$ 13. $x \leq -1$ 14. $x \geq 6$ 15. $x \geq 4$ 16. $x \leq 0$

OPEN-ENDED QUESTION

17.   Write two inequalities such that the graph of the set of points in common to
       the two rays they describe will be a segment.

REVIEW

1.   Simplify $\frac{-8}{-4}$.

2.   A school bus can carry at most 53 students. If each bus makes only one trip,
      find the least number of busses needed to transport 300 students to a
      football game.

3.   In a warehouse, shirts of the same size and color are stored in boxes of 12 or 16.
      A weekly inventory indicates that total number of this type of shirt in stock is
      282. A clerk said this is not possible. He said there must be a computer error.
      Explain why he is correct.

4.   Maria usually makes 70% of her basketball foul shots.
      This month she missed 9 of them. How many did she attempt?

5.   What is the total number of squares
      in this figure?

6.   Solve $-3x + 5 = 26$

7.   Estimate the value of $0.49 \cdot 0.00061432$

      (A)   0.003   (B)   0.0003   (C)   0.0004   (D)   0.004

7.2 Solving and Graphing Inequalities

OBJECTIVE   To graph rays described by inequalities that have to be solved

You have learned to solve equations by doing the same operation on each side to get a simpler equation. The same procedure holds for solving inequalities with one small exception pointed out below.

You can add or subtract the same number to each side of an inequality and still get a true inequality. For example: $3 \leq 5$ is true.

Add 4 to each side. Is the result true?

$$3 \quad \leq 5 \quad \textbf{TRUE!}$$

$$3 + 4 \ ? \ 5 + 4 \quad \textbf{Add 4 to each side.}$$
$$7 \quad \leq 9 \quad \textbf{TRUE!}$$

Similarly, you can add the same **negative** number to each side of an inequality.

Can you divide each side of an inequality by the same number and still get a true inequality?

Let's try an example. $8 \leq 12$ is true.

Divide each side by 4. Is the result true?

$$8 \leq 12 \qquad \textbf{TRUE!}$$
$$\frac{8}{4} \ ? \ \frac{12}{4} \qquad \textbf{Divide each side by 4.}$$
$$2 \leq 3 \qquad \textbf{TRUE!}$$

Let's now explore what happens if you **divide** each side of an inequality by the same **negative** number.

DISCOVERY   Write the inequality that is the result of dividing—

each side of -8 $\leq$ 20 by -4

each side of 6 $\geq$ -5 by -1

Can you guess what the rule is for dividing each side of an inequality

by the same negative number?

Before doing the next example let's quickly review the rule for division of signed numbers:

The quotient of **like** signs is **positive:** $\dfrac{\text{negative}}{\text{negative}} = \text{positive}$ $\dfrac{\text{positive}}{\text{positive}} = \text{positive}$

The quotient of **unlike** signs is **negative.** $\dfrac{\text{negative}}{\text{positive}} = \text{negative}$ $\dfrac{\text{positive}}{\text{negative}} = \text{negative}$

EXAMPLE 1   Write the inequality that is the result of dividing each side of
$20 \geq -15$ by -5.

Strategy $20 \geq -15$

                                      $\dfrac{20}{-5}$? $\dfrac{-15}{-5}$

Solution $-4 \leq 3$ **A negative is less than a positive.**

Note what happens when you divide each side of a "**greater than**"inequality:

$20 \geq -15$ by a negative number.

You get a ≤ symbol. $-4 \leq 3$

The $\geq$ symbol is **reversed** to a $\leq$ symbol when each side of an inequality is divided by a **negative** number.

We say that the **order** of the inequality is **reversed.**

Similarly, a $\leq$ symbol will be **reversed** to a $\geq$ symbol when you divide each side of the inequality by a negative number. For example, divide each side of $-8 \leq 4$ by -2.

                         $-8 \leq 4$

                         $\dfrac{-8}{-2}$? $\dfrac{4}{-2}$

                         $4 \geq -2$ **A positive is greater than a negative.**

The **order** of the inequality is **reversed.**

The same is true for **multiplication** of each side of an inequality by a **negative** number.

So, the procedure for solving an inequality will be the same as that for solving an equation, with one exception.

Division of each side of an inequality by a **negative** number will produce an inequality with the inequality symbol **reversed**.

EXAMPLE 2   Graph the ray defined by $3x + 5 \leq 26$.

Strategy $3x + 5 \leq 26$

$3x \quad \leq 21$ **Subtracting 5 from each side will NOT reverse the $\leq$. symbol.**

$x \quad \leq 7$ **Dividing each side by <u>positive</u> 3 will NOT reverse the $\leq$ symbol.**

Now graph the ray as illustrated in the last lesson.

Solution   1. Draw a dot.
2. Label 7 below it.
3. Draw the ray pointing **left** since $x \leq 7$.

7

EXAMPLE 3   Graph the ray defined by $4 - 2x \leq 10$.

Strategy $4 - 2x \leq 10$

$- 2x \leq 6$ **Subtracting 4 from each side will not reverse the $\leq$ symbol.**

$\dfrac{-2x}{-2} \geq \dfrac{6}{-2}$ **Dividing each side by <u>negative</u> 2 REVERSES the $\leq$ symbol.**

$x \geq -3$ $\dfrac{\textbf{positive}}{\textbf{negative}} = \textbf{negative.}$

Now graph the ray.

Solution   1. Draw a dot.
2. Label -3 below it.
3. Draw the ray pointing **right** since $x \geq -3$.

-3

EXAMPLE 4   Which inequality below would be most helpful in solving this problem?

Bart spent an evening playing video games and drinking sodas.

Each video game cost 25 cents to play and sodas cost 60 cents each.

Bart had only $8 to spend on video games and sodas.

If he had only 3 sodas and played as many games as he could, how many video games did he play?

(A)	$0.25x + 1.80 \leq 8$	(B)	$x + 1.80 \leq 8$
(C)	$0.60x + 0.75 \leq 8$	(D)	$3x + 0.25 \leq 8$

Strategy   Let **x** represent the number of games he can play.

To find the amount that he spends, use the idea that

amount spent on videos is :   number of games · cost of each

amount spent on sodas is: number of sodas · cost of each

His total spent is $8 or **less.**

$$\textbf{TOTAL SPENT} \qquad\qquad \leq 8$$

$$\downarrow$$

number of games · cost of each   +   number of sodas · cost of each ≤ 8

  x   ·   0.25   +   3   ·   0.60 ≤ 8

Solution   Thus, the most helpful inequality would be (A): $0.25x + 1.80 \leq 8$

SUMMARY

1.   What is the main difference between the way you solve an equation and an inequality?

Given $4 \leq 12$, name the inequality you get after doing the following.

2.   Add 2 to each side.   3. Divide each side by 2.   4. Divide each side by -2.

Given $12 \geq -6$, name the inequality you get after doing the following.

5.   Add -2 to each side.   6. Divide each side by -3.

7. Tell what steps you would use to graph the ray defined by $3x - 2 \geq 13$.

8. Tell the steps in graphing the ray defined by $-4x + 8 \leq 16$.

CLASSROOM PRACTICE

Graph the ray defined by each inequality.

1.	$3x - 6 \leq 9$	2.	$6x + 2 \geq 26$	3.	$8x - 2 \leq 22$
4.	$4 + 3x \leq 19$	5.	$7 + 4x \geq 23$	6.	$2x - 5 \geq 17$
7.	$-2x + 6 \leq 12$	8.	$-5 - 4x \leq 19$	9	$-3x + 7 \geq -8$
10.	$-10 - 5x \leq 15$	11.	$7 - 3x \leq -17$	12.	$-4x + 3 \geq -13$
13.	$-4x + 2 \geq -8$	14.	$-8 \geq -6x + 10$	15.	$10 \geq -3x + 1$

16. John is buying lunch for himself and his friend. Hot dogs cost $1.85 each and sodas cost $0.75 each. John has only $10 to spend. He orders 2 sodas. He wants to buy as many hot dogs as possible. Which inequality below would be appropriate in solving his problem?

(A) $x + 1.50 \leq 10$ (B) $0.75x + 1.85 \leq 10$

(C) $1.85x + 1.50 \leq 10$ (D) $1.50x + 1.85 \leq 10$

WRITTEN EXERCISES

Graph the ray defined by each inequality.

1.	$3x - 2 \leq 13$	2.	$4x + 4 \geq 20$	3.	$7x - 3 \leq 18$
4.	$4 + 2x \leq 18$	5.	$8 + 3x \geq 23$	6.	$-8x + 3 \geq 27$
7.	$-2x + 18 \leq 14$	8.	$-6x + 4 \leq 16$	9	$-5x + 10 \geq 30$
10.	$-2x - 4x \leq -6$	11.	$5 - 3x \leq -7$	12.	$7 - 5x \geq 32$
13.	$-7x - 1 \geq + 13$	14.	$16 \geq -6x - 8$	15.	$-2 \geq -5x + 13$
16.	$12 \geq -2x - 8$	17.	$6 - 4x \geq -14$	18.	$-21 \geq 4 - 5x$

19. Which inequality below would be most helpful in solving this problem?
Jim was given a cash birthday gift of $45. He bought two tennis balls at $1.75 each. He would like to buy as many compact disks as possible at $12 each. How many disks could he buy?

(A) $2x + 12 \leq 45$ (B) $x + 3.50 \leq 45$

(C) $1.75x + 24 \leq 45$ (D) $12x + 3.50 \leq 45$

OPEN-ENDED QUESTION

20.   Barry has 6 more tropical fish than Marcel. Together they have fewer than 12
        How many fish can Marcel have? Why would a ray not be a practical way to
        represent the solution to this problem? How many solutions can this problem
        have? Explain why.

REVIEW

     Use a calculator for exercises 1-2.

1.   Louis owed $348.19 on his credit card but forgot to pay the bill by the due date.
        Each month, the credit card company charges interest on the unpaid balances
        (amount he still owes) at the rate of 18% per year. Assume he makes no more
        charges on the card for the rest of the month. What would he have to pay,
        including interest on what he owes to pay the bill in full at the end of the next
        month?

        (**HINT:** Calculate the monthly interest as $\frac{1}{12}$ of the yearly interest rate.)

2.   Ninety men and seventy women participated in a tennis tournament. Prizes were
        awarded to the top 20 men participants and to the top 10% of the women
        participants. What percent of the people who participated in the tournament were
        awarded prizes? Round your answer to the nearest whole number percent.

3.   Find the weight of one pyramid if
        one cube weighs one pound and the
        scale is balanced.

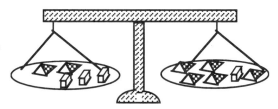

4.   Which of the following is **NOT** a way to find 105% of 60?

        (A) $60 + 0.05 \cdot 60$ (B) $0.105 \cdot 60$

        (C) $\frac{1}{20}$ of 60 added to 60   (D) $1.05 \cdot 60$

7.3 Angles and Their Measures

OBJECTIVES To use a protractor to measure an angle

To name an angle

You can now use the concept of **ray** to form **angles** as shown below.

Notice that the hands of a
clock form the same shape
angle at 3:00 regardless of the
lengths of the hands (angle's
sides). Thus, the sides of an
angle are **rays**.

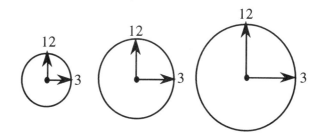

The symbol for **angle** is $\angle$.
In the diagram, the sides of the
angle are **rays**: $\overrightarrow{CA}$ and $\overrightarrow{CB}$.
C is called the **vertex** of the
angle.

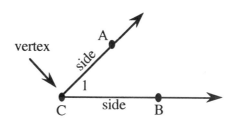

The angle may be named in three ways.

(1)   by three capital letters where the **middle letter** names the **vertex :**

$\angle$**ACB**   **or** $\angle$**BCA**

(2)   by the vertex alone where there is no possibility of confusion: $\angle$**C**

(3)   by a numeral placed between the rays: $\angle$**1**

DEFINITION

An **angle** is a geometric figure consisting of two rays with a common endpoint.

The **common endpoint** is called the **vertex** of the angle.

The **rays** are the **sides** of the angle.

EXAMPLE 1   Name each angle in as many ways as possible.

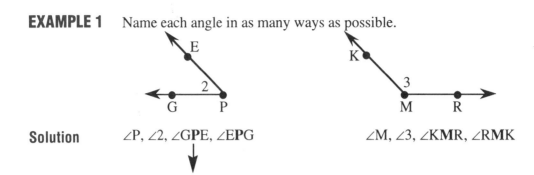

Solution   ∠P, ∠2, ∠GPE, ∠EPG   ∠M, ∠3, ∠KMR, ∠RMK

Vertex in **middle**

The Babylonians of ancient times observed
that the Earth took about **360** days to
rotate about the Sun.

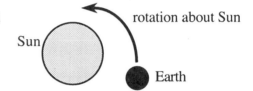

Therefore, it was decided to measure
angles in terms of **rotation** about a circle.
One full rotation was called 360 **degrees**
or 360°, where ($^\circ$) meant **degrees**.

Halfway around a circle would be 180°.
One fourth of the way around a circle
would be 90°.

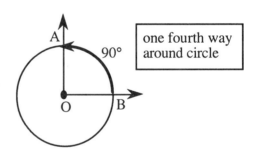

The number that tells you the **size** of the angle is called the **measure** of the angle.
In the figure above,   **m** ∠AOB = 90 or the
                         degree **m**easure of ∠AOB is 90.

Angles are measured in degrees ($^\circ$).

When writing the measure of an angle, we will **omit** the degree symbol ($^\circ$).

Thus, we write **m** ∠AOB = 90 which is understood to mean the degree **m**easure of ∠AOB
is 90.

A **protractor** is used to measure angle degrees.
In the figure at the right, m ∠BOC = 70.
Notice that in measuring the angle, the base of
the protractor is in line with OC⃗.

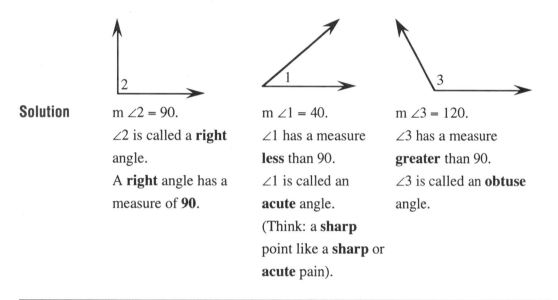

EXAMPLE 2   Use a protractor to find the measure of each angle below.

Solution   m ∠2 = 90.   m ∠1 = 40.   m ∠3 = 120.

∠2 is called a **right**   ∠1 has a measure   ∠3 has a measure
angle.   **less** than 90.   **greater** than 90.

A **right** angle has a   ∠1 is called an   ∠3 is called an **obtuse**
measure of **90**.   **acute** angle.   angle.

(Think: a **sharp**
point like a **sharp** or
acute pain).

DISCOVERY

In each of the drawings below notice that as the angle measure increases, the relationship
of the sides of each angle is changing.

How will the sides of an angle with measure be related to each other?

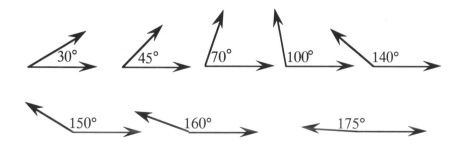

The results at the bottom of the previous page suggest the following for an angle of measure 180.

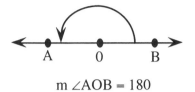

m ∠AOB = 180

The sides of ∠AOB, $\overrightarrow{OA}$ and $\overrightarrow{OB}$, are two rays that form a **line**. Since the sides of an angle of measure **180** form a (**straight**) line, the angle is called a **straight angle**.

This lesson has introduced you to four types of angles.

Their properties are easier to classify and distinguish using a **data table** as shown below.

ANGLE CLASSIFICATION TABLE

Angle Drawing	Name	Characteristics
(right angle drawing: A up, O corner, B right)	right ∠	m ∠AOB = 90
(acute angle drawing: A upper, O corner, B right)	acute ∠	m ∠AOB < 90 (but not 0)
(obtuse angle drawing: A upper left, O corner, B right)	obtuse ∠	m ∠AOB > 90 (but less than 180)
(straight angle drawing: A, O, B on a line)	straight ∠	m ∠AOB = 180

We make two agreements about angles in this book.

1. An angle measure **cannot** be **0**.

2. An angle measure **cannot** be greater than **180**.

EXAMPLE 3   Identify each type of angle.

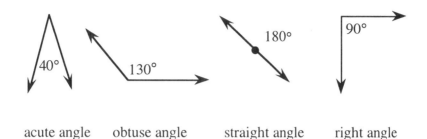

Solution   acute angle   obtuse angle   straight angle   right angle

The next example applies inequalities to angle measures.

First note a convenience for indicating that a number is **between** two given numbers.

For example, suppose **x** is some number
between 4 and 9.

x > 4 and at the same time x < 9.

We write 4 < x < 9.

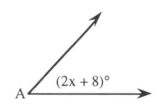

EXAMPLE 4   What are the restrictions on
              x if ∠A is acute?

Strategy   Recall the two restrictions
              on an acute angle.

(Note that in a drawing we **do** include the
degree symbol for an angle measure.)

angle measure < 90	**and**	angle measure > 0
2x + 8 < 90		2x + 8 > 0
2x < 82		2 x > -8
x < 41	**and**	x > -4

Thus, x > -4 and x < 41

This means that x is **between** -4 and 41. This can be written as

$$-4 < x < 41.$$

Solution   Thus, the restrictions on x are described by   -4 < x < 41.

SUMMARY

1.   What geometric figure is the side of an angle?

2.   The common endpoint of two sides of an angle is called the ___ of the angle.

3.   How do you read the expression m ∠ RST?

4.   How many ways are there of
     naming the angle at the right?

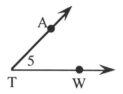

5.   Tell how to use a protractor to find m ∠ 5 above.

What is each of the following?

6.   right angle   7.   straight angle   8.   acute angle   9.   obtuse angle

10.   What angle measures are not used in this book?

11.   ∠ B is obtuse.
      What does this tell you about m ∠ B?

12.   How can you use the results of Exercise
      11 to find the restrictions on x?

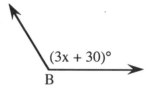

CLASSROOM PRACTICE

Name each angle four ways.

1.

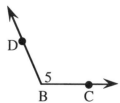

2.

3.

For each figure, answer the questions below. Use a protractor to find angle measures.

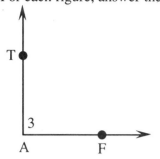

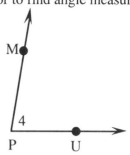

4. Name the angle
    four ways.

5. Measure the angle.

6. Identify the type of
    angle.

7. Name the angle
    four ways.

8. Measure the angle.

9. Identify the type of
    angle.

10. Name the angle
    four ways.

11. Measure the angle.

12. Identify the type of
    angle.

What type of angle does each of the following appear to be?

13.   14.   15.   16.

17. What are the restrictions on x
    if ∠A is acute?

18. What are the restrictions on x
    if ∠B is obtuse?

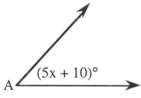

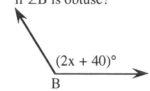

WRITTEN EXERCISES

1. What is the measure of a straight angle?

2. What is the measure of an acute angle?

3. What is the measure of a right angle?

4. What is the measure of an obtuse angle?

Name each angle four different ways.

5.   6.   7.

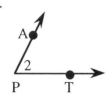   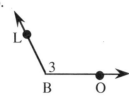   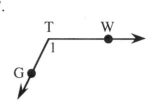

For each figure, answer the questions below. Use a protractor to find angle measures.

8.	Name the angle four ways.	11.	Name the angle four ways.	14.	Name the angle four ways.
9.	Measure the angle.	12.	Measure the angle.	15.	Measure the angle.
10.	Identify the type of angle.	13.	Identify the type of angle.	16.	Identify the type of angle.

What type of angle does each of the following appear to be?

17.   18.   19.   20.

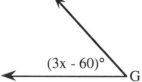

21.   What are the restrictions on x   22.   What are the restrictions on x
       if ∠P is obtuse?   if ∠G is acute?

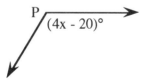   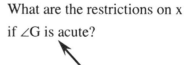

23.   ∠A is a right angle.
       m ∠A = 3x - 60. Find x.

In the rectangle at the right, $\overline{AC}$ and $\overline{BD}$ are called **diagonals** of the rectangle ABCD.

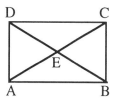

24.   Use a protractor to find m $\angle$DEA to the nearest whole number.

25.   Is $\angle$DEA a right angle?

OPEN-ENDED QUESTION

26.   Draw a four-sided figure such that each angle formed by the intersecting diagonals is a right angle. Do the sides of the four-sided figure have to meet at right angles? If not, draw a figure that illustrates your conclusion.

REVIEW

1.   On a multiple choice test each correct answer is worth 8 points. But 3 points are deducted for each wrong answer. Which formula below represents the total score S if R represents the number of right answers and I the number of incorrect answers?

(A)   S = 8 + R - 3 - I   (B)   S = 8R + 3I

(C)   S = 3I - 8R   (D)   S = 8R - 3I

2.   Mr. Tomlinson encourages his class to work together in small groups of 6 on Thursdays. On other days they work in groups of 3 or 9. When all students are present, there are always 2 students left over to summarize ideas. Which of the following could be the number of students in the class?

(A)   14   (B)   20   (C)   26   (D)   32

3.   Graph the ray defined by the inequality -2x - 4 $\geq$ 14.

4. $PQ = 5\frac{1}{4}$, $QR = 7\frac{1}{8}$, PR = ?

5.   PQ = 2x + 1, QR = 3x + 2, PR = 13.

Find QR.

Manipulative Discovery

Adjacent Angles

This activity will help pave the way for the next lesson on Adjacent Angles.

How many angles are in figure (1)?
Notice that ∠1 and ∠2 are **next** to each other.
In the next lesson these will be defined as
adjacent angles.
Do you see a third angle in figure (1)?

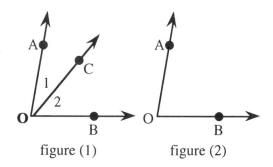

figure (1)   figure (2)

This will be easier to see if you use tracing
paper as indicated below. Little squares of
hamburger-patty paper work very well in
this kind of activity.
Use two such pieces of patty-paper.

Trace ∠1 on one sheet.   Trace ∠2 on a second sheet.

(Trace sides $\overrightarrow{OA}$ and $\overrightarrow{OC}$.)   (Trace sides $\overrightarrow{OC}$ and $\overrightarrow{OB}$.)
You will get this figure.   You will get this figure.

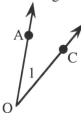 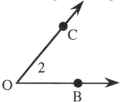

Use a protractor to find **m ∠1**.   Use a protractor to find **m ∠2**.

Slide this tracing onto figure (2) above   Slide this tracing onto figure (2), above

so that the two $\overrightarrow{OA}$s coincide.   so that the two $\overrightarrow{OB}$s coincide.

These two angles together should form the large angle and look the same as figure (1).

So, figure (1) is made up of **3** angles!   Use a protractor to find **m ∠AOB**.
What arithmetic relationship seems to exist for **m ∠1, m ∠2, and m ∠AOB?**

7.4 Adjacent Angles

OBJECTIVES   To identify adjacent angles

To apply the Angle Addition Property

Recall the Segment Addition Property.

Point C at the right divides the segment $\overline{AB}$ into

two segments: $\overline{AC}$ and $\overline{CB}$.

These two segments together make up the whole

segment $\overline{AB}$.   **AC + CB = AB**

Similarly, as you saw in the Manipulative Activity of the

previous page, $\overrightarrow{OC}$ divides the angle $\angle AOB$ into two
adjacent angles, $\angle 1$ and $\angle 2$.

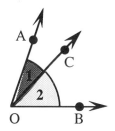

These two angles together make up the whole angle $\angle AOB$.
m $\angle 1$ + m $\angle 2$ = m $\angle AOB$

This is easier to visualize if the angles are drawn separately.

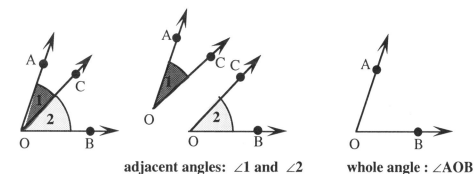

adjacent angles: $\angle 1$ and $\angle 2$ whole angle : $\angle AOB$

It is now easy to see why you cannot always label an angle using only one letter.
In the figure,above left, it would not be clear if you referred to $\angle O$.
There are **three different angles** with vertex O. The three angles are $\angle AOB$, $\angle 1$, and $\angle 2$.

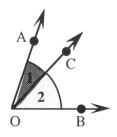

DEFINITION

Two angles that share a common side but do not overlap each other, are called **adjacent** angles.

$\overrightarrow{OC}$ is the **common** side to adjacent angles ∠1 and ∠2.

ANGLE ADDITION PROPERTY

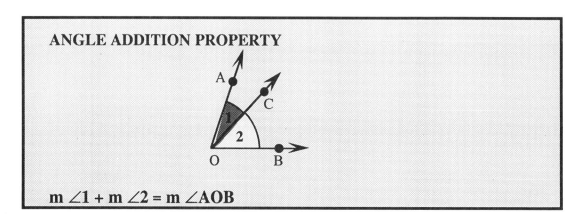

m ∠1 + m ∠2 = m ∠AOB

EXAMPLE 1   Given: m ∠PWR = 130, m ∠2 = 35.
Find m ∠1.

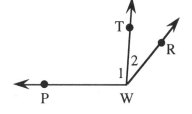

Strategy   Use the Angle Addition Property to write an equation.

m ∠1 + m ∠2 = m ∠PWR

Solution   m ∠1 + 35   = 130   **Solve for m ∠1. Subtract 35 from each side.**
m ∠1   = 95

Sometimes applications of the Angle Addition Property call for more algebraic connections. This is illustrated in the next example.

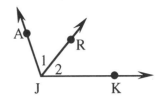

EXAMPLE 2   m ∠1 = x + 40, m ∠2 = 2x + 10,
                 m ∠AJK = 110. Find m ∠2.

Strategy   **1.** Use the Angle Addition Property to write an equation.
                        Solve the equation.

m ∠1	+	m ∠2		=	m ∠AJK	
x + 40	+	2x + 10		=	110	
1x + 40	+	2x + 10		=	110	**x = 1x**
		3x + 50		=	110	**Combine like terms.**
		3x		=	60	**Subtract 50 from each side.**
		x		=	20	**Divide each side by 3.**

    2. **x = 20** is not the answer to the problem.
        Use m ∠2 = 2x + 10 to find m ∠2.

$$m \angle 2 = 2 \cdot 20 + 10$$ **Substitute 20 for x in 2x + 10.**

$$m \angle 2 = \quad 40 \quad + 10$$

$$\mathbf{m \angle 2 =} \qquad \mathbf{50}$$

    3. **Check your answer.**
        Use m ∠1 = x + 40 to find m ∠1.

$$m \angle 1 = \mathbf{20} + 40 = 60$$ **Substitute 20 for x in x + 40.**

        Verify the Angle Addition Property.

m ∠1	+	m ∠2		=	m ∠AJK	
60	+	**50**		=	110	**True!**

Solution   Thus, **m ∠2 = 50**

You learned to apply **ratio** techniques to solving problems involving the Segment Addition Property. Now you will use the ratio idea in connection with the Angle Addition Property.

EXAMPLE 3   Write representations for m ∠1 and m ∠2.

$$m \angle 1 : m \angle 2 = 3 : 4 \qquad m \angle 1 = \frac{5}{6} \text{ of } m \angle 2.$$

↓

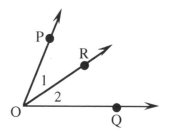

Solution   m ∠1 = 3x   m ∠1 = 5x

                       m ∠2 = 4x   m ∠2 = 6x

EXAMPLE 4 $m \angle 1 = \frac{2}{3}$ of m ∠2, m ∠AOB = 50.

                Find m ∠2.

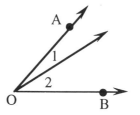

Strategy   Let m ∠1 = 2x, m ∠2 = 3x.

                Use the Angle Addition Property to write an equation.
                Solve the equation.

                m ∠1 + m ∠2 = m ∠AOB
                 2x   +   3x   =   50
                        5x   =   50
                         x   =   10

                Use m ∠2 = 3x to find m ∠2.

                     m ∠2 = 3 · **10**   **Substitute 10 for x in 3x.**

Solution   Thus, m ∠2 = 30   **Check on your own.**

SUMMARY

1   What are adjacent angles?

2.   What does the Angle Addition Property say?

3.   Angle Addition Property is similar to what other property? Explain.

Use the data below to answer Exercises 4-6.

Given: m $\angle 1 = 3x + 50$, m $\angle 2 = 2x + 40$, m $\angle SPR = 140$

Find m $\angle 2$.

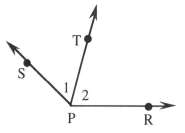

4.   What equation can you write to solve this problem?

5.   After solving the equation for x, how do you then find m $\angle 2$?

6.   How do you check the result?

7.   Using the diagram for Exercises 4-6, how do you write representations for m $\angle 1$ and m $\angle 2$ if m $\angle 1$: m $\angle 2 = 5 : 7$?

CLASSROOM PRACTICE

1.   m $\angle 1 = 29$, m $\angle 2 = 37$, m $\angle ABC = ?$

2.   m $\angle 1 = 17$, m $\angle ABC = 70$, m $\angle 2 = ?$

3.   m $\angle 2 = 46$, m $\angle ABC = 62$, m $\angle 1 = ?$

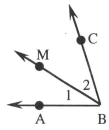

4.   m $\angle 1 = 2x + 10$, m $\angle 2 = 3x + 40$, m $\angle JLK = 75$

    m $\angle 2 = ?$

5.   m $\angle 2 = 2x + 5$, m $\angle 1 = 4x + 15$, m $\angle JLK = 80$

    m $\angle 1 = ?$

6.   m $\angle 1 = 2x - 10$, m $\angle 2 = 5x + 15$, m $\angle JLK = 110$

    m $\angle 2 = ?$

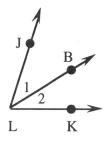

7.   m $\angle 2 = 3x - 10$, m $\angle 1 = x + 40$, m $\angle JLK = 130$,

    m $\angle 1 = ?$

8.   m $\angle 1$: m $\angle 2 = 3 : 7$, m $\angle TBH = 120$.

    Find m $\angle 2 = ?$

9.   m $\angle 1 = \frac{3}{4}$ of m $\angle 2$, m $\angle TBH = 77$.

    Find m $\angle 2$.

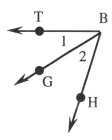

10.   m ∠2 = 32, m ∠1 = 43, m ∠TEH = ?

11.   m ∠1 = 17, m ∠3 = 19, m ∠GEB = ?

12.   m ∠TEH = 70, m ∠2 = 29, m ∠1 = ?

13.   m ∠BEG = 41, m ∠3 = 19, m ∠1 = ?

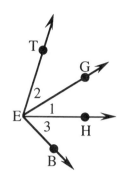

WRITTEN EXERCISES

1.   m ∠2 = 37, m ∠1 = 44, m ∠AYG = ?

2.   m ∠AYG = 72, m ∠2 = 46, m ∠1 = ?

3.   m ∠1 = 19, m ∠AYG = 60, m ∠2 = ?

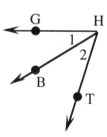

4.   m ∠1 = 3x + 15, m ∠2 = 2x + 25, m ∠GHT = 70.
       m ∠1 = ?

5.   m ∠2 = x + 18, m ∠1 = 2x + 12, m ∠GHT = 42.
       m ∠2 = ?

6.   m ∠1 = 2x - 14, m ∠2 = 5x + 18, m ∠GHT = 74.
       m ∠1 = ?

7.   m ∠2 = 4x - 20, m ∠1 = x + 30, m ∠GHT = 60.
       m ∠2 = ?

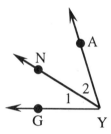

8.   m ∠1 : m ∠2 = 5 : 6, m ∠TDH = 33.
       Find m ∠1 = ?

9.   m ∠1 = $\frac{4}{9}$ of m ∠2, m ∠TBH = 39.
       Find m ∠1.

10.   m ∠1 = $\frac{3}{5}$ of m ∠2, m ∠TBH = 40.
       Find m ∠2.

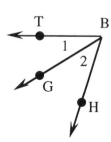

11.   m ∠2 = 19, m ∠1 = 27, m ∠TQR = ?

12.   m ∠1 = 37, m ∠3 = 23, m ∠SQP = ?

13.   m ∠RQT = 71, m ∠2 = 17, m ∠1 = ?

14.   m ∠SQP = 51, m ∠3 = 34, m ∠1 = ?

15.   m ∠1 : m ∠2 = 2 : 5, m ∠TQR = 70, m ∠2 = ?

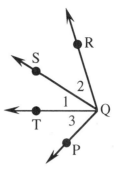

OPEN-ENDED QUESTION

16.   ∠AOT and ∠TOG are adjacent angles. m ∠AOG = 100, m ∠AOT = 3 · m ∠TOG.
      Draw the figure and find m ∠TOG.

REVIEW

1.   What symbols are missing from the pattern below at the positions x and y?

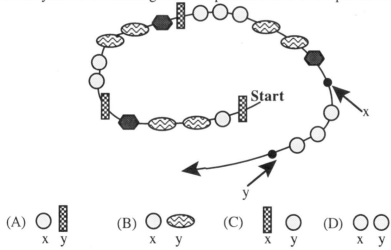

(A) ◯ ▮   (B) ◯ ⬭   (C) ▮ ◯   (D) ◯ ◯
    x y   x y   x y   x y

2.   Which of the four figures below can be made from folding the figure at the far
     left?

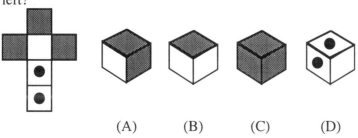

        (A)   (B)   (C)   (D)

3.   The attendance at the football game this week was 500. This figure is 140% of what it was last week. This means that

(A)   The number attending was 40 more than last week.

(B)   Last week's attendance was less than this week's attendance.

(C)   700 students attended this week.

(D)   40% less attended this week than last week.

4.   Tyrone's scores on three math tests are 80, 70, and 90. What must he get on the next test to have a final average of 84?

5.   If each of the following procedures was applied to a given number, which of them would give equal results?

        I   Subtract three times the number from itself.

        II   Divide the number by three.

        III Multiply the number by -2.

(A)   I and II   (B)   II and III

(C)   I and III   (D)   I, II, and III

6.   As shown in the figure below, the picture is not centered on the wall from left to right. How far to the left should it be moved to be centered?

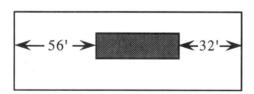

(A)   24'   (B)   12'

(C)   28'   (D)   Not enough information is given.

7.   Graph the ray defined by the inequality $2x + 4 \leq 10$.

8.   What are the restrictions on x if ∠A is acute?

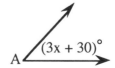

7.5 Angles and Circle Graphs

OBJECTIVES   To read and interpret circle graphs

To apply percent to comparison of measurement of angles

Frequently, circle graphs are used to present data.

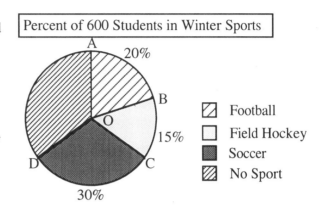

Percent of 600 Students in Winter Sports

Notice that this circle graph is divided into 4 **adjacent angles**. Thus, you can see that the idea of adjacent angles can have a practical connection to real-life situations.

DISCOVERY

The circle graph above displays only percents of students.
How can you find the actual number of students out for any sport?

EXAMPLE 1   Use the circle graph above to find the number of students in the school.

Solution   According to the **title** at the top of the circle graph, there are 600 students in the school.

Note that the graph does not give the number of students out for each sport.
Each is given in terms of a percent. However, you know from Example 1, above, that there are 600 students in the school.
Thus, finding the number of students out for a particular sport will involve finding a percent of a number. This is illustrated in the next example.

EXAMPLE 2   Use the circle graph from the previous page to find the number of
students out for Field Hockey.

Strategy   From the graph it is seen that 15% of the students are out for field
hockey, Thus 15% of **600** are out for Field Hockey.

To find 15% of 600, multiply:

$0.15 \cdot 600 = 90$.

Solution   Thus, 90 are out for field hockey.

EXAMPLE 3   Use the circle graph of the previous page to find the number of students
not out for any sport.

Strategy   First, find the **percent** not out for any sport.

All percents of the graph must add up to the **whole: 100%.**

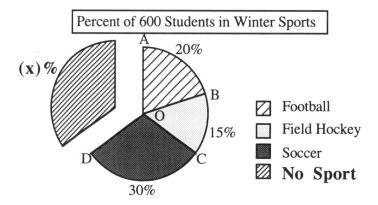

Solve: **x** + 20 + 15 + 30 = **100**

x +   65   = 100   **Combine like terms.**

x   = **35**   **Subtract 65 from each side.**

Thus, **35%** of 600 is the number of students not out for any sport.

Find **35%** of 600.

Multiply: $0.35 \cdot 600 = 210$.

Solution   Thus, 210 are not out for any sport.

EXAMPLE 4 The circle graph shows the numbers of Juniors in various math courses. The numbers in the graph are **not** angle measures. These figures represent **numbers** of students.

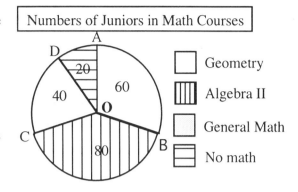

The number of students taking general math or not in any math course is what % of the total number of Juniors?

Strategy   **1.** First, find the **total** number of Juniors:
$60 + 80 + 40 + 20 = 200$

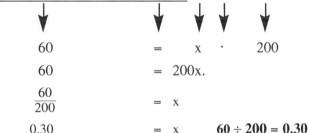

2. Find the number taking General Math or no math:
$40 + 20 = 60$

3. Write an equation. Solve the equation.

Number in <u>General Math or no math course</u> is what % of total Juniors?

$$60 = x \cdot 200$$
$$60 = 200x.$$
$$\frac{60}{200} = x$$
$$0.30 = x \qquad \mathbf{60 \div 200 = 0.30}$$

4. Write 0.30 as a percent: **30%**.

Solution   Thus, **30%** of the Juniors are in General Math or no math course.

Recall that all the way around a circle is 360°.

Thus, for any circle graph the sum of the measures of all the angles must be 360. This concept will be used in the next example. The Angle Addition Property will also be applied.

EXAMPLE 5   Use the circle graph on page 329 to find m ∠AOC.

Strategy   m ∠AOC = m ∠AOB + m ∠BOC
Thus, the percent of students represented by m ∠AOC is
20% + 15% = 35%.

Thus, m ∠AOC = 35% of 360.
So, find 0.35 · 360 = 126

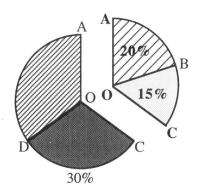

Solution   Therefore, m ∠AOC = 126.

SUMMARY

1.   How do you find how many students altogether were in the survey?
2.   How do you find the percent taking Latin ?
3.   How do you find the number of students taking German?
4.   How do you find the number of students taking Spanish or Latin?
5.   How do you find m ∠POR?

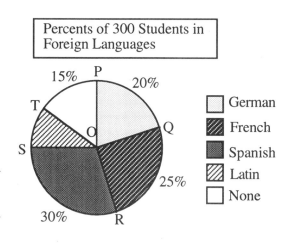

Percents of 300 Students in Foreign Languages

German
French
Spanish
Latin
None

CLASSROOM PRACTICE

1. How many people were surveyed?
2. How many bought a Plymouth?
3. How many bought a Subaru?
4. How many bought a Chevy?
5. How many bought a Toyota or a Ford?
6. Find m ∠AOB.
7. Find m ∠DOC.
8. Find m ∠AOE.
9. Find m ∠BOC.
10. Find m ∠EOD.
11. Find m ∠EOC.
12. Find m ∠DOA.

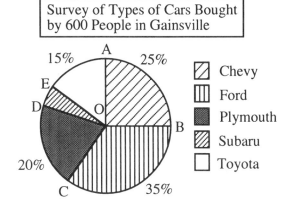

Survey of Types of Cars Bought by 600 People in Gainsville

Chevy
Ford
Plymouth
Subaru
Toyota

13. How many watched sports?
14. The number watching movies was what % of the total surveyed?
15. The number watching Ddocumentaries was what % of the number watching sports?
16. The number watching movies or documentaries was what % of the total number surveyed?

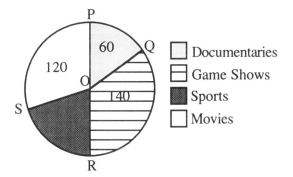

Survey of Favorite Types of T.V. Shows Watched by 400 People

Documentaries
Game Shows
Sports
Movies

WRITTEN EXERCISES

1. If a circle graph shows six angles, what is the sum of their measures?

The owner of a fast-food chain surveyed 300 people to determine what types of fast food people seem to prefer.

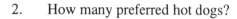

The circle graph at the right shows the results of the survey. Use this graph to answer Exercises 2-14 below.

2.   How many preferred hot dogs?

3.   How many preferred sandwiches?

4.   How many wanted chicken?

5.   How many selected hamburgers?

6.   How many wanted ribs?

7.   How many chose hamburgers or ribs?

Find the measure of each angle. (Round answer to the nearest tenth.)

8.   m ∠AOB   9.   m ∠DOC   10.   m ∠COB

11.   m ∠EOD   12.   m ∠EOC   13.   m ∠DOB

14.   Find the average for the numbers selecting hot dogs and chicken.

At the right is a circle graph showing the cereal choices of a sample of people in an apartment house. Use this graph to answer Exercises 15-20.

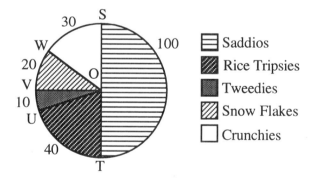

15.   Find the total number of people in the survey.

16.   The number of people choosing Crunchies is what % of the total?

17.   The number choosing Rice Tripsies is what % of the total?

18.   Tweedies fans represent what % of the total?

19.   The number wanting Crunchies is what % of the number wanting Rice Tripsies?

20.   The number selecting Snow Flakes is what % of the number choosing Crunchies?

21.   The graph below indicates the retail sales in billions of dollars for the major sneaker companies during 1989. Use it to answer the question that follows.

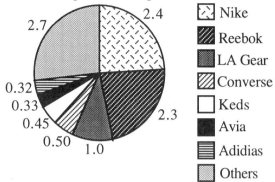

According to the graph, how much more than Converse's retail sales were Nike's retail sales?

(A) $1,950,000,000   (B) $1,900,000,000

(C) $1,950,000   (D) $1,900,000

OPEN-ENDED QUESTION

22.   The Student Government Association at Penns Grove High School has 60 members. They came up with the following methods for raising money.

12 voted for a dance.

27 wanted a car wash.

The rest wanted to sell football pennants.

Use a protractor to draw a circle graph to represent the various choices.

Indicate the percents of students in favor of each of the three choices.

Include a title for the graph and an explanation of the code for reading the graph.

REVIEW

Identify the type of angle with the given measure.

1.   70   2.   180   3.   146   4.   90

5.   Simplify $-4(-2)^3$

6   The width of a rectangle is $\frac{2}{3}$ of length. The perimeter is 40 ft. Find the length.

7.6 Rotation Patterns

OBJECTIVES   To predict a pattern of rolling an object along a line

To predict a pattern of rotating a geometric figure about its center

MANIPULATIVE DISCOVERY

The square in figure (a) has sides 5 inches long. If
it is rolled to the right along a line, what minimum
distance will it have traveled before the A is in the
position shown in figure (b)?

figure (a)   figure (b)

Discover this by **tracing** the small square on a
small sheet of tracing paper (hamburger patty
paper) and rolling it along a line to see what
actually happens.

EXAMPLE 1   The square at the right is 6 inches on each side. It is
rolled to the right along a line as shown. What minimum
distance will it have traveled before it is again upright?

Strategy   You might want to **trace** the small square on a small sheet of tracing paper
(hamburger patty paper) and roll it along a line to better understand this
problem. The square's position with each roll is shown below.

The square (**4 sides**) must be rolled **4**
times before **T** is again in the upright
position: **4 · 6 in. = 24 in.**

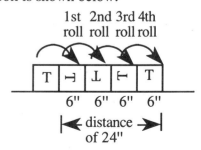

Solution   Thus, the square travels 24 inches before
the **T** is again upright.

The triangle at the right has 3 sides all **equal** in length. Such a triangle is called an **equilateral** triangle.

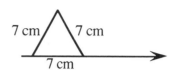

7 cm   7 cm

7 cm

EXAMPLE 2   The equilateral triangle at the right is 7 cm on each side. It is rolled to the right along the line. If the triangle stops so that the letter M is in an upright position, which of these distances could it have rolled?

M

(A)   24 cm   (B)   30 cm   (C)   14 cm   (D)   84 cm

Strategy   Discover this by **tracing** the triangle with the M on a small sheet of tracing paper (hamburger patty paper) and rolling it along a line to see what actually happens.

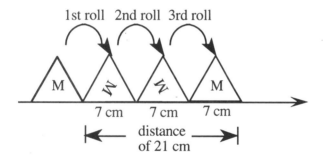

1st roll   2nd roll   3rd roll

M   Ｍ   Ｍ   M

7 cm   7 cm   7 cm

distance of 21 cm

The triangle (**3** sides) must be rolled **3** times before M is first in an upright position: **3 · 7 cm = 21 cm**.

The M will be in an upright position every **3** rolls, or after every **21 cm** rolled.

Now find which of the possible answers above is a **multiple** of **21**.

2 · **21** = 42

3 · **21** = 63

4 · **21** = **84**   **(D)**   **84 is a multiple of 21!**

Solution   Therefore, the triangle could have rolled **84 cm** before stopping with M upright

The last two examples suggest a pattern.

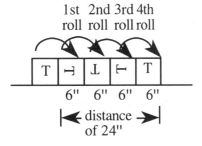

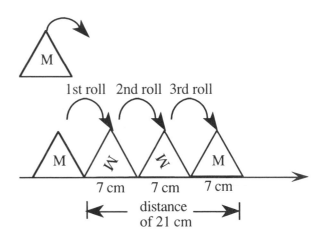

The **square** (**4** sides) must be rolled **4** times to the right before the **T** again becomes upright.

The **triangle** (**3** sides) must be rolled **3** times to the right before the **M** again becomes upright.

This suggests that the **7**-sided figure at the right with all sides of equal length would have to be rolled **7** times to the right before the **K** would again be in the upright position.

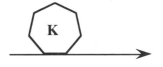

In general, a plane figure with **N** sides of the same length would have to be rolled to the right along a line **N** times for a letter in the center to be once again in an upright position.

DISCOVERY

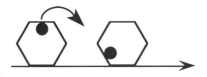

Each side of the hexagon measures 5 in. The hexagon is rolled to the right along the line.

What is the least number of inches the hexagon must travel to be in the position shown in the second figure?

EXAMPLE 3

The pentagon, 4 cm on a side, is rolled to the right long the line. If the pentagon is stopped so that the shaded circle is in the position shown in the second figure, which of the following distances could it have rolled?

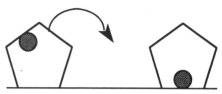

(A)   8 cm   (B)   16 cm   (C)   24 cm   (D)   32 cm

Strategy

5 rolls (traveled **5 · 4 cm, or 20 cm**) would take the circle **all** the way around to its **original** position.

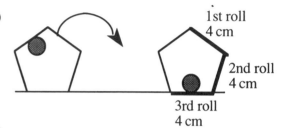

1st roll 4 cm

2nd roll 4 cm

3rd roll 4 cm

3 rolls (traveled **3 · 4 cm, or 12 cm**) would take the circle to the position shown in the second figure.

The circle will be in this position every time the pentagon has gone through **5** rolls (traveled **20 cm**)   **plus**   **12 more cm.**

Thus, the circle will be in the position shown in the second figure after the pentagon has traveled the following distances:

12 cm

12 cm + 1 · **20 cm**   =   32 cm

12 cm + 2 · **20 cm** = 12 cm + 40 cm   =   52 cm

12 cm + 3 · **20 cm** = 12 cm + 60 cm   =   72 cm

....

....

12 cm + **multiples** of **20 cm (in general)**

Solution

Thus, the correct answer choice is choice (D) or 32 cm.

Another kind of rotation pattern involves rotating a geometric figure about its center. This is illustrated in the next example.

EXAMPLE 4   If the square figure at the right is rotated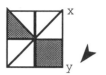
about its center so that the vertex at the
location labeled x ends up at the location
labeled y, which of the diagrams below
shows what the figure will look like then?

(A)   (B)   (C)   (D)

Strategy   Trace the original figure on a small sheet of tracing paper.

Holding the sheet in place with your pencil point placed at the center,
rotate the sheet 90° clockwise.

Solution   The result corresponds to (A).

SUMMARY

1. The pentagon is 7 in. on each side. If it is rolled to the right along a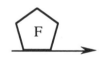
    line, how do you find the distance the pentagon rolls before the **F**
    again appears in an upright position?

2. Tell how to solve the following problem.
    The equilateral triangle is 4 cm on each side. It is rolled to the
    right along a line. Which of these distances could it have rolled
    so that the B will again be in an upright position?

    (A)   8 cm   (B)   16 cm   (C)   48 cm   (D)   80 cm

3. How do you solve this problem?
    The hexagon is 3 in. on a side and is rolled
    to the right along a line. Which of the
    following distances could it have rolled so that   figure (a)   figure (b)
    the shaded circle is in the position shown in
    figure (b)?

    (A)   6 in.   (B)   12 in.   (C)   36 in.   (D)   39 in.

4. This square is rotated about its center so that the vertex P ends up at the location labeled Q. How can you determine which of the following diagrams the figure will then look like?

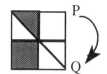

(A)   (B)   (C)   (D)

CLASSROOM PRACTICE

For each figure below, what minimum distance will it have rolled to the right along a line when the letter is again upright?

1. 4 in on a side

2. 5 cm on a side

3. 6 ft on a side

4. If the figure, 3 in. on a side, is rolled to the right along a line, which distance could it have rolled for the J to again be in an upright position?

    (A)   6 in.   (B)   12 in.   (C)   36 in.   (D)   39 in.

5. If the figure, 6 ft on a side, is rolled to the right along a line, which distance could it have rolled for the U to again be in an upright position?

    (A)   30 ft   (B)   48 ft   (C)   54 ft   (D)   78 ft

6. The hexagon in figure (a) is 5 in. on a side and is rolled to the right along a line. Which of the following distances could it have rolled so that the shaded circle is in the position shown in figure (b)?

    figure (a)   figure (b)

    (A)   45 in.   (B)   30 in.   (C)   50 in.   (D)   55 in.

7.   The hexagon in figure (a) is 3 in. on a side and is rolled to the right along a line. Which of the following distances could it have rolled so that the shaded circle is in the position shown in figure (b)?

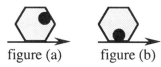

figure (a)   figure (b)

(A)   21 in.   (B)   15 in.   (C)   27 in.   (D)   42 in.

8.   This square is rotated about its center so that the vertex G ends up at the location labeled H. Which diagram below shows what the figure will then look like?

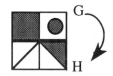

(A)   (B)   (C)   (D)

9.   This square is rotated clockwise about its center so that the vertex K ends up at the location labeled T. Which diagram below shows what the figure will then look like?

(A)   (B)   (C)   (D)

WRITTEN EXERCISES

For each figure below, what minimum distance will it have rolled to the right along a line when the letter is again upright?

1.   8 in. on a side   2. 4 cm on a side   3. 7 ft on a side

4. If the figure, 9 in. on a side, is rolled to the right along the line, what distance could it have rolled for the K to again be in an upright position?

(A)   9 in.   (B)   18 in.   (C)   36 in.   (D)   81 in.

5. If the figure, 9 in. on a side, is rolled to the right along the line, what distance could it have rolled for the L to again be in an upright position?

(A)   27 in.   (B)   45 in.   (C)   72 in.   (D)   81 in.

6. The heptagon in figure (a) is 8 cm on a side and rolled to the right along the line. Which of the following distances could it have rolled so that the shaded circle is in the position shown in figure (b)?

figure (a)   figure (b)

(A)   48 cm   (B)   80 cm   (C)   88 cm   (D)   96 cm

7. The octagon in figure (a) is 7 in. on a side and rolled to the right along the line. Which of the following distances could it have rolled so that the shaded square is in the position shown in figure (b)?

figure (a)   figure (b)

(A)   77 in.   (B)   63 in.   (C)   28 in.   (D)   14 in.

8. The pentagon in figure (a) is 3 in. on a side and rolled to the right along the line. Which of the following distances could it have rolled so that the shaded circle is in the position shown in figure (b)?

figure (a)   figure (b)

(A)   15 in.   (B)   21 in.   (C)   27 in.   (D)   51 in.

9.   This square is rotated clockwise about its center so that the vertex R ends up at the location labeled S. Which diagram below shows what the figure will then look like?

(A)   (B)   (C)   (D)

10.   This square is rotated counter-clockwise about its center so that the vertex C ends up at the location labeled D. Which diagram below shows what the figure will then look like?

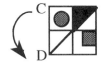

(A)   (B)   (C)   (D)

11.   The distance around a circle is called the **circumference**. The formula for the approximate circumference of a circle is $C = 6.28 \cdot r$, where r is the radius. Suppose that the circle is rolled to the right along the line until the letter T is again in an upright position. Write three distances it could have rolled.

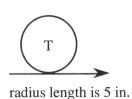

radius length is 5 in.

OPEN-ENDED QUESTION

12.   Suppose that the circle is rolled to the right along the line until the letter T is again in an upright position. Write three distances it could have rolled.
      Explain how you solved the problem.

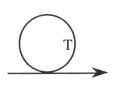

radius is 12 in.

REVIEW

1. Find the perimeter and area of rectangle ABCD for A(-2,4), B(6,4), C(6,7), and D(-2,7).

2. Complete the data table.

x	2(3x - 1) + 4
4	
	32

3. A store manager lists the selling price of a VCR at $412. If he plans a profit of 30% of the cost, what must the VCR have cost him to the nearest cent?

4. Suppose that x and y represent whole numbers.

   Then, for the equation $4x + 7y = 22$, what must be true about the value of y?

   (A)   y must be a multiple of 2.   (B)   y must be a multiple of 7.

   (C)   y must be divisible by 22.   (D)   y must be divisible by 7.

5. Kharad mistakenly multiplied by 6 instead of dividing by 6 while using his calculator. If the incorrect answer displayed by the calculator screen is 288, what is the correct answer?

6. What symbol is in the 111th position of the following pattern?

   obtuseobtuseobtuse...

7. m ∠1 = 43, m ∠2 = 38, m ∠BOA = ?

8. m ∠1 = $\frac{3}{7}$ of m ∠2, m ∠BOA = 30.

   m ∠2 = ?

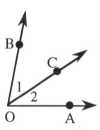

9. What is the total number of squares in this figure?

10. What fractional part of the drawing is not shaded?

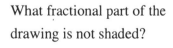

7.7 Simple Probability

OBJECTIVES   To find the probability of the occurrence of a simple event

When a coin is tossed, there are two **possible outcomes**, heads or tails.

These are **equally likely** to occur.

Assume that you are hoping that the coin will land with the tail facing up.

Then **tails** is called the **favorable** outcome.

The **probability** of getting **tails** is **1** out of **2**, or $\frac{1}{2}$.

PROBABILITY is the chance that a particular event will occur.

EXAMPLE 1   What is the probability that the spinner will

land on a section marked S?

Strategy   There are 8 sections.

Three sections are marked S.

There are **3** favorable outcomes out of **8**

possible outcomes

Solution   The chance or **probability** that the spinner will stop on a section marked **S**

is **3** out of **8**, or $\frac{3}{8}$

The **probability** of an event is determined by the following formula:

$$\text{probability of an event} = \frac{\text{number of } \textbf{favorable outcomes}}{\textbf{total} \text{ number of outcomes}}.$$

In this lesson you will see the application of angle measurement to illustrate probability relationships.

Notice in this picture of the circle with spinner that the three
sections marked S make up a portion of the **area** of the whole
circle.

In fact the **area** taken up by these three sections is $\frac{3}{8}$ of the **area**
of the entire circle.

Thus, the **probability** of the spinner landing on an S is
equivalent to finding the **ratio** of the **shaded area** to the **whole
circle's area**.

This idea is very useful in figuring the probability when the circle is **not** divided into
equal sections. This is illustrated in the next example.

EXAMPLE 2   If you spin the spinner once, what is the chance that it will
stop in region A?

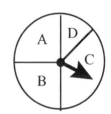

Strategy   Region A appears to be $\frac{1}{4}$ of the **area** of the entire circle.

Or, the angle forming region A appears to be a 90°angle.

Think of 360° as the entire circle. Then $\frac{90°}{360°} = \frac{1}{4}$.

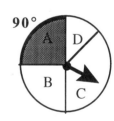

Solution   Thus, the **chance** of the spinner landing in section A is $\frac{1}{4}$.

The results above suggest the following when computing probabilities involving a
spinner on a circle. Think in terms of either :

            1. **area** of section in which spinner can land,

   or   2. measure of **angle** of section in which spinner can land.

EXAMPLE 3   If you spin the spinner of Example 2 of the previous page just once, what is the chance that it will stop in region C?

Assume that the angle that forms section D has a degree measure of 45.

Strategy

The degree measure of angle   m ∠POR = 45 as given above. m ∠ROQ = 180 - 45 = 135.
POQ, m ∠POQ = 180,

half of the entire circle of 360.

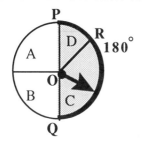   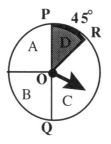   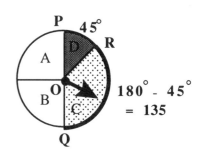

Solution   The chance that the spinner will stop in region C is $\frac{135}{360} = \frac{27}{72} = \frac{9}{24} = \frac{3}{8}$.

EXAMPLE 4   Members of the School Sports Club surveyed 650 students at Steinert High School. The club predicted that the probability of a student buying a fund-raiser ticket to a dance was approximately one-fourth. Suppose that the club can make a profit of $1.75 on each ticket they sell for $4.15.

Based on that probability, about how much profit can the club expect to make by selling fund raiser tickets? Which answer is closest?

(A) $290   (B) $391.20   (C) $675   (D) $4550

Strategy   1. Probability of $\frac{1}{4}$ means 1 out of 4.

Let x = number of students out of 650 who will buy tickets.

Think: 1 out of 4 **is the same as** x out of 650. Write a proportion.

$$\frac{1}{4} = \frac{x}{650}$$

$$1 \cdot 650 = 4 \cdot x \qquad \textbf{Cross multiply.}$$

$$650 = 4x$$

$$162.5 = x$$

The number of predicted buyers rounds to 163.

(continued on next page)

2.   Now find the profit.

$1.75 profit on each of 163 tickets: **$1.75 x 163 = $285.25**

Solution   Thus the probable profit will be about $285.25, closest to **choice (A)**.

There are two comments that need to be made about the solution to Example 4.

1.   This could have been found without using a proportion.

Find $\frac{1}{4}$ of 650, or $\frac{650}{4}$ = 162.5, which rounds to 163.

2.   Notice the extraneous information. The $4.15 selling price of the tickets had nothing do to with the solution. The solution was based only on the **$1.75 profit, NOT** the $4.15 selling price.

EXAMPLE 5   Each student in Hamilton High is participating in a $1.00 lottery to raise money for developing a new field hockey field. The winner will get half the money collected. One student will be picked at random. What is the probability that the winner will be a male student in grade 11?

NUMBER OF STUDENTS							
Grade 9		Grade 10		**Grade 11**		Grade 12	
M	F	M	F	**M**	F	M	F
26	24	34	17	**26**	25	27	21

Strategy   Number of outcomes is total population:

26 + 24 + 34 + 17 + 26 + 25 + 27 + 21 = **200**.

Number of favorable outcomes is number of 11th grade boys = **26**.

NUMBER OF STUDENTS							
Grade 9		Grade 10		**Grade 11**		Grade 12	
M	F	M	F	**M**	F	M	F
26	24	34	17	**26**	25	27	21

26 11th grade males

Solution   The probability that there will be a male winner in grade 11 is therefore

$$\frac{26}{200} = \frac{13}{100}.$$

EXAMPLE 6   A coin was tossed four times. The first three times it landed heads up.
The last time it landed tails up. What is the probability it will land heads up
the next time?

Strategy   The probability of a coin coming up heads is the same, no matter how many
times it is tossed.
There are **2** possible outcomes, heads or tails.
There is only **1** favorable outcome, heads.

Solution   Therefore the probability of getting heads on **any** throw is $\frac{1}{2}$.

Note, for the previous example, in real life you could toss a coin four times and it might
land heads up all four times.

Yet the **mathematical probability** of the coin landing heads up is $\frac{1}{2}$.

The formula for the probability of an event

$$\text{probability of an event} = \frac{\text{number of } \textbf{favorable} \text{ outcomes}}{\textbf{total} \text{ number of outcomes}}.$$

can be written in symbols: $\mathbf{p(e)} = \dfrac{\mathbf{f}}{\mathbf{t}}$

EXAMPLE 7   A bag contains 16 marbles. 3 marbles are blue and 7 are red.
The rest are green. One marble is drawn at random from the bag.
Find p(green).

Strategy   Find **p(green)** means find the **probability** of a **green** marble.
There are **16** possible outcomes: **t = 16**.
The number of **green** marbles is 16 - (3 + 7) = 16 - 10 = **6**.
The number of **favorable** outcomes is **6**: **f = 6**.

Solution $\mathbf{p(green)} = \dfrac{\mathbf{f}}{\mathbf{t}} = \dfrac{\mathbf{6}}{\mathbf{16}} = \dfrac{3}{8}$

A **die** (singular for **dice**) has dots on each of its six sides
corresponding to the numbers 1 through 6. The **two** dots shown at the
right correspond to the number **2**.

EXAMPLE 8   In one throw of a die, what is the probability that the upper face will show more than 2 dots?

Strategy   There are **6** possible outcomes (1 through 6): **t = 6**.

There are **4** numbers greater than 2: 3, 4, 5, and 6.

The number of **f**avorable outcomes is **4**: **f = 4**.

Use $p(e) = \dfrac{f}{t}$.

$p(\text{number greater than 2}) = \dfrac{4}{6} = \dfrac{2}{3}$.

Solution   Thus, the probability of tossing a number greater than 2 is $\dfrac{2}{3}$.

SUMMARY

1.   Explain the meaning of the formula $p(e) = \dfrac{f}{t}$.

2.   A person picks a coin out of a bag containing 2 pennies, 3 dimes, 5 quarters, and 1 nickel. If you are asked to find p(dime) what does this mean?

3.   If the pointer on the wheel is spun, how do you find p(landing on C)? Explain how the 40° is used in solving the problem.

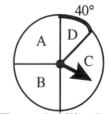

4.   318 students have bought tickets to the football game. The probability that a ticket buyer will buy a pennant is $\dfrac{1}{5}$. How do you find the approximate number of students who would be expected to buy a pennant?
What are two ways to solve this problem?

CLASSROOM PRACTICE

A bag contains 4 green marbles and 3 blue ones. One marble is drawn.

Find the probability of each event.

1.   p(green)

2.   p(blue)

If the pointer on the spinner is spun, find the indicated probability for where the pointer might land. (Exercises 3-8)

3.   p(5)

4.   p(2)

5.   p(1)

6.   p(Q)

7.   p(P)

8.   p(S)

9.   A bag of 15 marbles contains 3 green marbles, 6 blue ones, and the rest red. One marble is drawn at random. What is the probability that it will be red?

10. A bag contains 25 coins. There are 5 quarters, 6 dimes, 4 nickels, and the rest pennies. One coin is drawn at random. Find the probability that it will be a penny.

11. The School Stage Club is planing to sell candy bars to raise money for putting on a play. They allow for a profit of $0.45 on each $1.25 candy bar sold. The club predicted that the probability of a student buying a candy bar was one out of three. There are 640 students in the school. Based on the probability, about how much profit, to the nearest penny, does the club hope to make?

On one throw of a die, find the probability that the number of dots showing on the upper face will be the following:

12. 2   13.   less than 5   14.   an even number

15. Monica tosses a die 20 times. The last three times, 4 dots have shown on the upper face each time. What is the probability of 4 dots showing on the upper face on the next throw?

16. The school newspaper will feature a student of the month. One student will be selected at random from the total population. Find the probability that the selection will be a tenth-grade girl.

NUMBER OF STUDENTS							
Grade 9		Grade 10		Grade 11		Grade 12	
M	F	M	F	M	F	M	F
99	82	73	87	66	59	72	71

WRITTEN EXERCISES

A bag contains 6 orange marbles and 4 white ones. One marble is drawn.
Find the probability of each event.

   1.   p(orange)   2. p(white)

If the pointer on the spinner is spun, find the indicated probability for where the spinner
might land. (Exercises 3-9)

   3.   p(5)

   4.   p(4)

   5.   p(1)

   6.   p(not 2)

   7.   p(Y)

   8.   p(U)

   9.   p(W)

10.   Which spinner below would give you the best probability of spinning a K?

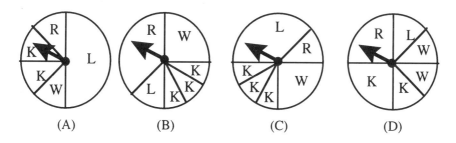

     (A)   (B)   (C)   (D)

11.   A bag of 20 marbles contains 4 red marbles, 8 blue ones, and the rest black. One
       marble is drawn at random. What is the probability that it will be black?

12.   A bag contains 32 coins. There are 10 quarters, 4 dimes, 3 nickels, and the rest
       pennies. One coin is drawn at random. Find the probability that it will be a penny.

13.   The P.T.A. plans to sell soda at a school play. Each soda costs the P.T.A. $0.35
       and is sold for $1.05. The P.T.A. predicted that the probability of a playgoer
       buying a soda would be one third. Suppose 175 people bought play tickets. Based
       on that probability, find to the nearest penny the **profit** the P.T.A. can expect.

On one throw of a die, find the probability that the number of dots showing on the upper face will be the following:

14.   5   15.   less than 4   16.   an odd number

17.   Assume that today is October 2. During the past 60 years there have been 450 October days that have had weather just like today. Of those, 150 have been followed by a nice sunny day. Which of the following is approximately the probability of a clear day tomorrow that would be predicted by a weatherman using the prediction rule described above?

    (A)   11%   (B)   33%   (C)   40%   (D)   none of these

18.   A summer camp for children from four local towns states that one child will be chosen at random to return next summer at no cost. Find the probability that the child will be a girl from Midtown.

NUMBER OF CHILDREN							
Newtown		Oldtown		Midtown		Fantown	
Boys	Girls	Boys	Girls	Boys	Girls	Boys	Girls
10	12	14	11	19	18	21	20

OPEN-ENDED QUESTION

19.   The probability that a student from a high school with 450 students will go to this week's football game is $\frac{2}{3}$. There are two different ways that you can find the number of students expected to attend the game. Explain each method in detail. Show that the answer is the same for each method.

REVIEW   CHAPTERS 1-7

Identify each type of angle.

1.   2.   3.   4.

   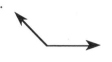

5.   Graph the ray defined by $-2x + 6 \leq 14$.

Use the figure below to answer excercises 6–7.

Give as many names as possible for the ray described by each inequality.

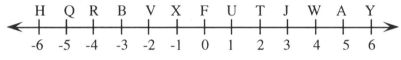

6. $x \leq -4$ 7. $x \geq 3$

8.   Which inequality below would be most useful in solving this problem?
        Bill earned $45 over two weeks at a part-time job. He bought three tee-
        shirts at $12 each. He would like to buy as many tapes as possible at $7.95 each.
        How many tapes could he buy?

        (A) $3x + 12 \leq 45$ (B) $12x + 7.95 \leq 45$
        (C) $7.95x + 36 \leq 45$ (D) $7.95x + 12 \leq 45$

9.   What are the restrictions on x if
        $\angle A$ is obtuse?

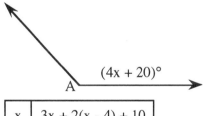

10.   Complete the table.

x	3x + 2(x - 4) + 10
5	
	12

Simplify.

11. $-2(3)^4$ 12. $-7 + 5 - 4 + 9$ 13. $(-4)(-6)$

14.   Insert the appropriate inequality symbol: 3.01^2 ? 1.9^5

15. m ∠BOA = 72, m ∠2 = 19.
    Find m ∠1.

16. m ∠1 = 2x - 8, m ∠2 = 3x + 10,
    m ∠BOA = 82. Find m ∠2.

17. m ∠2 = $\frac{5}{6}$ of m ∠1, m ∠BOA = 44.
    Find m ∠2

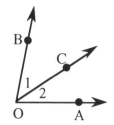

A small school can only afford to support four sports, 3 for boys and 1 for girls. At the right is a graph of the sports selections of 200 students of this school.

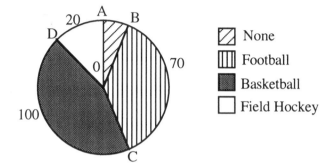

None — None

Football

Basketball

Field Hockey

18. How many students are not out for any sport?

19. The number out for football is what percent of the entire school enrollment?

20. Find the percent of all students out for field hockey.

21. Use the result of Exercise 20 to find m ∠DOA.

22. How many more students are out for basketball than football?

23. The heptagon is 8 cm on a side. What minimum distance will it have to roll along the line before the G is again in an upright position?

24. The hexagon in figure (a) is 4 cm on a side and rolled to the right along a line. Which of the following distances could it have rolled so that the shaded circle would be in the position shown in (b)?

figure (a)   figure (b)

    (A)   8 cm   (B)   32 cm   (C)   36 cm   (D)   40 cm

25. A bag contains 4 red balls, 6 white balls, 2 green balls, and 3 orange balls. One is drawn from the bag at random. Find the probability that it will be an orange ball.

26.   If the square figure at the right is rotated about its
       center so that the vertex at the location labeled P ends
       up at the location labeled Q, which diagram below
       shows what the figure will then look like?

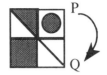

   (A)   (B)   (C)   (D)

If the spinner is spun once, find the
probability that it will land in the indicated
region.

27.   S

28.   not T

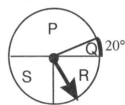

29.   If the spinner is spun once, find the
       probability that it will land in the
       region marked P.

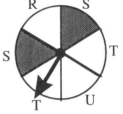

30.   A die is tossed 5 times. It lands with 3 dots showing on the upper face on the 4th,
       fifth, and sixth throws. What is the probability that 3 dots will show again on the
       next throw?

31.   On the scale below, the reading indicated by the arrow is between

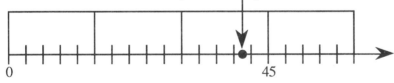

       (A)   18 and 19   (B)   33 and 35   (C)   39 and 42   (D)   43 and 44

32.   If the scale is balanced, what is the
       weight of one block if one pyramid
       weighs 3 pounds?

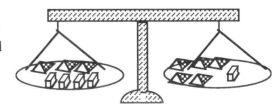

33. Which of the following is not equal to the other three?

(A) $\dfrac{15}{2}$ (B)   75   (C)   150% of 5   (D)   5 plus half of 5

34. As shown in the diagram, the picture is not centered on the wall from left to right. How far to the left should it be moved to be centered?

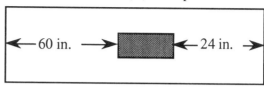

(A)   42 inches   (B)   36 inches

(C)   18 inches   (D)   Not enough information is given.

35. A stereo that regularly sells for $300 is advertised on sale at a discount of 20%. Which of the following computations will give the amount the customer must pay?

(A)   (300)(0.20)   (B)   300 + (300)(0.20)

(C)   300 - (0.20)(300)   (D)   300 + 0.20

36. The homes of Dee, Al, and Joy are along the same road. Dee's house is about 25 miles from Al's house. Joy's house is about 7 miles from Dee's house. About how far apart are the houses of Joy and Al?

(A)   about 18 miles apart

(B)   either about 18 miles or 32 miles apart

(C)   about 32 miles apart

(D)   about 25 miles apart

37. Examine the pattern **perpendicularperpendicularperpendicular...**
     What symbol is in the 45th position?

38. The number 79997 is a palindrome number. What is the very next larger palindrome number?

39. $GH = 2\frac{1}{4}$, $GK = 8\frac{1}{2}$, $HK = ?$

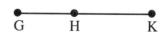

40. $GH : HK = 2 : 3$, $GK = 15$.
     Find HK.

41. The width of a rectangle is $\dfrac{5}{8}$ of the length. The perimeter of the rectangle is 52 cm. Find the length.

42. The scale on a road map is 2 inches = 8 miles. How many miles apart are two cities that measures 5 inches apart on the map?

43. Armadi used $12\frac{1}{2}$ gallons of gas to go on a 250-mile trip. How many miles per gallon did she get on the trip?

44. One car traveled 36 miles in 40 minutes. Find the average speed in miles per hour.

45. A 60 cent bag of peanuts weighed $1\frac{1}{2}$ ounces. At this rate, find the cost of one pound of those peanuts.

46. Pat's bowling average for four games was 160. What would he have to bowl on the fifth game to have an average of 168 for the five games?

The bar graph below shows Wanda's quiz scores for the first marking period. Use it to answer exercises 47-51.

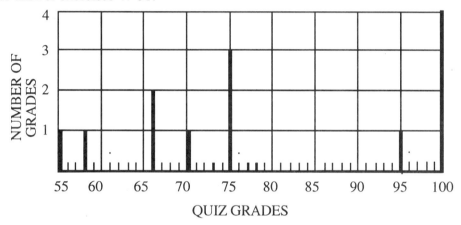

Find each of the following.

47. mean   48. median   49. mode   50. range

51. Which measure of central tendency best represents Wanda's performance? Explain why.

52. The length of a rectangle is 6 cm. The perimeter of the rectangle is 40 cm. Find the area of the rectangle.

OPEN-ENDED QUESTION

53. Draw the rectangle ABCD with vertices A(0,0), B(6,0), C(6,4), and D(0,4).
    Draw a rectangle with perimeter twice that of ABCD.
    Give the coordinates of its vertices.
    Is there more than one way to do this? Explain why.

Chapter

8

Angles Part II

8.1 Perpendiculars and Complementary Angles

OBJECTIVES   To apply the symbol for "is perpendicular to"

To solve problems about complementary angles

To apply the concept of "perpendicular to a line" to solving special probability problems

Recall that a **right angle** is an angle with measure 90.

∠CAB is a **right angle**.

The sides of a **right angle** are said to be **perpendicular**.

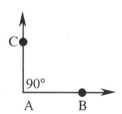

$\overrightarrow{AC}$ **is perpendicular to** $\overrightarrow{AB}$.

$\overrightarrow{AC}$ ⊥ $\overrightarrow{AB}$ The upside down T is read as **is perpendicular to**.

EXAMPLE 1   In which of the following figures can we say that the sides are perpendicular? In that case, write a statement using the new symbol for **is perpendicular to**.

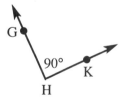

Solution   The angle measure is **NOT** 90. We **cannot** conclude that the sides are perpendicular.

The angle measure **is 90**. So, we can conclude that the sides are **perpendicular**.

$\overrightarrow{HK} \perp \overrightarrow{HG}$

In the figure at the right ∠1 and ∠2 are **adjacent angles**. There are **three** rays in the figure.

The rays $\overrightarrow{QP}$ and $\overrightarrow{QR}$ are called the **outer rays** of the adjacent angles.

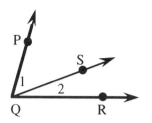

DISCOVERY

In the figure at the right, what can you conclude about m ∠AOB by the Angle Addition Property? Then, what kind of angle must m ∠AOB be? What relationship must therefore exist between the outer rays $\overrightarrow{OA}$ and $\overrightarrow{OB}$?

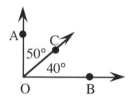

The discovery activity above suggests the following property about adjacent angles whose **outer rays are perpendicular:**

If the **outer rays** of two adjacent angles are **perpendicular,** then the **sum** of the angle measures is **90.**
This can be abbreviated as
If $\overrightarrow{OA}$ ⊥ $\overrightarrow{OB}$, then m ∠1 + m ∠2 = 90.

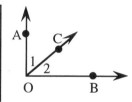

EXAMPLE 2   Given: $\overrightarrow{QR} \perp \overrightarrow{QP}$, m ∠2 = 37, m ∠1 = ?

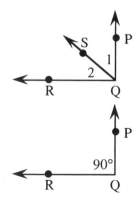

Strategy   What does $\overrightarrow{QR} \perp \overrightarrow{QP}$ tell you?
Since the outer rays are perpendicular,
m ∠RQP = 90.
Then, m ∠2 + m ∠1 = 90.
        37 + m ∠1 = 90
                m ∠1 = 90 - 37

Solution   So,   m ∠1 =   53   Outer rays are perpendicular.

EXAMPLE 3   Given: $\overrightarrow{HG} \perp \overrightarrow{HK}$,

m $\angle 1 = 2x + 10$, m $\angle 2 = 3x + 20$.

Find m $\angle 2$.

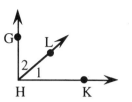

Strategy   Since the outer rays are perpendicular,

m $\angle 1$	+	m $\angle 2$	=	90.	
$2x + 10$	+	$3x + 20$	=	90	
		$5x + 30$	=	90	**Combine like terms.**
		$5x$	=	60	
		x	=	12	

Now use   m $\angle 2 = 3\mathbf{x}$ $+ 20$ to find m $\angle 2$.

m $\angle 2 = 3 \cdot \mathbf{12} + 20$ **Substitute 12 for x.**

Solution   So,   m $\angle 2 = 36 + 20$, or 56

Ratios can also be applied to problems involving perpendiculars and adjacent angles.
For example, in Example 3 above, you might be given that

m $\angle 1$: m $\angle 2 = 2 : 3$ or equivalently,

m $\angle 1 = \frac{2}{3}$ of m $\angle 2$.

Then you can find m $\angle 2$ if you know $\overrightarrow{HG} \perp \overrightarrow{HK}$. This is illustrated in the next example.

EXAMPLE 4   Given: $\overrightarrow{HG} \perp \overrightarrow{HK}$, m $\angle 1 = \frac{2}{3}$ of m $\angle 2$.

Find m $\angle 1$.

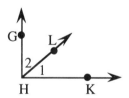

Strategy   Since m $\angle 1 = \frac{2}{3}$ of m $\angle 2$,

let m $\angle 1 = \mathbf{2}x$, and m $\angle 2 = \mathbf{3}x$

m $\angle 1$	+	m $\angle 2 = 90$	**The outer rays are perpendicular.**
$2x$	+	$3x = 90$	
		$5x = 90$	
		x $= 18$	

Solution   m $\angle 1 = 2x = 2 \cdot \mathbf{18} = 36$ **Substitute 18 for x.**

In the figure at the right, $\angle A$ and $\angle B$ are
NOT adjacent angles. Yet the **sum** of their
measures is **90**.

Each angle is said to be a **complement** of
the other.

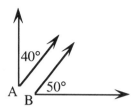

DEFINITION: Complementary Angles

Two angles are **complementary** if the **sum** of their measures is **90**.

Each angle is the **complement** of the other.

Notice in the first figure that complementary angles
need not be adjacent.

However, if the two angles are slid together so that
they are **adjacent**, then the resulting **outer rays** are
perpendicular.

This can be seen by tracing the 40° angle on tracing

paper and then sliding it so that the 40° and

50° angles are adjacent.

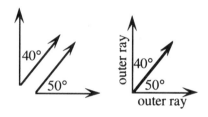

EXAMPLE 5   Is $\angle 1$ complementary to $\angle 2$? Explain why or why not.

Given: m $\angle 1 = 45$, m $\angle 2 = 55$ Given: $\overrightarrow{ED} \perp \overrightarrow{EF}$

            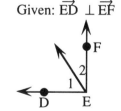

Solution   **NO:** $45 + 55 = 100$ **YES:**   Outer rays of two
                  Sum of measures is **NOT 90.**   adjacent angles are
                                                 perpendicular.

EXAMPLE 6   Find the measure of a complement of an angle with the given measure.

(a) 42   (b) 3x

Solution   90 - 42 = 48   90 - 3x

This **cannot** be simplified to 87x.

We close this lesson with a **probability** application involving the idea of **perpendicular**. The **distance** from a point to a segment or line is the **perpendicular** distance.

The distance from point P to $\overline{AB}$ is shown at the right.

The distance from point P to $\overline{AB}$ is $\overline{PQ}$ (the **perpendicular** from P to $\overline{AB}$).

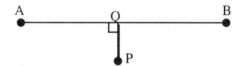

In calculating a probability, all possibilities must be equally likely. This is illustrated below.

EXAMPLE 7   Suppose that the 8-in.-by-6-in. paper at the right is covered with sugar. An ant is crawling on the paper. He never leaves the paper because of all the tasty sugar to eat. The ant is therefore equally likely to be on any part of the paper.

What is the probability that he will be no more than 2 inches from the top edge of the paper?

8 in.

6 in.

Strategy   Any point in the shaded box at the right is no more than 2 inches from the top edge of the paper.

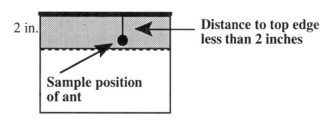

2 in.

Distance to top edge less than 2 inches

Sample position of ant

(continued on next page)

Think of the ant's position as equally likely in any region of the paper. This is better seen by dividing the paper into equal regions each 2 inches wide.

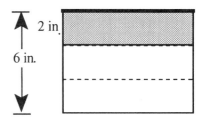

Solution   The probability of the ant being in the shaded region is $\frac{2}{6} = \frac{1}{3}$.

Notice in the last example that the width, 8 inches, of the paper had nothing to do with the solution. This is illustrated below.

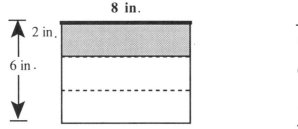

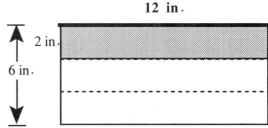

Probability of ant being in shaded region is $\frac{2}{6} = \frac{1}{3}$.

Probability of ant being in shaded region is $\frac{2}{6} = \frac{1}{3}$.

The probability is the **same** whether the width of the paper is **8 inches or 12 inches**.

SUMMARY

1.   What is the meaning of the symbol "$\perp$"?

2.   Name the outer rays of the adjacent angles.

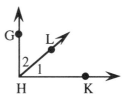

3.   Given the angle measures of two adjacent angles, what must be true if the outer rays are to be perpendicular?

4.   Given the measure of an angle, how do you find the measure of a complement of this angle?

5.   Given: $m\angle 1 = 4x$. Explain why the measure of a complement of this angle is **NOT** 86x.

Given: $\overrightarrow{QR} \perp \overrightarrow{QP}$

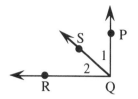

6. If m ∠ 1 = 38, how do you find m ∠ 2?

7. Given: m ∠ 1 = 4x - 10, m ∠ 2 = x + 30,
    What equation do you write to find m ∠ 2?

8. Given: m ∠ 1 = $\frac{4}{5}$ of m ∠ 2.

    What equation do you write to find m ∠ 2?

9. For exercise 9, if the solution of the equation is x = 10,
    what is the next step in solving the problem?

10. An ant is crawling on the 21-in.-by-12-in. sheet of
    paper shown. How do you find the probability
    that the ant is no more than 3 inches from the bottom
    edge of the paper?

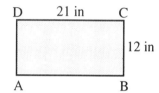

CLASSROOM PRACTICE

Given: $\overrightarrow{WT} \perp \overrightarrow{WL}$

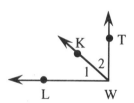

1. m ∠ 2 = 42, m ∠ 1 = ?

2. m ∠ 1 = 62, m ∠ 2 = ?

3. m ∠ 1 = 37, m ∠ 2 = ?

4. m ∠ 2 = 43, m ∠ 1= ?

5. m ∠ 1 = x + 12, m ∠ 2 = 4x + 8.
    Find m ∠ 2.

6. m ∠ 2 = 3x - 10, m ∠ 1 = 2x + 30. Find m ∠ 1.

7. m ∠ 2 = $\frac{2}{7}$ of m ∠ 1, m ∠ 1 = ?

8. m ∠ 1 = $\frac{1}{4}$ of m ∠ 2, m ∠ 2 = ?

Find the measure of a complement of the angle with the given measure.

9. 43   10. 75   11. y   12. 7k

An ant is crawling on the surface of the 30-in.-by-12-in. sheet of paper shown. Find the probability that the ant is no more than:

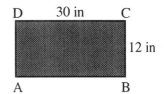

D   30 in   C

12 in

A   B

13.   4 inches from the bottom edge of the paper.

14.   6 inches from the left edge of the paper.

WRITTEN EXERCISES

Find the measure of a complement of the angle with the given measure.

1.   49   2. 62   3. m   4. 6d

Given: $\overrightarrow{DM} \perp \overrightarrow{DE}$

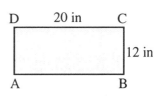

5. $m \angle 2 = 54$, $m \angle 1 = ?$

6. $m \angle 1 = 53$, $m \angle 2 = ?$

7. $m \angle 1 = 39$, $m \angle 2 = ?$

8. $m \angle 2 = 44$, $m \angle 1 = ?$

9. $m \angle 1 = 2x + 8$, $m \angle 2 = 3x + 12$.
          Find $m \angle 2$.

10. $m \angle 2 = 4x - 10$, $m \angle 1 = 2x + 40$. Find $m \angle 1$.

11. $m \angle 2 = \frac{3}{2}$ of $m \angle 1$, $m \angle 1 = ?$

12. $m \angle 1 = \frac{1}{5}$ of $m \angle 2$, $m \angle 2 = ?$

13. $\angle 1$ and $\angle 2$ are complementary angles. $m \angle 1 : m \angle 2 = 7 : 2$. Find $m \angle 1$.

An ant is crawling on the surface of a 6 in by 10 in sheet of paper. Find the probability that the ant is no more than:

D   20 in   C

12 in

A   B

14.   2 inches from side $\overline{AB}$

15.   5 inches from side $\overline{BC}$

OPEN-ENDED QUESTION

16.   A mosquito is flying around an empty room that measures 20 feet long by 16 feet
        wide by 9 feet high. At a particular moment, what is the probability that the
        mosquito will be no more than 3 feet from the floor? Write the answer as well as
        explanation of how you solved this problem.

        HINT: This problem is very similar exercises 14 and 15 above. The
        only difference is that it involves a box (3-dimensions) rather than a rectangle.

REVIEW

1.   Yolanda plans to buy two tires that cost between $60 and $70 each.
        There is a state sales tax of 6%. The total cost of the two tires is closest to
        which of the following?
        (A) $8.00   (B) $138   (C) $130   (D) $208

2.   Last week, Nadia earned $700. As part of estimating the amount of her
        paycheck, she first adds the following deductions and then rounds to the nearest whole
        number percent:

Federal tax	24.0%
FICA	7.2%
State Income Tax	4.5%
Unemployment Insurance	0.42%

        Her estimate of the amount of her paycheck is about
        (A) $252   (B) $539   (C) $952   (D) $448

3. Seventy men and fifty women participated in a walking marathon. Prizes were offered to the
    top 20 of the men and to the top 20% of the women participants. What percent of the
    participants were **not** awarded prizes?

4.   Rodney owes $315.39 on his credit card. He misses two monthly
        payments. The credit company charges 15.5% interest per year on the
        unpaid balance (amount owed).Assume that he makes no charges for
        these two months. What would he have to pay, including interest, to
        pay the bill in full at the end of two months? the nearest cent.

COMPUTER MANIPULATIVE ACTIVITY

This activity will help pave the way for the concept of supplementary angles introduced in the next lesson.

Use a computer software program that allows you to draw angles with a given measure and move the angles about the screen with a mouse. Examples of such a program are *Canvas, McDraw, Aldus Freehand,* and *Geometry Sketchpad*.

COMPUTER ACTIVITY

Use a computer software drawing program to draw ∠1 with measure 40 and ∠2 with measure 140 as shown at the right.

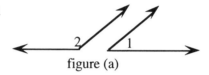

figure (a)

Use the mouse to slide ∠1 to be adjacent to ∠2. What do you notice about the outer rays?

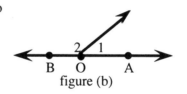

figure (b)

What kind of angle to the adjacent angles form together?

PRACTICE

Repeat the above activity for the following angles.

1.   m ∠ 1 = 50 and m ∠ 2 = 130   2. m ∠ 1 = 120 and m ∠ 2 = 60

3.   Form a generalization about this new relationship for a special pair of adjacent angles. The generalization is very similar to the property on page 362.

8.2 Supplementary Angles

OBJECTIVE   To solve problems about supplementary angles

Recall that a straight angle has a measure of 180.

The sides are rays that together form a line.

O is between A and B .

Notice that the rays extend in **opposite** directions.

They are called **opposite rays**.

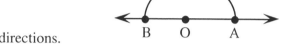

Each figure below shows a pair of adjacent angles.

In the second figure, the outer rays $\overrightarrow{OA}$ and $\overrightarrow{OB}$ form a **line**.

In this case, ∠AOB is a **straight angle** and the outer rays are **opposite** rays.

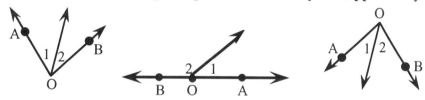

(In this book, if a diagrams appears to be that of a straight angle, this may be assumed without being stated in writing.)

Recall that the measure of a **straight angle** is **180.**

So, for the middle figure above, m ∠AOB = 180. This suggests the following property:

If the outer rays of two adjacent angles form a **straight angle,** then the sum of the measures of the angles is **180.**

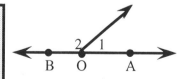

Recall from the last lesson, if the sum of the measures of two angles is 90, then the angles are **complementary**.

There is a similar definition of angles whose measures add up to 180.

In the figure at the right, ∠A and ∠B are **not** adjacent. Yet the sum of their measures is 180. ∠A and ∠B are called **supplementary** angles.

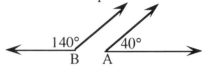

DEFINITION   Supplementary Angles

Two angles are **supplementary** if the sum of their measures is **180**.
Each angle is a **supplement** of the other.

MANIPULATIVE DISCOVERY

Use a protractor to measure the two angles at the right.

Why are the angles supplementary?

Use a small sheet of tracing paper to trace ∠2.

Slide ∠1 to be adjacent to ∠2.

What is true about the outer rays, $\overrightarrow{OA}$ and $\overrightarrow{OB}$, of the two adjacent angles?

What kind of angle do the two adjacent angles form together?

Form a generalization about this special relationship of **supplementary angles**.

The discovery activity above suggests the following property about adjacent angles whose **outer rays form a straight angle**.

If the outer rays of two adjacent angles form a **straight angle**, then the angles are **supplementary**.

EXAMPLE 1   Are the pairs of angles supplementary? Explain why or why not.

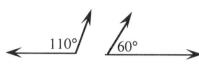

Solution   **NO.** 110 + 60 = 170, **NOT** 180. The sum of the angle measures is **NOT** 180.

YES. The outer rays form a **straight angle**. So, the angles are **supplementary**.

EXAMPLE 2   Find the measure of a supplement of the angle with the given measure.

140	63	2x

Solution   **180** - 140 = 40   **180** - 63 = 117   180 - 2x

EXAMPLE 3   Find m ∠1.

Strategy   Assume from the figure that $\overrightarrow{HG}$ and $\overrightarrow{HK}$ are **opposite rays**, forming a **straight angle**.

So, m ∠1 + m ∠2 = **180**.

m ∠1 + 119 = 180

m ∠1   = 180 - 119

Solution   m ∠1   = 61

EXAMPLE 4   m ∠2 = 40, m ∠3 = 60.
Find m ∠1.

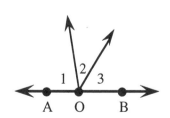

Strategy   Assume ∠AOB is a **straight angle**.

So,   m ∠1 + m ∠2 + m ∠3 = 180

m ∠1 + **40** + **60** = 180

m ∠1   + **100** = 180

m ∠1   = 80

Solution   Therefore, m ∠1 = 80.

EXAMPLE 5   ∠1 and ∠2 are supplementary.

m ∠1 = 3x + 10, m ∠2 = 2x - 5.

Find m ∠1.

Strategy   Use **angles are supplementary** to write an equation.

m ∠1	+	m ∠2	=	180
3x + 10	+	2x - 5	=	180
	5x + 5		=	180	**Combine like terms.**
	5x		=	175
	x		=	37

Now use   m ∠1 = 3**x** + 10 to find m ∠1.

m ∠1 = 3 · **37** + 10   **Substitute 37 for x in 3x + 10.**

m ∠1 = 111 + 10

Solution   Thus,   m ∠1 = 121

Just as with complementary angles in the last chapter, the solution of supplementary angles problems might involve ratios. This is illustrated in the next example.

EXAMPLE 6   ∠1 and ∠2 are supplementary.

m ∠1 = $\frac{2}{3}$ of m ∠2. **(or m ∠1 : m ∠2 = 2 : 3)**

Write an equation you could use to find m ∠1.

Strategy   Represent the angle measures in terms of one letter or variable

m ∠1 = $\frac{2}{3}$ of m ∠2.

Let m ∠1 = **2**x. Let m ∠2 = **3**x.

Use ∠1 and ∠2 are supplementary to write an equation.

m ∠1 + m ∠2 = 180

2x   +   **3x**   = 180   **Substitute 2x for m ∠1 and 3x for m ∠2 .**

Solution   Thus, **5x** = 180 is an equation you could use to find m ∠1.

SUMMARY

1. Give an example of two angles that are supplementary.

2. How can you tell from a picture of two adjacent angles whether the two angles are supplementary?

3. How do you find the measure of a supplement of an angle with a given measure, say 113?

Given: m ∠1 and m ∠2 are supplementary.

4. m ∠1 = 3x + 10, m ∠2 = 2x + 40. What equation can you write to find m ∠1?

5. m ∠1 = $\frac{4}{5}$ of m ∠2. What equation can you write to find m ∠1?

6. How can you tell from a drawing of two adjacent angles if the angles are supplementary?

CLASSROOM PRACTICE

Is each pair of angles supplementary? Explain why or why not.

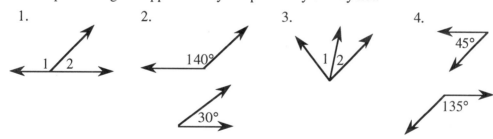

1.   2.   3.   4.

In exercises 5–9 find the measure of a supplement of each angle with the given measure.

5.   160   6. 35   7. 62   8. 4t   9. 108

10.   m ∠1 = 117, m ∠2 = ?

11.   m ∠1 = 26, m ∠2 = ?

12.   m ∠1 = 2x - 15, m ∠2 = 3x + 5. Find m ∠1.

13.   m ∠2 = 3x + 20, m ∠1 = x + 40. Find m ∠2.

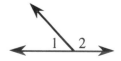

14. $\angle 1$ and $\angle 2$ are supplementary. m $\angle 1 = 4x + 10$, m $\angle 2 = 2x + 20$. Find m $\angle 2$.

15. $\angle 1$ and $\angle 2$ are supplementary. m $\angle 1 = 6x - 10$, m $\angle 2 = 4x - 30$. Find m $\angle 1$.

16.   m $\angle 1 = \frac{3}{7}$ of m $\angle 2$. Find m $\angle 2$.

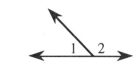
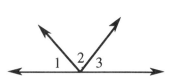

17.   m $\angle 1 : $ m $\angle 2 = 5 : 7$. Find m $\angle 1$.

18.   m $\angle 1 = 65$, m $\angle 2 = 75$, m $\angle 3 = ?$

19.   m $\angle 1 = 2x$, m $\angle 2 = 3x$, m $\angle 3 = 4x$. Find m $\angle 2$.

20.   m $\angle 1 = 30$, m $\angle 2 = 2x + 10$, m $\angle 3 = x + 20$. Find m $\angle 2$.

WRITTEN EXERCISES

Find the measure of a supplement of the angle with the given measure.

1.   42   2. 115   3. 5x   4. 79   5. 112

Is each pair of angles supplementary? Explain why or why not.

6.   7.   8.

     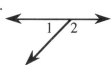   

9.   m $\angle 1 = 114$, m $\angle 2 = ?$ 10.   m $\angle 2 = 72$, m $\angle 1 = ?$

11.   m $\angle 2 = 115$, m $\angle 1 = ?$ 12.   m $\angle 1 = 66$, m $\angle 2 = ?$

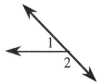

13.   m $\angle 1 = 3x + 20$, m $\angle 2 = 2x + 30$. Find m $\angle 1$.

14.   m $\angle 1 = 2x - 10$, m $\angle 2 = 3x + 30$. Find m $\angle 2$.

15.   m $\angle 1 = 4x + 30$, m $\angle 2 = x + 50$. Find m $\angle 1$.

16.   m $\angle 1 = 5x + 7$, m $\angle 2 = 3x + 13$. Find m $\angle 2$.

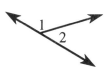

17. ∠1 and ∠2 are supplementary. m ∠1 : m ∠2 = 3 : 7. Find m ∠2.

18. ∠1 and ∠2 are supplementary. m ∠1 = $\frac{4}{5}$ of m ∠2. Find m ∠1.

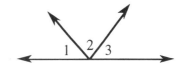

19. m ∠1 = 85, m ∠2 = 75, m ∠3 = ?

20. m ∠1 = 8x, m ∠2 = 3x, m ∠3 = x.
     Find m ∠2.

21. m ∠1 = 30, m ∠2 = 7x + 10, m ∠3 = 3x + 20.
     Find m ∠2.

OPEN-ENDED QUESTION

Sometimes it is helpful to use a **DATA TABLE** to solve a problem. This is illustrated in the next problem.

22. Suppose ∠1 and ∠3 are complementary.
     Will m ∠2 be different for different values of m ∠1
     and m ∠3? Try some sample values for m ∠1.
     See if you can use the results of completing the
     data table at the right to draw a conclusion.
     (**HINT:** Use the idea of complementary angles to
     find m ∠3 and then the idea of supplementary angles
     to find m ∠2.)

m ∠1	m ∠3	m ∠2
10		
20		
35		
40		

REVIEW

1. Find the measure of a complement of the angle with measure 42.

2. Solve 2(3x - 2) = 4.

3. Solve $\frac{x}{4}$ = 4.

4. Which of the following is not equal to the other three?

    (A)   125% of 40   (B) $\frac{5}{4} \cdot 40$ (C)   0.125 · 40   (D)   50

5. Simplify: -7 + 3 - 9 +4   6. Simplify: $\frac{-8}{-4}$

7. A school bus can carry at most 39 students. If each bus makes only one trip, find the least number of busses needed to transport 150 sophomores to a class picnic at the end of the school year.

8. 12 is not a factor of 64 because

    (A)   64 is not an odd number.   (B)   3 is not a factor of 64.

    (C)   2 is not a factor of 64.   (D)   4 is a factor of 12 but not of 64.

9. Cassette tapes are stored in boxes of 8 or 12. A weekly inventory indicates that the total number of cassettes in stock is supposed to be 302. Why is this not possible?

10. Find the least common multiple of 3 and 4.

11. Suppose that m and n represent whole numbers.
    Then for the equation $5m + 3n = 24$, what must be true about the value of m?

    (A)   m must be divisible by 5.   (B)   m must be divisible by 3.

    (C)   m must be a multiple of 5.   (D)   m must be even since 24 is even.

12. Jenny mistakenly multiplied by 7 instead of dividing by 7 while using her calculator. If the incorrect answer displayed on the calculator is 245, what is the correct answer?

13. Mr. Johnson encourages his class to work together in small groups of 3 on Wednesdays. On other days they work together in groups of 4 or 8. When all students are present, there are always 2 students left over to write up group conclusions. Which of the following could be the number of students in the class?

    (A)   13   (B)   14   (C)   26   (D)   30

14. As cars come off the assembly line, inspectors spot-check them. Ricci checks the 4th car and every 4th one after that. Donna checks the 6th car and every 6th one after that. If 96 cars are produced in one day, how many of them will have been inspected twice?

8.3 Solving Equations of the Form ax + b = cx + d

OBJECTIVE   To solve equations with variable terms on both sides

The next lesson introduces a new type of angle pair, **vertical angles**. You will need to solve equations like 3x + 20 = x + 40 in applications of the property of vertical angles. You have solved equations like 2x + 20 = 40 in which the variable (letter) is on only one side. An equation can contain the variable on each side, as in 3x + 20 = x + 40.

DISCOVERY

What can you subtract from each side of the equation 3x + 20 = x + 40 to get an equation with the variable on only one side? **HINT:** The resulting equation will contain only 3x or only 1x.

EXAMPLE 1   Solve 3x + 20 = x + 40.

Strategy	3x + 20	=	**1x** + 40	**x = 1x**
	3x **- 1x** + 20	=	1x **- 1x** + 40	**Subtract 1x from each side.**
	2x + 20	=	40	
	2x	=	20	**Subtract 20 from each side.**
Solution	x	=	10	**Divide each side by 2.**

You could also have solved 3x + 20 = x + 40 by first subtracting 3x from each side.

EXAMPLE 2   Solve 3x + 20 = x + 40 by first subtracting 3x from each side.

Strategy	3x **- 3x** + 20	=	1x **- 3x** + 40	**Subtract 3x from each side.**
	20	=	-2x + 40	
	20 **- 40**	=	-2x + 40 **- 40**	**Subtract 40 from each side.**
	-20	=	-2x	
Solution	10	=	x	$\frac{-20}{-2} = 10$

Note that the results of Example 1 and Example 2 are the same: **x = 10** in both solutions.

Sometimes equations contain fractions.

For example, consider the equation $\frac{3}{2}x - 1 = \frac{4}{5}x + 6$.

This equation looks like the type you solved in Example 1.

It would be easier to solve if there were no fractions.

You can change the equation to one with no fractions!

Multiply each side by the **Least Common Multiple (LCM)** of the denominators **2** and **5** .

Recall that the LCM of two numbers is the smallest number that 2 and 5 both divide into exactly: **10**.

The solution of the equation $\frac{3}{2}x - 1 = \frac{4}{5}x + 6$ is shown in the next example.

EXAMPLE 3   Solve $\frac{3}{2}x - 1 = \frac{4}{5}x + 6$.

Strategy   Eliminate the fractions.

Multiply each side by the LCM of 2 and 5.

$$10(\tfrac{3}{2}x - 1) \quad = \quad 10(\tfrac{4}{5}x + 6) \qquad \textbf{Multiply each side by 10.}$$

$$10 \cdot \tfrac{3}{2}x - 10 \cdot 1 \quad = \quad 10 \cdot \tfrac{4}{5}x + 10 \cdot 6 \quad \textbf{DISTRIBUTE the 10.}$$

$$15x - 10 \quad = \quad 8x + 60 \qquad 10 \cdot \tfrac{3}{2} = \overset{5}{\cancel{10}} \cdot \tfrac{3}{\underset{1}{\cancel{2}}} = 15$$

$$10 \cdot \tfrac{4}{5} = \overset{2}{\cancel{10}} \cdot \tfrac{4}{\underset{1}{\cancel{5}}} = 8$$

Solve $15x - 10 = 8x + 60$.

Subtract either 8x or 15x from each side.

$15x - \mathbf{8x} - 10$	$=$	$8x - \mathbf{8x} + 60$	**Subtract 8x from each side.**
$7x - 10$	$=$	60	
$7x$	$=$	70	**Add 10 to each side.**
Solution x	$=$	10	**Divide each side by 7.**

Notice that we chose to subtract **8x** rather than **15x** from each side above.

This resulted in a positive coefficient of x, **7**, rather than a negative number.

Many times there are several ways to solve the same problem.

This is illustrated in the next example.

EXAMPLE 4   Which sequence of steps will **NOT** solve the equation $\frac{1}{2}x + 4 = 10$?

(A)   Subtract 4 from each side, then multiply each side by 2.

(B)   Multiply each side by 2, then subtract 4 from each side.

(C)   Divide each side by $\frac{1}{2}$, then subtract 8 from each side.

(D)   Subtract 4 from each side, then divide each side by $\frac{1}{2}$.

Verify that the three which will solve the equation do give the same answer.

Strategy   In this type of situation, you will have to go through each choice to determine which one is incorrect.

Check (A)

$$\frac{1}{2}x + 4 = 10$$

$$\frac{1}{2}x = 6 \qquad \textbf{First subtract 4 from each side.}$$

$$2 \cdot \frac{1}{2}x = 2 \cdot 6 \qquad \textbf{Multiply each side by 2.}$$

$$1x = 12$$

Check (B)

$$\frac{1}{2}x + 4 = 10$$

$$2 \cdot (\frac{1}{2}x + 4) = 2 \cdot 10 \qquad \textbf{First multiply each side by 2.}$$

$$2 \cdot \frac{1}{2}x + 2 \cdot 4 = 20$$

$$1x + \textbf{8} = 20$$

$$1x = 12 \qquad \textbf{Subtract 8 from each side, NOT 4.}$$

Choice (B) is **wrong**.

Let's now check that the other two choices are correct and do give the same solution.

(continued on next page)

Check (C) $\frac{1}{2}x + 4 \qquad\qquad = 10$

$(\frac{1}{2}x + 4) \div \frac{1}{2} \qquad = \quad 10 \div \frac{1}{2}$ **First, divide each side by $\frac{1}{2}$.**

$\frac{1}{2}x \div \frac{1}{2} \quad + \quad 4 \div \frac{1}{2} = \qquad 20$ **$10 \div \frac{1}{2} = 10 \cdot 2 = 20$**

$\qquad\qquad 1x \quad + \quad 8 \quad = \qquad 20$ **$\frac{1}{2}x \div \frac{1}{2} = 1x \qquad 4 \div \frac{1}{2} = 4 \cdot 2 = 8$**

$\qquad\qquad\qquad x \qquad\qquad = \qquad 12$ **Subtract 8 from each side.**

Choice (C) gives the same solution as Choice (A), x = 12.

Check (D) $\frac{1}{2}x + 4 \qquad\qquad = 10$

$\qquad \frac{1}{2}x \qquad\qquad\qquad = \quad 6$ **First subtract 4 from each side.**

$\qquad 1x \qquad\qquad\qquad = \quad 12$ **Divide each side by $\frac{1}{2}$.**

$\qquad\qquad\qquad\qquad\qquad\qquad$ **$6 \div \frac{1}{2} = 6 \cdot 2 = 12$**

Choice (D) gives the same solutions as Choices (A) and (C), x = 12.

Thus, the sequence of steps in choice **(B)** will **NOT** solve $\frac{1}{2}x + 4 = 10$.

Solution   The other three choices all give the same solution, x = 12.

SUMMARY

1. The lesson suggested that to solve an equation like 4x - 2 = 2x + 12, you might begin by using two different approaches. What are these two approaches?
2. What are two ways to change the equation 4x - 7 = x - 22 to an equation with only one variable?
3. By what number can you multiply each side of $\frac{2}{3}m + 21 = -3 + \frac{3}{2}m$ to get an equation with no fractions? This number is called the ___ ___ ___ of 3 and 2.
4. Give several ways to solve the equation $\frac{3}{4}x - 6 = 9$.

CLASSROOM PRACTICE

Solve.

1. 6x + 7 = 3x + 16
2. 7y - 9 = 3y + 19
3. 6 + 10x = 8x + 14
4. 5n - 4 = 3n + 18
5. 6p + 13 = 9p - 5
6. 11x + 8 = -2 + 9x

7. $7y - 11 = -10 + 8y$ 8. $4 + 6x = 7x - 5$ 9. $4x + 5 = 7 - 2x$

10. $8x - 12 = 6x + 14$ 11. $8a - 7 = 3a + 13$ 12. $6 - x = 3x - 18$

13. $\frac{3}{2}b + 2 = 11$ 14. $\frac{2}{3}a + 7 = 9$ 15. $\frac{3}{10} + \frac{4}{5}x = \frac{1}{2}$

16. $\frac{3}{4}x - 6 = \frac{1}{2}x + 3$ 17. $\frac{2}{3}a + 2 = -3 + \frac{3}{2}a$ 18. $\frac{1}{5}b + 7 = \frac{1}{2}b + 4$

WRITTEN EXERCISES

Solve.

1. $4x - 7 = 2x + 13$ 2. $3a - 5 = 7a + 15$ 3. $4m - 7 = 6m + 9$

4. $7k - 4 = 3k + 20$ 5. $9p + 8 = 6p - 19$ 6. $13f + 5 = 11f - 7$

7. $10g - 22 = 8g - 14$ 8. $7a + 8 = 3a - 16$ 9. $x - 3 = 72 - 4x$

10. $-6a - 15 = -17 - 9a$ 11. $8 - 2y = 5y + 1$ 12. $a + 11 = -2a + 5$

13. $\frac{5}{3}x - 7 = 8$ 14. $\frac{3}{4}x + 7 = 16$ 15. $6 + \frac{1}{2}x = 8$

16. $\frac{2}{3}b - 6 = \frac{1}{2}b - 5$ 17. $\frac{3}{4}m - 5 = \frac{2}{3}m - 4$ 18. $\frac{2}{3}x - 5 = 4 - \frac{1}{2}x$

19. Which of these sequences of steps transforms the equation $\frac{1}{3}x + 2 = 12$ into the equation $x = 30$?

(A)   Subtract 2 from each side and then multiply each side by $\frac{1}{3}$.

(B)   Multiply each side by 3 and then subtract 2 from each side.

(C)   Subtract 2 from each side and then divide each side by 3.

(D)   Multiply each side by 3 and then subtract 6 from each side.

20. Which of these sequences of steps will **NOT** solve the equation $\frac{1}{4}x - 5 = 8$?

(A)   Multiply each side by 4 and then add 5 to each side.

(B)   Add 5 to each side and then multiply each side by 4.

(C)   Multiply each side by 4 and then add 20 to each side.

(D)   Add 5 to each side and then divide each side by $\frac{1}{4}$.

21.   The formula for changing temperature from Celsius to Fahrenheit is $F = \frac{9}{5}C + 32$.

If the temperature of something is 140° F, what is the temperature in degrees Celsius?

OPEN-ENDED QUESTION

22.   Write a description of at least three different sequences of steps you could use to solve the equation $\frac{3}{4}x + 5 = 14$. Then show that the resulting value of x is the same for each of the sequences.

REVIEW

1.   18 is **NOT** a factor of 96 because
   (A)   96 is not a prime number.
   (B)   18 is not a prime number.
   (C)   6 is not a factor of 96.
   (D)   9 is not a factor of 96.

2.   A new bicycle regularly priced at $219 is on sale at 30% off that price. Find the sale price of that bicycle.

3.   The profits or losses of five branches of a store are indicated in the table below.

Store Branch	1	2	3	4	5
Net Profit / Loss	+$565	$+481	-$235	+875	+$345

What is the range of these data?

4.   The number of Central High School students who gave to the United Fund this year was 318. This figure is 135% of what it was the previous year. This means that
   (A)   35 more students gave to the Fund.
   (B)   The number of Central High student contributors decreased from last year to this year.
   (C)   The school raised more money this year than it did last year.
   (D)   The number of contributors increased from last year to this year.

8.4 Vertical Angles

OBJECTIVES   To identify vertical angles

To apply the Vertical Angles Property

DISCOVERY

In the figure at the right, name a pair of angles that are **not adjacent** and also **not straight**. Name a second pair.

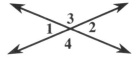

∠1 and ∠2 are vertical angles.

| **DEFINITION**   **Vertical Angles** |
| Each pair of **non-adjacent** angles / **non-straight** angles formed by two intersecting lines is called a pair of **vertical** angles. |

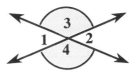

∠3 and ∠4 are vertical angles.

EXAMPLE 1   In which figure below are ∠5 and ∠6 vertical angles?

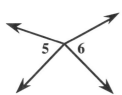

∠5 and ∠6 are **not** vertical angles since they are **not** formed by intersecting "straight" lines.

∠5 and ∠6 are vertical angles since they **are** formed by two intersecting lines.

DISCOVERY

In the figure at the right, recall that ∠AOB
is a straight angle.

m ∠1 = 180 - 40 = 140.

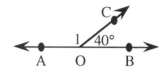

What kind of angles are ∠3 and ∠2?

They are vertical angles.

What do you think is true about m ∠2 and m ∠3?

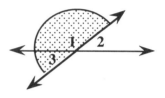

Suppose m ∠2 = 40.

Find m ∠1. (**What do you know about ∠3 and ∠1?**)

Then find m ∠3.

What do you conclude?

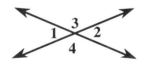

The DISCOVERY activity above suggests the following property.

THE VERTICAL ANGLES PROPERTY

Vertical Angles have equal measure.   m ∠1 = m ∠2

m ∠3 = m ∠4

You can verify this property intuitively by the following manipulative activity.

MANIPULATIVE ACTIVITY

Use tracing paper to trace ∠1 in the figure of the property above.

Turn the tracing over. Try to slide it so that it fits exactly over ∠2.

Therefore, m ∠1 = m ∠2.

Repeat this activity for ∠3. Use tracing to verify that m ∠3 = m ∠4.

NOTE: Throughout this text you may assume from a drawing that if the angles look like vertical angles, then they are indeed vertical angles.

EXAMPLE 2   Given: m ∠1 = x + 40

m ∠2 = 3x + 20

Find m ∠2.

Strategy   Assume from the drawing that the angles are vertical.

1.   Use vertical angles have equal measure to write an equation.

m ∠1	=	m ∠2	
1x + 40	=	3x + 20	**x = 1x**
40	=	2x + 20	**Subtract 1x from each side.**
20	=	2x	**Subtract 20 from each side.**
10	=	**x**	**Divide each side by 2.**

2.

m ∠2	=	3x + 20	**Find m ∠2.**
m ∠2	=	3 · **10** + 20	**Substitute 10 for x.**
m ∠2	=	30 + 20	

Solution   So, m ∠2 = 50

EXAMPLE 3   Find the measure of each numbered angle.

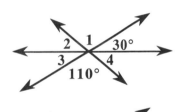

Strategy   Copy (or trace) the figure.

Look for vertical angles.

For example, shade the sides of the 30°

angle, and then extend the sides of the

30° angle to better see the angle vertical

to it. Now it is easier to see that

 m ∠3 = 30 by the Vertical Angles

Property.

(continued on next page)

Now repeat the process for the 110° angle.

Shading shows that ∠1 and the 110° angle

are vertical angles.

So, m ∠1 = 110.

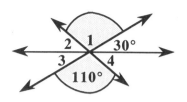

Find m ∠2 using m ∠1 = 110 and the 30° ∠.

The three angles together form a **straight** ∠.

So,   m ∠2 + 110 + 30 = 180

         m ∠2 +   140   = 180

         m ∠2   = 40

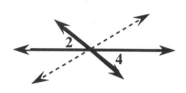

Finally, ∠2 and ∠4 are vertical angles.

So, **m ∠2 = m ∠4 = 40.**

We now have all the numbered angle

measures:

Solution   m ∠1 = 110, m ∠2 = 40, m ∠3 = 30, and

m ∠4 = 40.

SUMMARY

1.   How do you recognize vertical angles?

2.   If two lines intersect, what do you know about the vertical angles formed?

3.   Name two pairs of vertical angles.

4.   How do you find m ∠1?

5.   What do you know about ∠2 and the 132° ∠?

6.   How do you find m ∠2?

7.   How can you now find m ∠3?

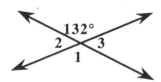

8.   m ∠1 = 3x - 10, m ∠2 = x + 30. How do you find m ∠2?

9.   How do you use the result of exercise 8 to find m ∠3?

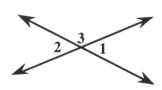

CLASSROOM PRACTICE

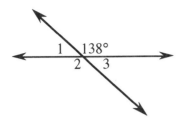

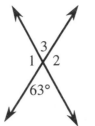

1.   m ∠1 = ?
2.   m ∠2 = ?
3.   m ∠3 = ?

4.   m ∠1 = ?
5.   m ∠2 = ?
6   m ∠3 = ?

7.   m ∠1 = ?
8.   m ∠2 = ?
9.   m ∠3 = ?
10.   m ∠4 = ?

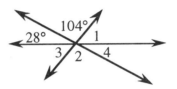

Given: m ∠1 = 3x + 20, m ∠2 = x + 30

11.   Find m ∠2.
12.   Find m ∠3.

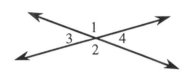

Given: m ∠3 = 4x + 10, m ∠4 = x + 40

13.   Find m ∠4.
14.   Find m ∠2.

WRITTEN EXERCISES

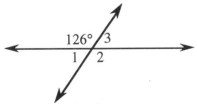

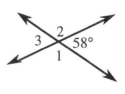

1.   m ∠1 = ?
2.   m ∠2 = ?
3.   m ∠3 = ?

4.   m ∠1 = ?
5.   m ∠2 = ?
6.   m ∠3 = ?

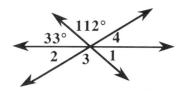

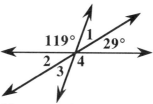

7.   m ∠1 = ?

8.   m ∠2 = ?

9.   m ∠3 = ?

10.   m ∠4 = ?

11.   m ∠2 = ?

12.   m ∠1 = ?

13.   m ∠3 = ?

14.   m ∠4 = ?

Find the indicated angle measure.

15.   m ∠4 = 2x - 20, m ∠3 = x + 1, m ∠3 = ?

16.   m ∠3 = 3y - 20, m ∠4 = y + 40, m ∠4 = ?

17.   m ∠2 = 5x - 10, m ∠1 = x + 30, m ∠2 = ?

18.   m ∠1 = 7x - 4, m ∠2 = 3x + 12, m ∠3 = ?

19.   m ∠4 = 6x + 12, m ∠2 = x + 32, m ∠1 = ?

20.   m ∠4 = 5x + 8, m ∠3 = 3x + 24, m ∠2 = ?

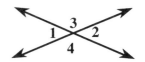

OPEN-ENDED QUESTION

21.   Write an explanation of the sequence of steps used
        to solve the following problem. Indicate the roles
        played by the meaning of perpendicular and the
        Vertical Angles Property.

        Given: $\overrightarrow{OC} \perp \overrightarrow{OA}$.

        m ∠2 = 5x, m ∠1 = 4x.

        Find m ∠3.

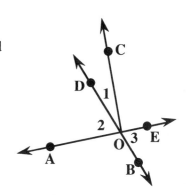

REVIEW

1.   Examine the pattern **psag2k3psag2k3psag2k3....**
       What symbol will be in the 104th position?

2.   Solve the inequality -4x + 8 ≤ 20.

3. The number 969 is a palindrome number.
    Find the very next larger palindrome number.

4. What are the restrictions on x if
    ∠P is obtuse?

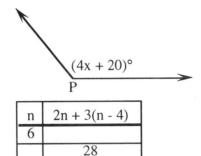

$(4x + 20)°$

P

5. Complete the table.

n	2n + 3(n - 4)
6	
	28

6. The hexagon in figure (a) is 6 cm
    on a side and is rolled to the right
    along a line. Which of the
    following distances could it have
    rolled so that the shaded circle is
    in the position shown in figure (b)?

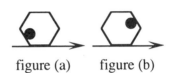

figure (a)   figure (b)

    (A)   24 cm   (B)   36 cm   (C)   48 cm   (D)   54 cm

7. Find the next term in the sequence 5, 16, 49, 148, ...

8. Find the measure of a complement of an angle with measure 53.

9. The basketball team scored 60 points in the last game. Their score increased by
    25% this week. Which of the following computations will give their score this
    week?
    (A) $0.25 \cdot 60$ (B) $60 + 0.25 \cdot 60$
    (C) $60 + 0.25$ (D) $60 - 0.25 \cdot 60$

10. As shown in the diagram, the
    picture is not centered on the wall
    from left to right. How far to the
    left should it be moved?

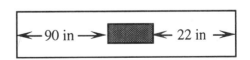

$\longleftarrow$ 90 in $\longrightarrow$ ▬ $\longleftarrow$ 22 in $\longrightarrow$

    (A)   22 in.   (B)   56 in.   (C)   34 in.   (D)   68 in.

8.5 Three Dimensional Visualization
Revolving a Plane Figure About an Axis

OBJECTIVES To draw a cone, cylinder, or sphere

To identify the three dimensional figure obtained by rotating or
revolving a two dimensional figure about one of its sides or about a line

In the last chapter you learned to predict the results of rolling a square or triangle or
hexagon etc, along a line.

Now you will extend this concept to the three-dimensional world, space.

For example, you will be able to predict what kind of three-dimensional figure is formed
by rotating a rectangle 360° about one of its sides.

First you will learn to draw some 3-D figures like those below.

SPHERE   CONE   CYLINDER

When drawing these, do not be concerned about the shading as shown above.

Draw a simple figure using dashed segments or arcs to represent segments or arcs that
would be invisible unless the figure were made of glass or clear plastic.

EXAMPLE 1   Draw a cone.

Strategy   Suppose a small cone like the one shown above were sitting on a table.

Imagine your stepping back 50 or 60 feet from the table with the cone.

Imagine moving even further away from the cone.

What would the cone begin to look like?

It might look like a triangle with two sides equal in length

(an **isosceles** triangle).

This suggests a way for drawing the cone. **(continued)**

1. From some point A draw two segments $\overline{AB}$ and $\overline{AC}$ of equal length as shown below.

2. Join B and C with an oval (arc), **not** circular, but almost straight.

3. Now draw a dashed oval as shown below to represent the part of the base of the cone that would be invisible.

Solution

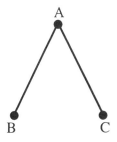 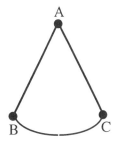 

EXAMPLE 2   Draw a cylinder.

Strategy   Suppose a small cylinder like the one shown at the right were sitting on a table.
Imagine your stepping back 50 or 60 feet from the table with the cylinder. Imagine moving even further away from the cylinder.
What would the cylinder begin to look like?
It might look like a **rectangle**.

1. Draw two vertical segments equal in length: $\overline{AB}$ and $\overline{CD}$.

2. Join A and C with an oval.

3. Join B and D with an oval dashed at the top and solid at the bottom.

Solution

EXAMPLE 3   Draw a **sphere (ball)**.

Strategy   Suppose a small **sphere** like the one shown at the
right were sitting on a table.
Imagine your stepping back 50 or 60 feet from the
table with the sphere. Imagine moving even
further away from the sphere.
What would the sphere begin to look like?
It might look like a **circle**.

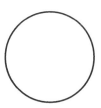

1. Draw a circle.

2. Draw half an oval
    in the middle as
    shown.

3. Draw a dashed
    oval as shown
    below.

EXAMPLE 4   The rectangle at the right is rotated 360° about the side $\overline{AB}$.
What three dimensional figure is formed?

Strategy   Think of the pages of a ring binder notebook.
Suppose the ring binder is closed and stood up.
Then the pages are fanned out like a revolving door in a
restaurant or hotel. What shape is formed?
The figures below show the pattern of fanning out pages of a
ring binder. The results of one page position at a time are
shown below as if in slow motion.

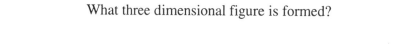

   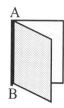   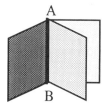   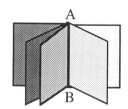   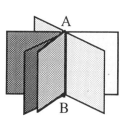

(continued on next page)

The last figure shows the result displayed as a **cylinder**.

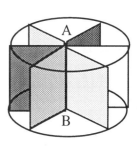

Solution

Thus, if the original rectangle is revolved about the side $\overline{AB}$, the three-dimensional figure formed is a **cylinder**.

EXAMPLE 5

The triangle at the right is rotated 360° about the side $\overline{AB}$.
What three-dimensional figure is formed?

Strategy

Think of the pages of a **triangular ring** binder notebook.
The strategy is the same as the that of the last example.
The ring binder is closed and then stood up. The pages are then fanned out like a revolving door in a hotel. What shape is formed?

The figures below show the pattern of fanning out pages of a ring binder. The results of one page position at a time are shown below as if in slow motion.

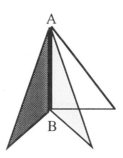
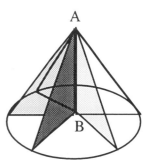

Solution

The last figure shows the result displayed as a **cone**.

EXAMPLE 6   The quarter circle is rotated 360° about the side

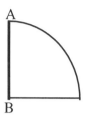

$\overline{\text{AB}}$. What three-dimensional figure is formed?

Strategy   The strategy is the same as that of the last two examples. Think of fanning out the pages of a quarter circle. The results of one page position at a time are shown as if in slow motion.

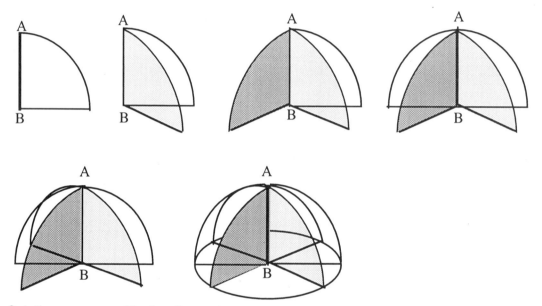

Solution   The last figure shows the result displayed as a **half ball** or **half sphere**. It is called a **hemisphere**.

You have seen that rotating a triangle or rectangle about a side can produce a cone or cylinder.

The three-dimensional figure may not always be **vertical**.

Notice the following pattern on the next page.

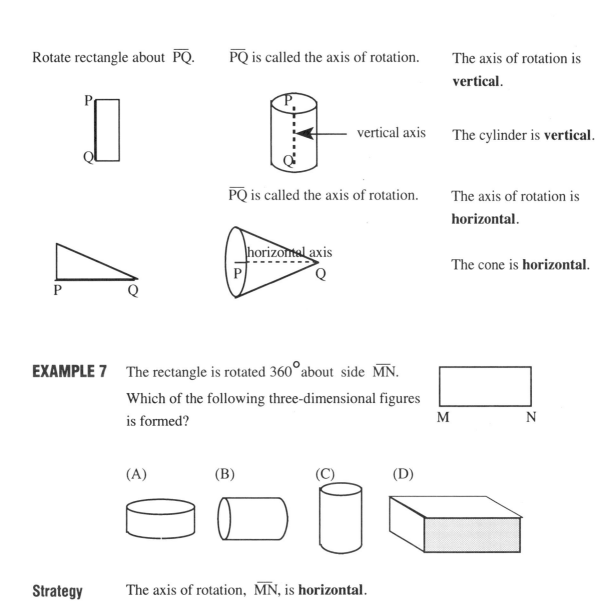

Rotate rectangle about $\overline{PQ}$. $\overline{PQ}$ is called the axis of rotation.   The axis of rotation is **vertical**.

vertical axis   The cylinder is **vertical**.

$\overline{PQ}$ is called the axis of rotation.   The axis of rotation is **horizontal**.

horizontal axis   The cone is **horizontal**.

EXAMPLE 7   The rectangle is rotated 360° about side $\overline{MN}$.

Which of the following three-dimensional figures is formed?

(A)   (B)   (C)   (D)

Strategy   The axis of rotation, $\overline{MN}$, is **horizontal**.

So, the resulting cylinder will be **horizontal**.

Solution   The correct figure is (B).

Sometimes the plane figure being rotated is a combination of two or more of the ones shown in this lesson. This is illustrated on the next page.

EXAMPLE 8   The figure at the right is rotated 360° about $\overline{ST}$.

Which of the following three-dimensional figures is formed?

(A)   (B)   (C)   (D)

      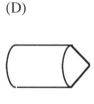   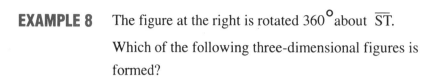

Strategy   Separate the two figures: triangle and rectangle. Rotation of each separately about its axis will produce a **vertical cone** on top of a **vertical cylinder**.

Solution   Therefore, the resulting figure is **(C)**, a **vertical cone** on top of a **vertical cylinder**.

SUMMARY

Tell how to draw each of the following three-dimensional figures.

1.   sphere   2. cylinder   3. cone

What three dimensional figure is formed by rotating the given plane figure 360° about the labeled side?

4.   5.   6.

7.   Tell how to determine what three-dimensional figure is formed by rotating the figure at the right 360° about $\overline{PQ}$.

CLASSROOM PRACTICE

Copy each given figure. Then complete the drawing to form the indicated three-dimensional shape.

1.   cylinder   2.   cone   3.   sphere

What three-dimensional figure is formed by rotating the given plane figure 360° about the labeled side?

4.

(A)   horizontal cone
(B)   horizontal cylinder
(C)   vertical cylinder
(D)   vertical cone

5.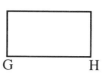

(A)   horizontal cone
(B)   horizontal cylinder
(C)   vertical cylinder
(D)   vertical cone

6.

(A)   sphere
(B) $\frac{1}{4}$ of a sphere
(C)   hemisphere
(D)   vertical cone

What three-dimensional figure is formed by rotating the given plane figure 360° about the labeled side?

7.

(A)   (B)   (C)   (D)

8.   (A)   (B)   (C)    (D)

9.   (A)   (B) 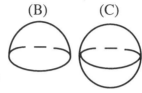   (C)   (D)

WRITTEN EXERCISES

Draw each of the following three-dimensional figures.

1.   sphere   2.   vertical cone   3.   vertical cylinder

4.   horizontal cone   5.   horizontal cylinder   6.   hemisphere

What three-dimensional figure is formed by rotating the given plane figure 360°
about the labeled side?

7.   8. 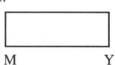   9.

(A)   horizontal cone   (A)   vertical cylinder   (A)   sphere

(B)   horizontal cylinder   (B)   sphere   (B)   quarter of sphere

(C)   vertical cylinder   (C)   horizontal cylinder   (C)   hemisphere

(D)   vertical cone   (D)   hemisphere   (D)   vertical cone

What three-dimensional figure is formed by rotating the given plane figure 360° about the labeled side?

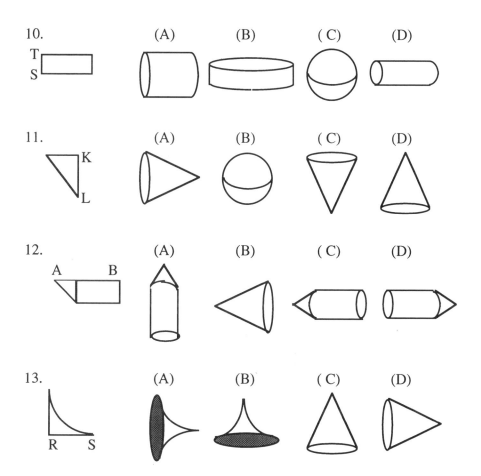

10.   (A)   (B)   (C)   (D)

11.   (A)   (B)   (C)   (D)

12.   (A)   (B)   (C)   (D)

13.   (A)   (B)   (C)   (D)

OPEN-ENDED QUESTION

14.   Describe the three-dimensional figure that is formed by rotating this plane figure 360° about the labeled side. Then draw the figure.

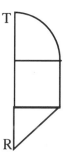

REVIEW   CHAPTERS 1-8

Find the measure of each angle.

1.   complement of an angle with measure 36

2.   supplement of an angle with measure 3x

$\overrightarrow{RA} \perp \overrightarrow{RE}$

3.   m ∠2 = 49, m ∠1 = ?

4.   m ∠1 = 3x, m ∠2 = 7x, m ∠1 = ?

Which pair of angles are supplementary? Tell why or why not.

5.   6.

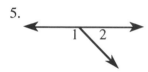   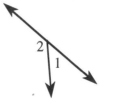

7.   m ∠2 = 129, m ∠1 = ?

8.   m ∠1 = 3x + 10, m ∠2 = 2x + 5.
      Find m ∠2.

9.   m ∠1 : m ∠2 = 3 : 7. Find m ∠2.

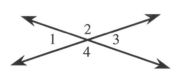

m ∠4 = 104

10.   Find m ∠1.

11.   Find m ∠2.

12.   m ∠1 = 4x - 10, m ∠2 3x + 20.
       Find m ∠1.

Find each angle measure.

13.   m ∠3 = ?

14.   m ∠2 = ?

15.   m ∠1 = ?

16.   m ∠4 = ?

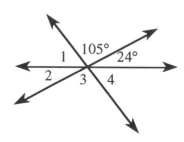

What three-dimensional figure is formed by rotating the given plane figure about the labeled side? (Exercises 17-20)

17.
P   Q

18.
R   S

19.
T
Y

20.
B
A

(A)   (B)   (C)   (D)

Solve each equation.

21. $4x - 3 = 2x + 8$

22. $\frac{3}{4}x + 8 = \frac{1}{2}x + 12$

23.   Which sequence of steps will **NOT** solve the equation $\frac{2}{3}x - 5 = 7$?

   (A)   Multiply each side by 3, add 5 to each side, then divide each side by 2.

   (B)   Add 5 to each side and then divide each side by $\frac{2}{3}$.

   (C)   Multiply each side by 3, add 15 to each side, then divide each side by 2.

   (D)   Add 5 to each side, multiply each side by 3, then divide each side by 2.

24.   Assume that the pattern below continues. How many squares will be in Row 8?

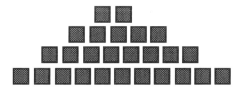

25.   At the right are three views of a die. The letters A, B, C, D, and E appear exactly once on the faces of this die. What letter is opposite B?

1st view   2nd view   3rd view

26. If the window is to be centered on the wall, it should be how many feet from the left vertical edge of the wall?

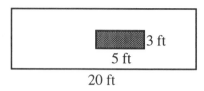

At the right is a graph of the results of a survey of the foreign language choices of 400 students.

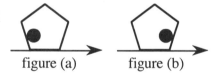

27. The number of students choosing Latin is what percent of the number of students choosing French?

28. The number of students taking no foreign language is what percent of the total number of students?

29. Find m ∠DOA.

30. Complete the table.

n	$3n + 2(n - 6)$
8	
	38

31. The pentagon (a) is 8 cm on a side. It is rolled to the right along a line. Which of the following distances could it have rolled so that the black circle would be in position (b)?

(A) 24 cm   (B) 40 cm   (C) 64 cm   (D) 72 cm

32. Amanda earns $6.50 an hour for the times worked Monday through Friday and $7.50 an hour on weekends. Use the time-card below to find her week's earnings.

Name: Amanda Jones   Date: 11/30/93
DAY: Mon. Tues. Wed. Ths. Fri. Sat. Sun.

HRS: $4\frac{1}{2}$ $3\frac{1}{2}$ 6 $7\frac{1}{2}$ 0   4 $3\frac{1}{2}$

(A) $147.25   (B) $188.50   (C) $196.   (D) $244.75

33.   Last year there were 30 students out for football. The number of students out for football this year is 10% more than the number last year. How many students are out for football this year?

34.   Janet's average for the first four math tests is 70. What grade must she get on the fifth test to have an average of 76 on the five tests?

35.   A basketball team lost 20% of the games played this season. The team won 16 games. How many games were lost?

36.   Last week José earned $400. To estimate the amount of his paycheck, he first adds and then rounds to the nearest whole number percent the following deductions:

    Federal Tax   23%
    State Income Tax   7.5%
    FICA   6.5%
    Unemployment Insurance   0.42%

His estimate of his paycheck is ____:

(A) $148   (B) $152   (C) $248   (D) $260

37. $0.399 \cdot 0.0212$ is approximately

(A)   0.08   (B)   0.008   (C)   0.0008   (D)   0.00008

38.   Stan's grandfather gave him $2 on his tenth birthday, $4 on his eleventh birthday, and $8 on his twelfth birthday. His grandfather says that the pattern determines that he will give his grandson $14 on his 13th birthday. Stan says that the pattern determines that his grandfather will give Stan $16 on his 13th birthday. Stan's sister says that either amount could be correct, since each follows a pattern that begins with " 2, 4, 8." Who is correct?

(A)   Stan only   (B)   Stan's grandfather only

(C)   Stan's sister   (D)   nobody

39.   A medium-size school bus can transport no more than 28 students as passengers. If each bus makes no more than one trip, what is the smallest number of buses that can transport 377 students from one place to another?

40.   Bart spent an evening playing video games and drinking sodas. Each video game costs 25 cents to play, and sodas cost 60 cents each. Bart had $8.00 to spend on video games and sodas. If he had only 3 sodas and played as many video games as possible, how many video games did he play?

(A)   9   (B)   24   (C)   17   (D)   29

41.   An electrician charges $40 for each hour worked plus an additional $35 service
       charge. If C represents the electrician's total charges in dollars and h represents
       the number of hours worked, which formula below could be used to calculate C?
       (A)   C = 40 + 35 + h   (B)   C = 40 + 35h
       (C)   C = 40 · 35 + h   (D)   C = 40h + 35

Identify each type of angle.

42.   43.   44.

          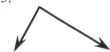   

45.   Which inequality below would be most useful in solving this problem?
           Jon earned $55 over two weeks at a part-time job. He bought 2 shirts at $12.95
           each. He would like to buy as many rolls of film as possible at $6.00 each.
           How many rolls could he buy?
       (A)   6x + 12.95 ≤ 55   (B)   6x + 25.90 ≤ 55
       (C)   12.95x + 6 ≤ 55   (D)   12.95x + 12 ≤ 55

46.   What are the restrictions on x if
       ∠A is acute?

$(4x - 30)°$

A

47.   Insert the appropriate inequality symbol: 1.8^6 ? 5.02^2.

48. $AB = \frac{2}{3}$ of BC, AC = 25.
       Find BC.

A   B   C

49.   A bag contains 5 red balls, 3 green ones, and 4 orange balls. One is drawn from
       the bag at random. What is the probability that it will be orange?

Rectangle ABCD has coordinates A(2, 3), B(8, 3), C(8, 6), and D(2, 6).

50.   Find the perimeter of ABCD.   51.   Find the area of ABCD.

52.   A room measures 12 ft by 21 ft. Find the cost of carpeting the room if carpet costs
       $35 a square yard.

53.   An 80-cent bag of candy weighed $2\frac{1}{2}$ ounces. At this rate, find the cost of a one
        pound bag of the candy.

54.   The length of a rectangle is 8 cm more than the width. The perimeter is 40 cm.
        Find the length.

The bar graph below shows Malmud's math quiz scores for the first five weeks of school.
Use it to answer exercises 55-59.

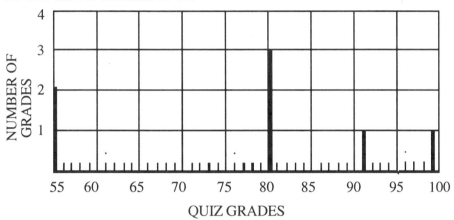

Find each of the following.

55.   mean   56.   median   57.   mode   58. range

59.   Which is the better measure of central tendency, the mean or the median?
        Explain why.

60.   Mr. Burke traveled 30 miles in 40 minutes. Find his average speed in miles per
        hour.

61.   14 is not a factor of 49 because
        (A)   49 is not an even number.   (B)   7 is not a factor of 49.
        (C)   2 is not a factor of 49.   (D)   14 must be a factor of 49 and is not.

62.   Cassette tapes are stored in boxes of 6 or 12. A weekly inventory indicates that
        the total number of cassettes in stock is supposed to be 104. Why is this not
        possible?

63.   Suppose that m and n represent whole numbers.
        Then for the equation 5m + 14n = 21, what must be true about the value of m?
        (A)   m must be divisible by 7.   (B)   m must be divisible by 5.
        (C)   m must be a multiple of 24.   (D)   m must be odd since 21 is odd.

64.   Sally is running a game booth at the school fair. She carefully collects exactly 30 cents from every player. At the end of the fair, she must count the money collected. She counted it four times, getting a different total each time. Which of the following could be the correct total?

(A) $22.45   (B) $22.50   (C) $22.60   (D) $22.65

65.   Which point on the number line could represent the product of the numbers represented by X and W?

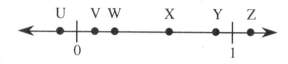

66.   Which of these is one way to find $\frac{3}{4}$ of a number?

(A)   Multiply the number by $\frac{4}{3}$.

(B)   Divide the number by 4 and divide the result by 3.

(C)   Divide the number by 4 and multiply the result by 3.

(D)   Divide the number by 3 and multiply the result by 4.

67.   The scale on a map is $\frac{1}{2}$ inch = 30 miles. How far apart are two cities that are shown as being 4 inches apart on that map?

OPEN-ENDED QUESTION

68.   The figure at the right shows two rectangles and two squares.
Trace them with tracing paper.
Then cut out the four figures,
Form a square region putting all four shapes together so that they lie flat.
Except for vertices and edges (sides), no part of any shape may cover any part of another shape. Sketch a picture of the region you have formed. Include in your sketch the outlines of the pieces you fitted together to form the region.
Find the perimeter and the area of the square region that the four pieces form.

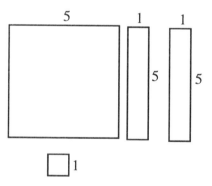

Chapter

▶ 9

Geometric Transformations

9.1 Lengths of Segments Parallel to an Axis

OBJECTIVES   To determine whether a segment is parallel to an axis, given the
coordinates of the endpoints of the segment

To find the length of a segment parallel to an axis, given the coordinates
of the endpoints of the segment

You have learned to find the
length of a segment on a number
line.

For example,

$$AH = |2 - (-4)| = |2 + 4|$$
$$= |6| = 6.$$

Suppose you are given the
coordinates of two points on a
plane: A(3, 5) and H(7. 5).
You can find AB by graphing

the two points, drawing $\overline{AH}$,
and then counting the blocks
between A and H. You will now
learn how to predict AH
without drawing the segment.

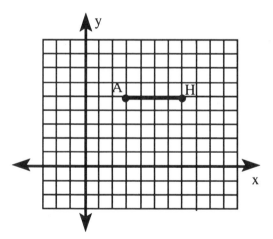

In the figure above, $\overline{AH}$ is said to be **parallel** to the x-axis.
The segment and the x-axis do **not** meet in the plane, no matter how far they are
extended.

In the next chapter, you will formally study the properties of **parallel** lines and segments.
However, an introduction to the nature of parallels is now necessary to develop the ideas
of this chapter.

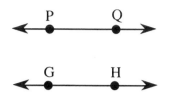

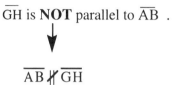

The two lines above are **parallel**.

$\overleftrightarrow{PQ}$ is **parallel to** $\overleftrightarrow{GH}$

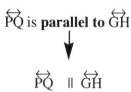

$\overleftrightarrow{PQ}$ ‖ $\overleftrightarrow{GH}$

The top and bottom edges of a door are parallel.

$\overline{AB}$ ‖ $\overline{CD}$

These two segments are **NOT** parallel.

$\overline{GH}$ is **NOT** parallel to $\overline{AB}$.

$\overline{AB}$ ∦ $\overline{GH}$

EXAMPLE 1   Given: A(2, 6), B(7, 6). To which axis is $\overline{AB}$ parallel?

Strategy   First graph the two points A and B.

Then draw the segment $\overline{AB}$.

Solution $\overline{AB}$ is parallel to the x-axis.

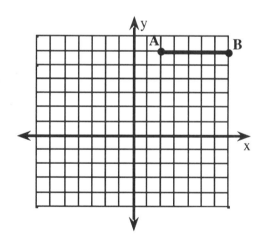

You can now find the length of the segment $\overline{AB}$ in a way very similar to finding the length of a segment on a number line, as shown at the top of page 410.

EXAMPLE 2   Find AB in the graph of $\overline{AB}$ in Example 1 on the previous page.

Strategy $\overline{AB}$ ∥ the x-axis, a number line!

So, first think of sliding $\overline{AB}$ straight down, as shown by the dashed segments, on to the x-axis.

$\overline{PQ}$ will have the same length as $\overline{AB}$.

PQ is a length on a number line.

$PQ = |\,7 - 2\,| = |\,5\,| = 5.$

Solution   So, AB = 5.

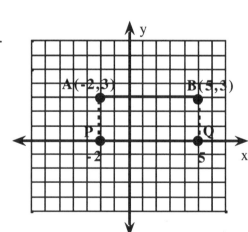

EXAMPLE 3   Given: A(-2, 3), B(5, 3)

To which axis is $\overline{AB}$ parallel? Find AB.

Strategy   First graph A and B, Draw $\overline{AB}$.

$\overline{AB}$ ∥ the x-axis.

Think of sliding $\overline{AB}$ straight down onto the x-axis.
AB = PQ, a distance on a number line.
$PQ = |\,5 - (-2)\,| = |\,5 + 2\,| = |\,7\,| = 7$

Solution   So, AB = 7

The last two examples suggest two patterns. Given the coordinates of a segment $\overline{AB}$, how can you determine without graphing: if $\overline{AB}$ ∥ the x-axis? ∥ the length AB?

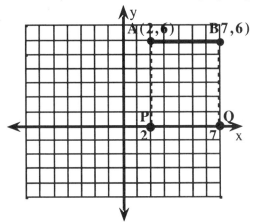

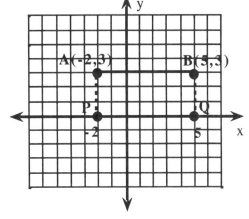

For A(2, **6**) and B(7, **6**) the **y**-coordinates are the same, each **6**. $\overline{AB}$ ∥ the **x-axis**.

AB = ┃ 7 - 2 ┃.

AB = absolute value of the **difference** of the **x-coordinates**.

For A(-2, **3**) and B(5, **3**) the **y**-coordinates are the same, each **3**. $\overline{AB}$ ∥ the **x-axis**.

AB = ┃ 5 - (-2) ┃.

AB = absolute value of the **difference** of the **x-coordinates**.

DISCOVERY   Predict for A(7, 5) and (7, -4):

(1)   the axis to which $\overline{AB}$ will be parallel.   (2)   the length AB.

EXAMPLE 4   Given: A(3, 4) and B(3, -2). To which axis is $\overline{AB}$ parallel? Find AB.

Strategy   Graph A and B. Draw $\overline{AB}$.

$\overline{AB}$ ∥ the **y**-axis.

Slide $\overline{AB}$ over to the y-axis.

AB = PQ, a distance on a number line.

AB = ┃ 4 - (-2) ┃ = ┃ 4 + 2 ┃

Solution   AB = 6.

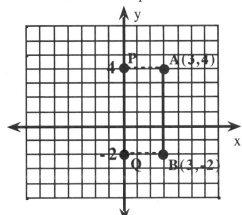

You should be able to now see a pattern for segments parallel to the y-axis.
It is similar to the pattern for segments parallel to the x-axis.
The next example illustrates both patterns.

EXAMPLE 5   For the given coordinates of A and B:

To which axis will $\overline{AB}$ be parallel?   Find AB.

A(-3, 4),   B(7, 4)   A(-2, -5), B(-2, 6)

Strategy   A(-3, 4), B(7, 4)   A(**-2**,-5), B(**-2**,6)

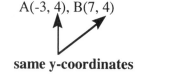

same y-coordinates   **same x-coordinates**

So, $\overline{AB}$ ‖ **x-axis**.   So, $\overline{AB}$ ‖ **y-axis**.

A(**-3**, 4),   B(**7**, 4)   A(-2, **-5**),   B(-2 ,**6**)

AB = | **7 - (-3)** | AB = | **6 - (-5)** |

Solution   AB = | 7 + 3 | = | 10 | = 10   AB = | 6 + 5 | = | 11 | = 11

You have now seen that:

1. $\overline{AB}$ ‖ the **x**-axis if the **y-coordinates are the same.**

2. $\overline{AB}$ ‖ the **y**-axis if the **x-coordinates are the same.**

3.   If $\overline{AB}$ ‖ to an axis, AB = the
     | difference of coordinates that are **not** the same |.

SUMMARY

1.   Tell how you can use the coordinates of the endpoints of a segment to predict
      if the segment is parallel to the x-axis.

2.   Tell how you can use the coordinates of the endpoints of a segment to predict
      if the segment is parallel to the y-axis.

3.   How do you find AB for A(3, 7) and B(8, 7)?

4.   How do you find AB for A(3, -2) and B(3, 8)?

CLASSROOM PRACTICE

For each of the following: To which axis is $\overline{AB}$ parallel? Also, find AB.

  1.   A(2, 5), B(8, 5)   2.   A(3, -1), B(12, -1)   3.   A(4, 6), B(4, 11)
  4.   A(-4, 2), B(-4, -15)   5.   A(6, 1), B(13, 1)   6.   A(-3, 2), B(6, 2)
  7.   A(3, 5), B(3, 14)   8.   A(4, -5), B(4, 8)   9.   A(-7, 1), B(-7, -8)
 10.   A(-2, -6), B(-5, -6)   11.   A(-9, -3), B(-9, 5)   12.   A(-6, -5), B(-3, -5)

WRITTEN EXERCISES

For each of the following: To which axis is $\overline{AB}$ parallel? Also, find AB.

  1.   A(4, 3), B(9, 3)   2.   A(6, 5), B(10, 5)   3.   A(3, 1), B(3, 12)
  4.   A(2, 7), B(2, 11)   5.   A(3, 2), B(13, 2)   6.   A(4, 7), B(4, 9)
  7.   A(1, 4), B(17, 4)   8.   A(8, 6), B(8, 19)   9.   A(11, 3), B(6, 3)
 10.   A(-5, 7), B(9, 7)   11.   A(-4, 3), B(6, 3)   12.   A(-5, 2), B(6, 2)
 13.   A(4, -3), B(4, 8)   14.   A(6, -5), B(6, 4)   15.   A(-8, -3), B(-8, 4)
 16.   A(-1, -4), B(5, -4)   17.   A(-2, -7), B(-2, 8)   18.   A(-4, -5), B(7, -5)
 19. $A(3\frac{1}{2}, 7)$, B(5, 7)   20. $A(2\frac{4}{5}, 3)$, B(6, 3)   21. $A(-5, 3\frac{1}{4})$, $B(-5, 8\frac{1}{2})$

Determine if AB = MN.

 22.   A(3, 4), B(7, 4)   M(5, 2), N(5, 6)
 23.   A(-2, 3), B(7, 3)   M(4, -5), N(4, 4)
 24.   A(6, -8), B(6, 7)   M(3, -6), N(3, 11)

OPEN-ENDED QUESTION

 25.   Given: A(2, 3), B(2, 7). Find the coordinates of C(? , ?) such that $\overline{AC}$ ‖ the
        x-axis and AB = AC. Is there more than one answer? Explain why or why not.

REVIEW

1.   Which of these figures cannot be folded to make a box?

(A)   (B)   (C)   (D)

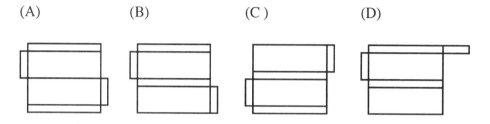

2.   What symbols are mising from the pattern below at the positions x and y?

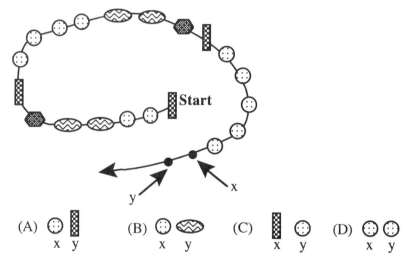

(A) x y   (B) x y   (C) x y   (D) x y

3.   The formula for changing temperature from Celsius to Fahrenheit is
      $F = \frac{9}{5} C + 32$. If the temperature of something is $40^\circ C$, find the temperature in
      degrees Fahrenheit.

OPEN-ENDED QUESTION

4.   A mosquito is flying around an empty room that measures 24 feet long by 18 feet
      wide by 9 feet high. At a particular moment, what is the probability that the
      mosquito will be no more than 4 feet from the shorter wall of the room?
      Write the answer as well as an explanation of how you got your answer.

9.2 Symmetry: Applying Reflections

OBJECTIVES   To determine if two geometric figures are symmetric with respect to the x-axis or y-axis

To find the coordinates of the mirror image of a point with respect to an axis

To find the coordinates of the endpoints of a segment with respect to an axis

To draw the flip of a geometric figure about a line

The first figure below is that of a tree leaf. The two halves are said to be **symmetric**

with respect to $\overline{AB}$, the central segment, called the **axis of symmetry**.

Leaf	Two halves pulled apart	Flip left half over horizontally.	If the flipped half is slid to the right, it will cover exactly the right half.

 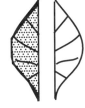 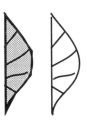 

figure (a)   figure (b)   figure (c)   figure (d)

You can see the results of the actual flip yourself by using tracing paper.

Trace on tracing paper the left half in figure (b).

Turn the tracing over.

It will look like the left half of figure (c).

Now slide the tracing to perfectly cover the second half of figure (c).

Figure (d) shows that the two halves are exactly the same **size** and **shape**.

The figures are said to be **congruent.**

We shall learn more about congruent figures later in this lesson.

A good test for **symmetry** with respect to a line or
segment is shown below.

$\overline{AB}$ is called the **axis of symmetry**.

$\overline{PQ} \perp$ the axis of symmetry.

$\overline{PQ}$ is **bisected** by the **axis of symmetry**.

P and Q are said to be **mirror images** of each other.

Similarly, $\overline{RS}$ is **bisected** by the axis of symmetry.

R and S are **mirror images** of each other.

Any segment joining the two halves and perpendicular
to the axis of symmetry is **bisected** by the axis of
symmetry. This is necessary for symmetry to exist.

EXAMPLE 1   Find the coordinates of the mirror image of the point A(-5,3) with
                 respect to the y-axis.

Strategy

First, graph the point A(-5, 3).
From A, draw a perpendicular to the y-
axis meeting it at M.

Solution

Extend $\overline{AM}$ to the right to a point C

so that AM = MC (M bisects $\overline{AC}$).
Read the coordinates of point C: C(5, 3).

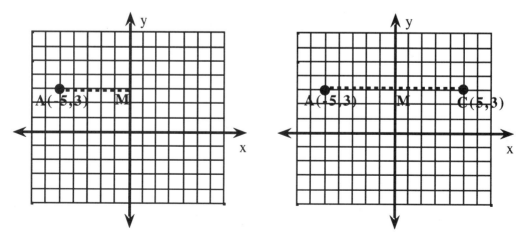

Thus, the **mirror image** of A(-5, 3) with respect to the y-axis is **C(5, 3)**

An easy way to verify that C is the mirror image of A is as follows:

1. First trace on tracing paper only the y-axis, points A and C, and the dashed segment $\overline{AC}$.

2. Fold the tracing paper in half along the y-axis.

3. The two points A and C **coincide**.

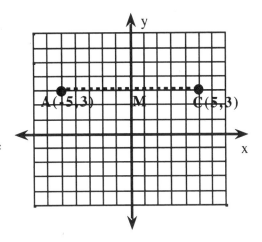

EXAMPLE 2   Find the coordinates of the mirror image of the point A(-2,-4) with respect to the y-axis.

Strategy

First, graph the point P(-2,-4).

From P, draw a perpendicular to the x-axis, meeting it at M.

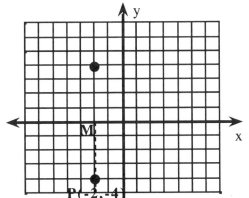

Solution

Extend $\overline{PM}$ up to a point Q so that

PM = MQ (M bisects $\overline{PQ}$).

Read the coordinates of point Q: (-2,4)

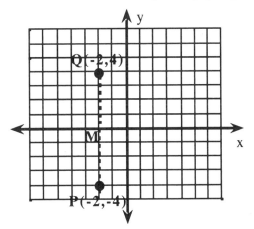

Thus, the mirror image of the point P(-2, 4) with respect to the x-axis is **Q(-2, 4)**.

You can draw the **mirror image** of a **segment,** with respect to an axis, by:

1. first finding the **mirror image** of the **endpoints** of the segment,

2. then connecting the **mirror images** with a segment.

EXAMPLE 3   Given: A(-5, 2), B(-3, 4).

Draw $\overline{PQ}$, the mirror image of $\overline{AB}$ with respect to the y-axis.

Find the coordinates of the endpoints of $\overline{PQ}$.

Strategy

1.   Graph A(-5, 2) and B(-3, 4),   **2.** Draw perpendiculars from A to M

Draw $\overline{AB}$.   and from B to N on the y-axis.

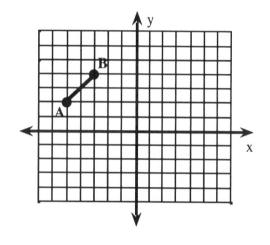
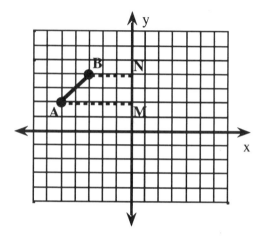

3.   Extend dashed segments to
the right so that AM = MP
and BN = NQ.

Draw $\overline{PQ}$.

Solution   The **mirror image** of $\overline{AB}$

is $\overline{PQ}$: P(5, 2), Q(3, 4).

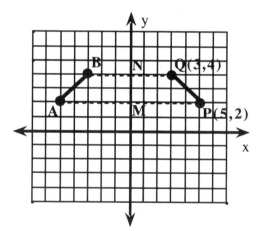

Segments $\overline{AB}$ and $\overline{PQ}$ are **congruent**.

This can be verified by **tracing** $\overline{AB}, \overline{PQ}$, and the y-axis on tracing paper.
Then fold the tracing paper along the y-axis, the **axis of symmetry**.

You will see that $\overline{AB}$ and $\overline{PQ}$ **coincide**.

Think of $\overline{AB}$ as **flipped** about the **axis of symmetry** onto $\overline{PQ}$.

Let's now take a close look at the idea of **congruency**.
Both figures at the right have the same
perimeter: 5 + 5 + 5 + 5 = 20.
But the **shapes** are different!

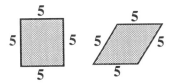

These two figures have the **same shape**.
But the figures do **not** have the same size.
Figure (b) is smaller than figure (a).

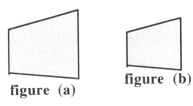

These two figures have the **same size** and **shape.**
If you trace figure (c) on tracing paper, you can then
slide the tracing to exactly cover the figure (d).
The triangles are **congruent**.
The mathematical symbol for **is congruent to** is ≅.

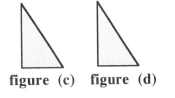

DEFINITION   **Congruent Figures**

If two geometric figures have the **same size and
shape**, then the figures are said to be **congruent.**
Figure (c) **is congruent to** figure (d).

figure (c)   ≅   figure (d)

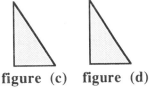

EXAMPLE 4   Graph the flip of the
geometric figure ABCDEF
about the y-axis. Give the
coordinates of the mirror
images of the **vertices** A, B,
C, D, E, and F.
Is the mirror image ≅
figure ABCDEF?
(continued on next page)

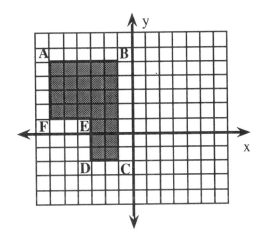

Strategy

Draw mirror images of A, B, C, D, E, and F.   Join mirror images in order:

P to Q to T to S to T to U.

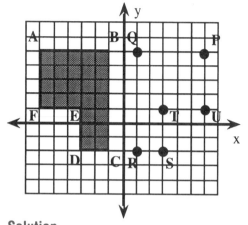

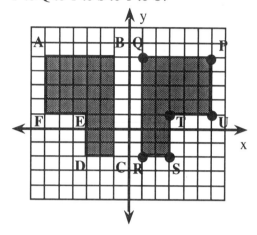

Solution

The **mirror image**

of A(-6, 5)	is	P(6, 5)
of B(-1, 5)	is	Q(1, 5)
of C(-1, -2)	is	R(1, -2)
of D(-3, -2)	is	S(3, -2)
of E(-3, 1)	is	T(3, 1)
of F(-6, 1)	is	U(6, 1)

The **mirror image** of

Trace the left figure ABCDEF on tracing paper. Flip the trace over.

Slide the trace to exactly cover the right figure PQRSTU.

The two figures coincide. Thus ABCDEF ≅ PQRSTU.

Note below how you can pick out **corresponding** sides, or sides that are **mirror images** of each other.

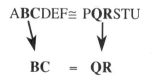

The axis of symmetry is not always vertical or horizontal.

It is also possible to draw the flip of a figure without the aid of coordinates.

Given a figure and an axis of symmetry, you can draw the **flip** of a figure with respect to the **axis of symmetry** as shown below in Example 5.

EXAMPLE 5   Draw the flip of the figure with respect to the

axis $\overline{AB}$.

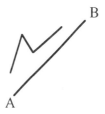

Strategy   Trace the drawing on a sheet of tracing paper. Holding the tracing in place, fold the traced

drawing over on the axis of symmetry, $\overline{AB}$. You will be able to see the flip through the paper. Trace it again in this position to see it better.

Solution   Now you can see both the original as well as the **FLIP** as shown at the right.

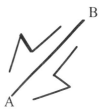

The **flip** of a figure with respect to an axis is also called a **reflection** of a figure In an axis. When you look in a mirror you are seeing a **reflection** or **mirror image** of yourself.

The resulting figure of Examples 4 and 5 can be referred to in three ways;
1. the **flip** of a figure about an axis
2. the **mirror image** of a figure with respect to an axis
3. the **reflection** of a figure in a line or axis

SUMMARY

1.   What does it mean for two geometric figures to be symmetric with respect to a line?

2.   How do you find the mirror image of the point P(-5, 4) with respect to the y-axis?

3.   How do you find the mirror image of the point P(-6, -3) with respect to the x-axis?

4.   Given: A(-4, 2) and B(-5, -7). How do you find the flip of $\overline{AB}$ about the y-axis?

5.   Explain how to find the reflection of a geometric figure in a non-vertical line.

6.   How can you verify that the flip of a geometric figure about an axis is congruent to the original figure?

7.   What is the meaning of the symbol $\cong$?

8.   Give two other names for the flip of a geometric figure about an axis.

CLASSROOM PRACTICE

Find the coordinates of the mirror image of point B with respect to the y-axis.

1.   B(6, 3)   2. B(-9, -2)   3. B(-1, 6)   4. B(8, -3)

Find the coordinates of the mirror image of point A with respect to the x-axis.

5.   A(5, 4)   6. A(-8, -1)   7. A(6, -7)   8. A(7, -6)

For the given coordinates of the points A and B, draw the reflection of $\overline{AB}$ in the y-axis.
Label the mirror image as $\overline{PQ}$. Then give the coordinates of the endpoints of the mirror image.

9.   A(2, -3), B(7, -5)   10.   A(8, 6), B(3, 5)   11. A(-9, -6), B(-4, -3)
12.   A(1, 9), B(7, 3)   13.   A(-6, 10), B(-3, 4)   14. A(3, -7), B(6, -5)

For the given coordinates of the points A and B, draw the reflection of $\overline{AB}$ in the x-axis.
Label the mirror image as $\overline{PQ}$. Then give the coordinates of the endpoints of the mirror image.

15.   A(-5, -3), B(7, -8)   16.   A(-4, 9), B(2, 3)   17.   A(0, 8), B(9, 3)

18.   Draw the reflection of the figure below in $\overleftrightarrow{AB}$.

19.   Graph the flip of ABCD about the
        y-axis. Name the coordinates of
        the mirror images of A, B, C, D:
        P, Q, R, S.
        Show that ABCD ≅ PQRS.

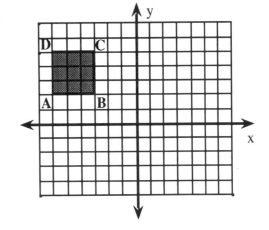

For the results of Exercise 19, name the
mirror image of each.

20. $\overline{AB}$ 21. $\overline{BD}$

22.   Graph the flip of ABCDEF
        about the x-axis. Name the
        coordinates of the mirror images
        of A, B, C, D, E, F:
        P, Q, R, S, T, U.
        Show that ABCDEF ≅ PQRSTU.

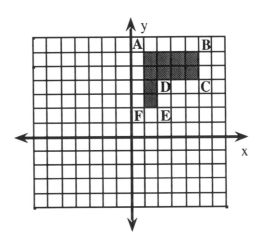

For the results of Exercise 22, name the
mirror image of each.

23. $\overline{BD}$ 24. $\overline{AE}$

WRITTEN EXERCISES

Find the coordinates of the mirror image of point M with respect to the y-axis.

1.   M(-7, 1)   2. M(9, -4)   3. M(-3, -8)   4. M(7, 6)

Find the coordinates of the mirror image of point T with respect to the x-axis.

5.   T(-8, 4))   6. T(-6, -6)   7. T(9, 5)   8. T(10, -2)

For the given coordinates of the points A and B, draw the reflection of $\overline{AB}$ in the y-axis.

Label the mirror image as $\overline{PQ}$. Give the coordinates of the endpoints of the mirror image.

  9.   A(-8, 3), B(-1, 6)   10.   A(-6, -7), B(-2, 5)   11.   A(-5, 7), B(-1, -9)

12.   A(4, 5), B(0, -3)   13.   A(6, 8), B(3, -10)   14.   A(7, 2), B(3, -6)

For the given coordinates of the points C and D, draw the flip of $\overline{CD}$ about the x-axis.

Label the mirror image as $\overline{ST}$. Then give the coordinates of the endpoints of $\overline{ST}$.

15.   C(-12, -2), D(-3, -8)   16.   C(-7, 1), D(-2, 9)   17.   C(2, -1), D(7, -6)

18.   Draw the reflection of this figure in the axis shown.

19.   Graph the flip of ABC about the x-axis. Name the coordinates of the mirror images of A, B, C: P, Q, R.
Show that ABC ≅ PQR.

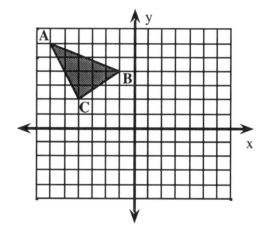

For the results of Exercise 19, name the mirror image of each.

20. $\overline{AC}$ 21. $\overline{BC}$

22.   Graph the flip of ABCDEF about the y-axis. Name the coordinates of the mirror images of A, B, C, D, E, F: P, Q, R, S, T, U.

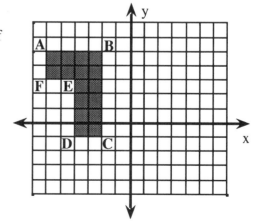

For the results of Exercise 22, name the mirror image of each.

23. $\overline{BE}$ 24. $\overline{CF}$

OPEN-ENDED QUESTION

25.   Suppose you were asked to graph

$\overline{AB}$ with endpoint coordinates
A(-4, 5) and B(-2, 2). Write how to
get the remaining three segments of
the figure at the right by using a
series of flips. Is there more than
one way?

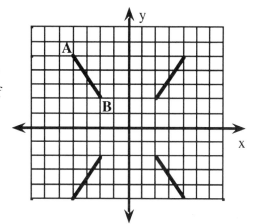

REVIEW

1.   Which of the following is **not** equal to the others?

       (A)   25% of 80   (B) $\frac{1}{5}$ of 100   (C)   100 ÷ 0.5   (D)   10 ÷ 0.5

2.   Which sequence of steps will **NOT** solve the equation $\frac{1}{3}$ x + 6 = 12?

       (A)   Subtract 6 from each side. Then multiply each side by 3.

       (B)   Multiply each side by 3. Then subtract 6 from each side.

       (C)   Divide each side by $\frac{1}{3}$. Then subtract 18 from each side.

       (D)   Subtract 6 from each side. Then divide each side by $\frac{1}{3}$.

3.   On a 5-hour trip, Meg traveled at an average speed of 20 mph for the first hour
       and at an average speed of 50 mph for the next 4 hours. Find her average
       speed for the 5 hours.

4.   A typical walking rate is 1 mile in 20 minutes. If a jogger can jog about 3 times
       that speed, how far would that jogger be able to jog in 2 hours?

       (A)   2 to 3 miles   (B)   5 to 6 miles

       (C)   15 to 20 miles   (C)   30 to 35 miles

For each of the following, to which axis is $\overline{AB}$ parallel? Also find AB .

    5.   A(3, 8), B(10, 8)   6. A(-1, 7), B(-1, -4)

9.3 Slides, Reflections, and Congruent Triangles

OBJECTIVES   To identify corresponding parts of congruent triangles

To find missing measures of congruent triangles

We have been referring informally to triangles.
Triangle ABC (Δ ABC) is formed by three segments joining
three points, A, B, and C. Notice that the three points do not all
lie on the same line.

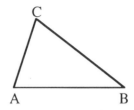

Each of these points is a **vertex** (plural: **vertices**) of the triangle.
The segments are the **sides** of the triangle.

Recall from the previous lesson that the **flip** of a geometric figure about an axis results in
a geometric figure **congruent** to the original figure.

EXAMPLE 1   Graph the points A(-7, 3), D(-3, 3), B(-1, 11). Draw Δ ADB.

Graph the **flip** of Δ ADB about the y-axis.

Give the coordinates of the **mirror images** of A, D, and B: M, R, and T.

Strategy   First graph the three points:
A, D, and B. Draw Δ ADB.
Graph the **mirror images** in
the y-axis: M, R, T.

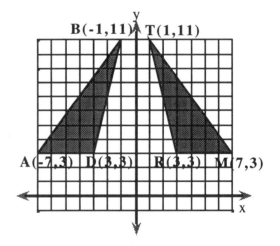

original vertices	mirror images
A(-7, 3)	M(7, 3)
D(-3, 3)	R(3, 3)
B(-1, 11)	T(1, 11)

Solution

Trace Δ ADB on tracing paper.
Flip it over. Slide it onto Δ MRT. The two triangles coincide.   **Δ ADB ≅ Δ MRT.**

Notice that the corresponding sides of the two triangles from Example 1 appear to have the same length. Also, it appears that corresponding angles have the same measure.

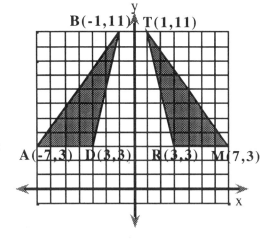

sides = in length   angles = in measure

AD = MR   m ∠B = m ∠T

AB = MT   m ∠D = m ∠R

DB = RT   m ∠A = m ∠M

You will be asked to verify this in the next example.

EXAMPLE 2   Copy the graph above on graph paper. Use a ruler to verify the equality of the side lengths above. Estimate the side lengths to the nearest $\frac{1}{4}$ inch.

Use a protractor to verify the equality of the angle measures above. Estimate the angle measures to the nearest whole number.

Solution

sides = in length	angles = in measure
AD = MR = 1 in	m ∠B = m ∠T = 22
AB = MT = $2\frac{1}{2}$ in	m ∠D = m ∠R = 104
DB = RT = $2\frac{1}{4}$ in	m ∠A = m ∠M= 54

DEFINITION: Congruent Triangles

Two triangles are congruent (≅) if:

corresponding angles have the same measure and

corresponding sides have the same length.

To apply the above definition, you first have to know how to pick out the angle of a triangle that is **opposite** a given **side**. This is illustrated on the next page.

Notice below that **small letters** are used to designate **sides** and
CAPITAL letters are used to designate **angles**.

Side **a** is opposite ∠**A**.   Side **b** is opposite∠**B**.   Side **c** is opposite∠**C**.

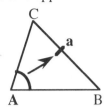   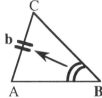   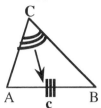

Notice that the number of **tick marks** on a side matches the number of **arcs** on the
opposite angle.

The triangles at the right are
congruent. The sets of tick marks
and arcs indicate that
corresponding angles have the
same measure and **corresponding**
sides have the same length.

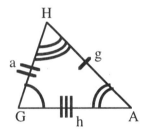   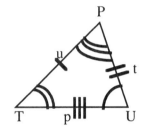

To indicate that the two triangles are congruent, write

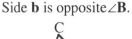

△ GAH ≅ △UTP

The order of the letters always indicates the **corresponding vertices**.

EXAMPLE 3   Given: △ PWG ≅ △ SEM
                Identify the corresponding sides and the corresponding angles.
                Draw the two triangles and mark the corresponding parts.

Strategy   1. Use the order of the letters to identify the pairs of corresponding parts.
                corresponding sides:

            △ **PW**G ≅ △ **SE**M   △ P**WG** ≅ △ S**EM**   △ **P**W**G** ≅ △ **S**E**M**
Solution   PW = SE   WG = EM   PG = SM
            (continued on next page)

2. corresponding angles:

$\triangle$ PW**G** $\cong$ $\triangle$ SE**M**	$\triangle$ **P**WG $\cong$ $\triangle$ SEM	$\triangle$ P**W**G $\cong$ $\triangle$ S**E**M

Solution   m $\angle$**G** = m $\angle$**R**   m $\angle$**P** = m $\angle$**S**   m $\angle$**W** = m $\angle$**E**

3. Now let's draw the two triangles.

Strategy   First, draw a triangle. Label it $\triangle$ PWG.

Then draw a second triangle that looks congruent to the first.

Label it with letters in the same relative order as the corresponding parts of the first triangle.

Solution

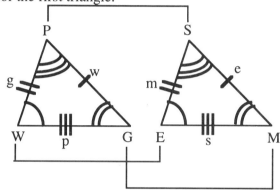

EXAMPLE 4   Given: $\triangle$ AGC $\cong$ $\triangle$ ZWP

Complete each of the following.

AC = ?   m $\angle$P = m $\angle$?

Strategy   Corresponding parts match order of letters.

$\triangle$ **AGC** $\cong$ $\triangle$ **ZW**P	$\triangle$ A**G**C $\cong$ $\triangle$ ZW**P**

Solution   **AC = ZP**   m $\angle$**C**= m $\angle$**P**

You have seen that the **flip** of a triangle about an axis produces a triangle congruent to the original triangle.

A **slide** can also produce a triangle congruent to the original triangle.

For example, suppose that each vertex of a triangle is **slid**

10 units to the right and then 3 units up.

The new triangle will be congruent to the original, as seen in the next example.

EXAMPLE 5   Given: D(1, 2), A(9, 4), G(3, 8)

Graph the points and draw △ DAG.

Graph △ PZS ≅ △ DAG, obtained by moving △ DAG 10 units to the

right and 3 units up.

DG = __? Verify this with a ruler.

m ∠A = m ∠?

Strategy   First graph D, A, and G.

Then graph the results of moving each of these points 10 units to the

right and 3 units up.

D(1, 2)	goes to	P(1 + **10**, 2 + **3**)	or	P(11, 5)
A(9, 4)	goes to	Z(9 + **10**, 4 + **3**)	or	Z(19, 7)
G(3, 8)	goes to	S(3 + **10**, 8 + **3**)	or	S(13, 11)

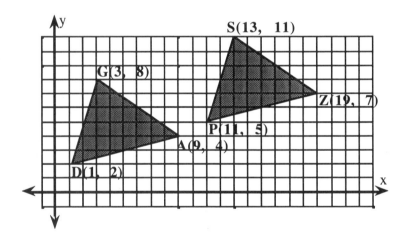

Solution   DG = PS = $1\frac{1}{2}$ in. to the nearest $\frac{1}{4}$ in.

m ∠A = m ∠Z = 52 to the nearest whole number angle measure.

SUMMARY

1.   Given: A(-1, 3), B(-8, 3), C(-5, 9)

How do you graph the flip of △ ABC about the y-axis?

2.   How do you verify for Example 1 that the triangle and its flip are congruent?

3. Given: Δ PAG ≅ Δ MEW. How do you identify the corresponding sides and angles?

4. How do you draw the two congruent triangles of Exercise 3 and label the corresponding parts?

5. Given: A(1, 2), B(6, 1), C(3, 7). How do you graph the slide of Δ ABC 7 units to the right and 5 units up? What will be true about the two triangles?

6. How do you use the definition of congruent triangles to verify that the triangle resulting from the slide in Exercise 5 is congruent to the original triangle?

CLASSROOM PRACTICE

For the given coordinates of A, B, and C, graph the points and draw Δ ABC.
Graph the flip of Δ ABC about the y-axis.
Give the coordinates of the mirror images of A, B, and C: P, Q, and R, respectively.
Use a ruler and protractor to verify that Δ ABC ≅ Δ PQR.

1. A(-10, 2), B(-1, 3), C(-6, 12)   2. A(4, 0), B(8, 0), C(2, 14)

3. A(-12, 1), B(-8, 1), C(-1, 10)   4. A(1, 1), B(12, 3), C(1, 14)

Identify the corresponding sides and angles of each given pair of triangles.
Draw the two triangles and mark the pairs of corresponding parts.

5. Δ ASM ≅ Δ UPW   6. Δ SAD ≅ Δ MRU   7. Δ VSQ ≅ Δ GET

Given: Δ DOG ≅ Δ PYE

8. DG = ?   9. m ∠O = ?   10. YE = ?

11. m ∠E = ?   12. PY = ?   13. m ∠D = ?

14. Given: A(1, 1), B(9, 1), C(1, 12)
Find the coordinates of Δ PQR formed by sliding Δ ABC 3 units to the right and 4 units up.

15. Verify by ruler and protractor that the two triangles of Exercise 14 are congruent.

WRITTEN EXERCISES

For the given coordinates of A, B, and C, graph the points and draw Δ ABC.

Graph the flip of Δ ABC about the y-axis.

Give the coordinates of the mirror images of A, B, and C: P, Q, and R, respectively.

Use a ruler and protractor to verify that Δ ABC ≅ Δ PQR.

   1.   A(-12, 3), B(-2, 3), C(-4, 10)   2. A(2, 2), B(14, 2), C(10, 8)

Identify the corresponding sides and angles of each given pair of triangles.

Draw the two triangles and mark the pairs of corresponding parts.

   3.   Δ HJE ≅ Δ POR   4. Δ DFA ≅ Δ ZUR   5. Δ FIG ≅ Δ NOW
   6.   Δ FAP ≅ Δ SUJ   7. Δ WEB≅ Δ ROK   8. Δ HIT ≅ Δ SAK

Given: Δ TUP ≅ Δ MAK

   9.   UP = ?   10.   MK = ?   11.   MA = ?
   12.   m ∠U = ?   13.   m ∠K = ?   14.   m ∠M = ?

Given: Δ BNA ≅ Δ DEH

   15.   DE = ?   16.   BA = ?   17.   NA = ?
   18.   m ∠H= ?   19.   m ∠B = ?   20.   m ∠E = ?

Given: A(1, 1), B (3, -8), C(5, 10)   (Exercises 21-28)

   21.   Find the coordinates of Δ PQR formed by sliding Δ ABC 7 units to the right and 4
         units down.

   22.   Verify by ruler and protractor that the two triangles of Exercise 21 are congruent.

Complete.

   23.   BC = ?   24.   m ∠C = ?   25.   AB = ?
   26.   m ∠Q = ?   27.   PR = ?   28.   m ∠P = ?

OPEN-ENDED QUESTION

29.   The coordinate axes divide the plane into 4
quadrants as labeled in the figure at the right.
Given: A(-8, 2), B(-1, 2), C(-10, 7)
Graph △ ABC. What flip will produce a triangle in
Q4 that will be congruent to △ ABC? Is there
another flip or series of flips that will also do this?

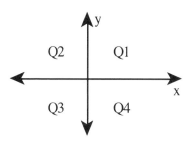

REVIEW

1.   Joe ordered tables to be set up for the junior-senior prom. Each of the available
tables accommodated 8 people. He knew that 251 people would come to the
prom. He used his calculator to divide 251 by 8 and got 31.375. Therefore, he
ordered 31 tables to be set up for the prom. His decision was
   (A)   good because he ordered just enough tables to accommodate everyone
coming to the junior-senior prom.
   (B)   bad because he ordered too few tables to accommodate everyone
coming to the junior-senior prom.
   (C)   bad because he ordered more tables than were needed.
   (D)   good because he allowed for some extra seating for chaperones.

2.   If each of the following procedures was applied to a given number, which of
them would give equal results?
               I   subtract twice the number from itself
               II   divide one by the number
               III   multiply the number by -1
   (A)   I and III   (B)   II and III   (C)   I and II   D) I, II, and III

3.   Suppose the 36 students in a sophomore class sold an average of 4.25 class play
tickets. If each ticket to the play cost $4, how much money did the students bring
in from the sale o tickets to that play?
   (A) $144   (B) $153   (C) $612   (D) Not enough information

4. It cost a store $50.60 to assemble a bicycle. If the store is to make a 25% profit on the sale of each bicycle, which of the following computations will give the number of dollars the store must charge for each bicycle?

(A)   (0.25)(50.60)   (B)   (0.25)(50.60) + 0.25

(C)   50.60 + 0.25   (D)   50.60 + (0.25)(50.60)

5. Find the complement of an angle with measure 42.

6. Solve $\frac{2}{3}x - 5 = \frac{1}{2}x + 1$

7. m $\angle 1$ = 43, m $\angle 3$ = ?

8. m $\angle 1$ = 4x + 20, m $\angle 2$ = 2x + 50,

    m $\angle 3$ = ?

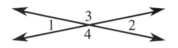

9. What three dimensional figure is formed by rotating the figure at the right about $\overline{AB}$?

10. A diagram of a rectangle with dimensions 6 inches by 8 inches is placed in a copy machine which is set to enlarge all dimensions by 10%. Will the resulting figure fit on an $8\frac{1}{2}$ " x 11" sheet of paper?

(A)   Yes, it will fit with room to spare.

(B)   Yes, it will just fit with no room to spare.

(C)   No, one dimension will fit, but no the other.

(D)   No, both dimensions will be too large.

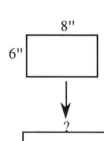

11. An ant is crawling on the surface of a sheet of paper measuring 30 inches by 24 inches. Find the probability that the ant will be no more than 3 inches from the left edge of the paper.

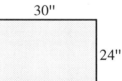

9.4 Combinations of Slides, Flips, and Rotations

OBJECTIVES   To predict results of geometric transformations of figures by combinations of slides, flips, and rotations

You have learned to predict the results of **slides** and **flips** of geometric figures.
Slides and **flips** are examples of **transformations,** or movements of geometric figures.
These two types of **transformations** do not change the size or shape of the figures.
A third type of **transformation** is a **rotation** of a figure about a point.
This is illustrated in the next example.

EXAMPLE 1   Draw the result of rotating the shaded figure 180° clockwise about the origin.

Strategy   Trace the shaded figure on tracing paper. Hold the tracing in place with your pencil point at the origin.

Use your other hand to rotate the traced figure as shown below.

Rotate the tracing 90° clockwise.   Rotate another 90° clockwise.

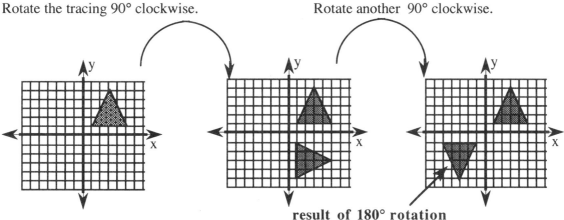

result of 180° rotation

Solution   Thus, the result of the rotation is the figure you see in the third drawing.

Can the transformation shown in Example 1 of the previous page be done using **flips** or **slides?** This idea is explored in the next two examples.

EXAMPLE 2   The figure at the right is the same as that of Example 1.
Draw the result of flipping the shaded figure about the y-axis and then flipping the result about the x-axis.
How does this final result compare with that of the rotation in Example 1?

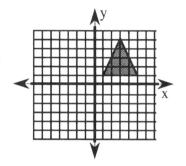

Strategy   First **flip** the shaded triangle about the y-axis.
Trace the axes and the shaded figure on tracing paper.

1. Holding the left side of the y-axis in place, fold the tracing along the y-axis.
    If it is not easy to fold this way, pick the tracing up and fold. Then lie it back down so that the axes coincide.
    The result is the drawing shown here at the right.

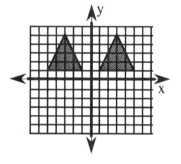

You may now want to trace over the tracing so that you can see it better after the next folding or flip.

2. Now let's **flip** the traced figure about the x-axis.
    Fold the tracing along the x-axis.

Solution   The result of the **two flips** is the drawing shown at the right.

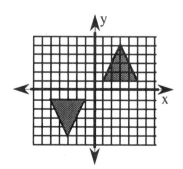

3. The result is the same as **rotating** the original figure 180° clockwise about the origin as in Example 1.

You have now applied two kinds of geometric transformations:

1. **rotation** about the origin
2. **flip** about an axis

(also known as **reflection** in an axis)

You just saw in Examples 1 and 2 that a **flip or rotation** produced the **same** result! Is this always true?

A third type of geometric transformation a **slide**, was introduced in Example 5, Lesson 9.3. One might think that a **rotation, flip**. or **slide** of a geometric figure will all produce the same image.

DISCOVERY

Draw the result of **sliding** the shaded triangle 8 units to the right. Give the coordinates of the resulting image.

Then draw the **flip** of the original figure about the y-axis. Give the coordinates of the resulting image.

Does the **translation (slide)** produce the same image as the **flip**?

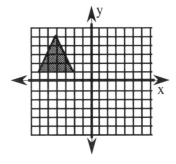

EXAMPLE 3   Draw the image of the **translation (slide)** of the rectangle 6 units to the right. Give the coordinates of the four vertices of the image.

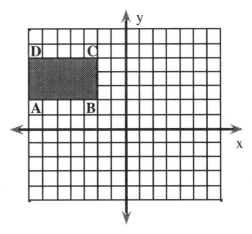

Strategy   Trace the shaded rectangle.

Slide the right edge, $\overline{BC}$, 6 units to the right. Label the result PQRS.

(solution on next page)

A(-7, 2) slides to   P(-7 + **6**, 2)

or P(-1, 2).

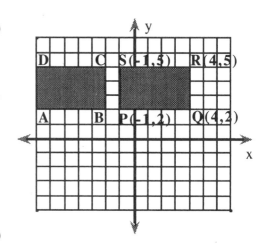

B(-2, 2) slides to   Q(-2 + **6**, 2)

or Q(4, 2).

C(-2, 5) slides to   R(-2 + **6**, 5)

or R(4, 5).

D(-7, 5) slides to   S(-7 + **6**, 5)

or S(-1, 5).

Solution   Thus the slide of ABCD 6 units
to the right results in the image
PQRS.

EXAMPLE 4   Draw the image of the **flip** about the y-axis of rectangle ABCD of
Example 3.
Give the coordinates of the four vertices of the image.
Is the result of the flip the same as the **slide** of ABCD as shown above?

Strategy   Trace ABCD and the y-axis on
tracing paper.
Fold the tracing paper on the
y-axis.

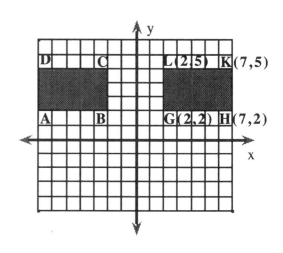

Solution   **1.**   The result is GHKL
with coordinates
G(2, 2), H(7, 2), K(7, 5), L(2, 5)

The coordinates of GHKL are
NOT the same as for PQRS of
Example 3 above.

2.   The result of the **slide** is **different**
from the result of the **flip**.

EXAMPLE 5   If the shaded figure at the right is reflected in the y-axis and then translated 6 units up, which graph below represents the resulting image?

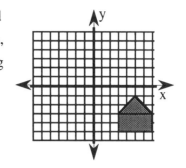

(A)   (B)   (C)

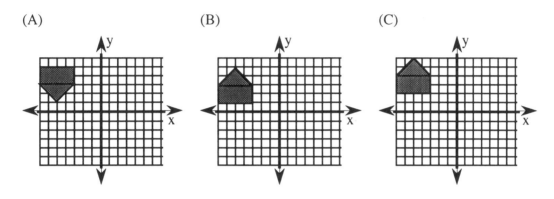

Strategy

Trace the shaded figure and the y-axis on tracing paper.	Flip about the y-axis: fold the traced drawing on the y-axis.	Slide the tracing so that the base, $\overline{AB}$, is moved up 6 blocks.

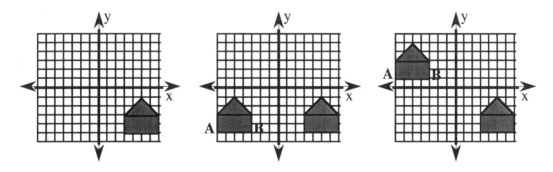

Solution   Thus, the solution is choice (B) above.

As you get more practice with geometric transformations, you will be able to visualize them in your mind without the need to actually use tracing paper.

SUMMARY

1. What three kinds of geometric transformations are discussed in this lesson?
2. Another name for **flip** about an axis is _____.
3. Another name for a **slide** is _____.
4. A geometric figure is reflected in the y-axis, and then the result is reflected in the x-axis. What single transformation will produce the same result?
5. Describe how to use tracing paper to visualize a rotation of a geometric figure 180°.
6. Describe how to use tracing paper to visualize a reflection of a geometric figure in the y-axis.
7. Describe how to use tracing paper to visualize a slide of a geometric figure 4 units up.

CLASSROOM PRACTICE

Draw the result of each transformation or combination of transformations for the figures below. (Exercises 1-10)

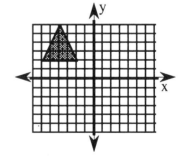

1. Reflect the figure in the y-axis.
2. Reflect the figure in the x-axis.
3. Rotate the figure 180° about the origin.
4. Translate the figure 6 units down.
    Give the coordinates of each vertex of the image.
5. Translate the figure 8 units to the right and then reflect the result in the x-axis.
    Give the coordinates of each vertex of the image.
6. The transformation of Exercise 5 produces the same image as what other transformation in Exercises 1-4?

7.   Reflect the figure in the y-axis and then reflect the result in the x-axis.

8.   Rotate the figure 180° about the origin.

9.   Reflect the figure in the x-axis and then translate the result 8 units to the right.

10. Which transformations of Exercises 7-9 produce the same result?

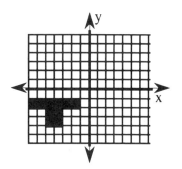

WRITTEN EXERCISES

Draw the result of each transformation or combination of transformations for the figures below. (Exercises 1-13)

1.   Reflect the figure in the x-axis.

2.   Reflect the figure in the y-axis.

3.   Rotate the figure 180° about the origin.

4.   Translate the figure 5 units up.

5.   Reflect the figure in the y-axis and then reflect the result in the x-axis.

6.   Reflect the figure in the y-axis and then translate the result 5 units up.

7.   Is the result of Exercise 6 the same as that of any other transformations in Exercises 1-5?

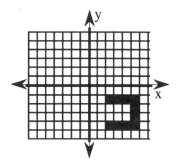

8.   Reflect the figure in the y-axis and then reflect the result in the x-axis.

9.   Translate the figure 9 units to the right and then reflect the result in the x-axis.

10. Translate the figure 6 units down and then translate the result 9 units to the right.

11. Rotate the figure 180° about the origin.

12. Reflect the figure in the x-axis and then translate the result 9 units to the right.

13. Do any of the transformations of Exercises 8-13 produce the same result?

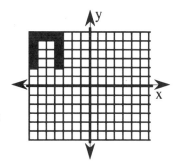

14.   Performing which set of transformations on the
       lightly shaded figure will **NOT** result in the lightly
       shaded figure covering the heavily shaded figure
       completely?

       (A)   reflection in the y-axis followed by
              reflection in the x-axis

       (B)   translation of 8 units to the right followed
              by flip about the x-axis

       (C)   reflection in the y-axis followed by slide 2
              units down

       (D)   reflection in the x-axis followed by
              reflection in the y-axis

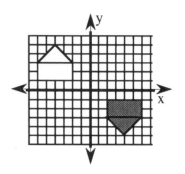

15.   If the figure were translated 2 units down and then
       reflected in the y-axis, which picture below would
       show the result?

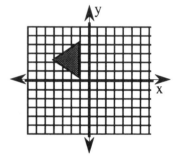

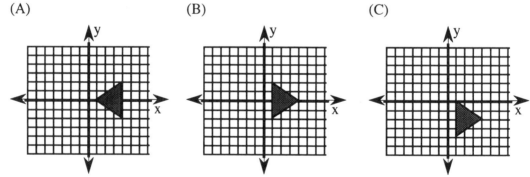

(A)   (B)   (C)

OPEN-ENDED QUESTION

16.   Draw a figure such that the image is the same for each of the following
       transformations : slide of 8 units to the right, reflection in the y-axis, rotation of
       $90°$ clockwise about the origin.

REVIEW   CHAPTERS 1-9

For each of the following: to which axis is $\overline{AB}$ parallel? Also, find AB.

1.   A(5, 2), B(5, 11)   2.   A(-4, 3), B(7, 3)

3.   Find the coordinates of the mirror image of M(-4, 7) with respect to the y-axis.

4   Find the coordinates of the mirror image of P(2, -3) with respect to the x-axis.

5.   Draw the reflection of this figure in the axis shown.

6.   Reflect the figure in the y-axis.
      Then reflect the result in the x-axis.

7.   Translate the figure 9 units to the right and then reflect the
      result in the x-axis.

8.   Translate the figure 6 units down and then translate the
      result 9 units to the right.

9.   Rotate the figure 180° clockwise about the origin.

10.   Reflect the figure in the x-axis and then slide the figure 9
      units to the right.

11.   Are any of the transformations of exercises 6-11 the same?

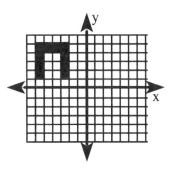

12.   Below is a list of transformations of the heavily
      shaded region. Which one will **NOT** result in the
      heavily shaded figure completely covering the lightly
      shaded one?

      (A)   reflection in y-axis followed by reflection in
            x-axis

      (B)   translation 8 units to the right followed by
            reflection in x-axis

      (C)   translation 8 units right followed by reflection in y-axis

      (D)   Rotate the figure 180° clockwise about the origin

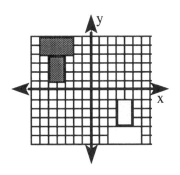

13.   Graph Δ ABC: A(-14, 2), B(-10, 2), C(-3, 11).

       Graph the reflection of Δ ABC about the y-axis.

       Give the coordinates of the mirror images of A, B, C: P, Q, R, respectively.

       Use a ruler and protractor to verify that Δ ABC ≅ Δ PQR.

14.   Δ GRW ≅ Δ MUE.

       Identify the corresponding sides and angles of the two triangles.

       Draw the two triangles and mark the pairs of corresponding parts.

15.   How many more sales of   **Types of Meals Bought by 200 Customers**
       cheeseburgers were there   **at a Fast Food Restaurant at Noon Hour**
       than of hot dogs?

16.   The number of sales of fried
       chicken was what percent of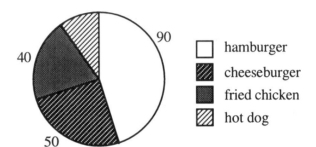
       the number of sales of
       cheeseburgers?

Find the measure of each angle.

17.   supplement of an angle with measure 44

18.   complement of an angle with measure 5x

$\overrightarrow{RA} \perp \overrightarrow{RE}$

19.   m ∠2 = 39, m ∠1 = ?

20.   m ∠1 = x, m ∠2 = 8x, m ∠2 = ?

Which pair of angles are supplementary? Tell why or why not.

21.   22.

   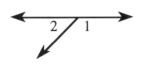

23. m $\angle$1 = 4x + 20, m $\angle$2 = x + 30.
    Find m $\angle$2.

24. m $\angle$1 : m $\angle$2 = 5 : 7. Find m $\angle$1.

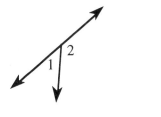

25. m $\angle$2 = 5x - 20, m $\angle$4 = 3x + 30.
    Find m $\angle$1.

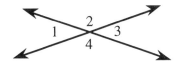

Find each angle measure.

26. m $\angle$4 = ?

27. m $\angle$1 = ?

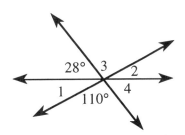

28. What three-dimensional figure is
    formed by revolving the figure

    about $\overline{KM}$?

    K   M

    (A)   horizontal cylinder   (B)   horizontal cone

    (C)   vertical cone   (D)   vertical cylinder

Solve each equation.

29. 6x - 4 = 4x + 10   30. $\frac{3}{4}$ x + 9 = 24.

31. Which sequence of steps will solve the equation $\frac{4}{5}$ x + 2 = 10?

    (A)   Multiply each side by 5, add 2 to each side, then divide each side by 4.

    (B)   Add 2 to each side and then divide each side by $\frac{4}{5}$.

    (C)   Multiply each side by 5, subtract 10 from each side, then divide each side
    by 4.

    (D)   Subtract 2 from each side, multiply each side by $\frac{4}{5}$.

32. Assume that the pattern below continues. How many squares will be in the seventh row?

33. At the right are three views of a
     die. The letters A, B, C, D, E, and F
     appear exactly once on the faces of
     this die. What letter is opposite E?

1st view   2nd view   3rd view

34. If the window is to be centered on
     the wall, it should be how many
     feet from the right vertical edge of
     the wall?

35. Complete the table.

n	$3n + 2(n - 4)$
6	
	32

36. The pentagon in figure (a) is 9 cm on a
     side and rolled to the right along a line.
     Which of the following distances could it
     have rolled so that the shaded circle
     would be in the position shown in figure (b)?

figure (a)   figure (b)

(A)   27 cm   (B)   45 cm   (C)   54 cm   (D)   90 cm

37. Amanda earns $5.50 an hour for the times worked Monday through Friday and
     $8.50 an hour on weekends. Use the time-card below to find her week's earnings.

Name: Amanda Jones   Date: 11/30/93
DAY: Mon. Tues. Wed. Ths. Fri. Sat. Sun.

HRS: $4\frac{1}{2}$ $3\frac{1}{2}$ 6 $7\frac{1}{2}$ 0   4 $3\frac{1}{2}$

38.   Last year there were 40 students out for football. The number of students out for football this year is 20% more than the number last year. How many students are out for football this year?

39.   Janet's average for the first five math tests is 80. What grade must she get on the sixth test to have an average of 82 on the six tests?

40.   A basketball team lost 30% of the games played this season. The team won 14 games. How many games were lost?

41.   Last week José earned $500. To estimate the amount of his paycheck, he first adds and then rounds to the nearest whole number percent the following deductions:

    Federal Tax   25%
    State Income Tax   7.5%
    FICA   6.5%
    Unemployment Insurance   0.52%

His estimate of his paycheck is _____:

(A) $200   (B) $300   (C) $445   (D) $700

42. $0.799 \cdot 0.0419$ is approximately

(A)   0.32   (B)   0.032   (C)   0.0032   (D)   0.00032

43.   A medium-size school bus can transport no more than 41 students as passengers. If each bus makes no more than one trip, what is the smallest number of buses that can transport 609 students from one place to another?

44.   An electrician charges $30 for each hour worked plus an additional $45 service charge. If C represents the electrician's total charges in dollars and h represents the number of hours worked, which formula below could be used to calculate C?

(A) $C = 30 + 45 + h$ (B) $C = 45 + 30h$

(C) $C = 30 \cdot 45 + h$ (D) $C = 45h + 30$

45.   Identify the type of angle.

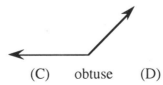

(A)   acute   (B)   straight   (C)   obtuse   (D)   right

46.   What are the restrictions on x if ∠A is acute?

$(2x - 12)°$

47.   Which inequality below would be most useful in solving this problem?

Jon earned $105 over two weeks at a part-time job. He bought 3 shirts at $15.95 each. He would like to buy as many cassette taps as possible $9.95 each. How many tapes could he buy?

(A) $3x + 9.95 \le 105$ (B) $3x + 15.95 \le 105$

(C) $47.85x + 9.95 \le 105$ (D) $47.85 + 9.95x \le 105$

48.   Insert the appropriate inequality symbol: 6.02^3 ? 1.9^{10}

49. $AB = \frac{3}{4}$ of BC, AC = 28.

Find AB.

50.   A bag contains 5 red balls, 3 green ones, and 4 orange balls. One is drawn from he bag at random. What is the probability that it will be orange?

Rectangle ABCD has coordinates A(5, 7), B(14, 7), C(14, 13), and D(5, 13).

51.   Find the perimeter of ABCD.   52.   Find the area of ABCD.

53.   A room measures 18 ft by 30 ft. Find the cost of carpeting the room if carpet costs $29 a square yard.

54.   An 80-cent bag of candy weighed $5\frac{1}{2}$ ounces. At this rate, find the cost, to the nearest penny, of a one-pound bag of the candy.

55.   The length of a rectangle is 4 cm more than the width. The perimeter is 56 cm. Find the length.

56.   Mr. Lamberti traveled 30 miles in 45 minutes. Find his average speed in miles per hour.

57.   14 is not a factor of 35 because

(A)   35 is not an odd number.   (B)   2 is not a factor of 35.

(C)   7 is not a factor of 35.   (D)   14 must be a factor of 35 and is not.

58.   What is the units digit in the 57th term of the pattern below?

$8^1, 8^2, 8^3, 8^4, ...$

59.   Examine this pattern:

PIZZAPIZZAPIZZA...

If this pattern continues, what symbol will be in the 47th position?

The bar graph below shows a basketball team's point scores in two weeks of games. Use it to answer exercises 60-66.

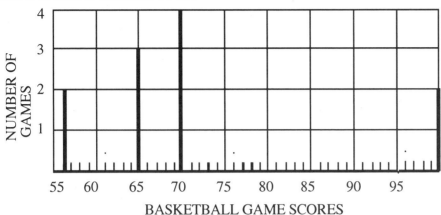

BASKETBALL GAME SCORES

Find each of the following.

60.   mean   61.   median   62.   mode   63. range

64.   Which is the better measure of central tendency, the mean or the median? Explain why.

65.   Suppose that a and b represent whole numbers.
       Then for the equation $3a + 28b = 36$, what must be true about the value of a?
       (A)   a must be divisible by 4.   (B)   a must be divisible by 3.
       (C)   a must be a multiple of 36.   (D)   a must be odd since 3 is odd.

66.   An ant is crawling on the surface of this 12-in.-by-8-in. sheet of paper. Find the probability that the ant is no more than 3 inches from side $\overline{BC}$.

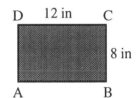

OPEN-ENDED QUESTION

67.   Complete the following pattern. Write an explanation of how you derived your answer.

       4 out of 11 games are lost   Fraction of games won is: $\dfrac{11 - 4}{11} = \dfrac{7}{11}$

       3 out of 7 applications are accepted   Fraction of applications rejected is $\dfrac{7 - 3}{7} = \dfrac{4}{7}$

       5 out of n games are won   Fraction of games lost is ?

10.1   Transversals and Special Angles

OBJECTIVE   To identify alternate interior, alternate exterior, and corresponding angles

In the figure of the house at the right, $\overline{AB}$ cuts across (**transverses**) the 5 edges of shingles. $\overline{AB}$ is called a **transversal** to the segments q, m, r , n, and p.
Note that the five edges are **parallel**.

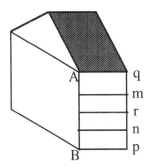

In this figure, $\overline{GH}$ is a **transversal** to segments p, q, and r. However, this time the segments being **transversed** are not parallel.

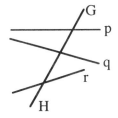

You will discover in the next lesson that the measures of angles at which a transversal cuts several segments determine whether the segments being transversed are parallel.

DEFINITION   Transversal

A **transversal** is a line, ray, or segment that intersects two or more lines, rays, or segments in the same plane, each at a different point.

EXAMPLE 1   Identify the transversal and lines it
                                transverses.

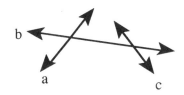

Solution   b is a transversal to a and c since b intersects
                                both lines in different points, all
                                in the same plane.

Note that b is **NOT** a transversal to a and c since it
does **NOT** intersect each line at a different point.
It cuts them all at the **same** point, **P**.

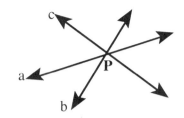

EXAMPLE 2 $\overline{AC}$ is a transversal to two different
pairs of segments. Name them.

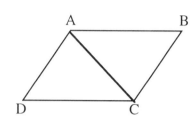

Strategy   Shade each pair of segments $\overline{AC}$
intersects **NOT** at the same point.

Solution

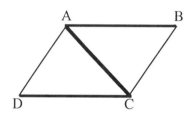   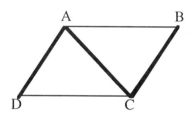

$\overline{AC}$ is a transversal to $\overline{AB}$ and $\overline{CD}$. $\overline{AC}$ is a transversal to $\overline{AD}$ and $\overline{BC}$..

In the figure, p is a transversal to q and r.
There are eight angles (**excluding straight angles**)
formed by the transversal to the lines q and r.

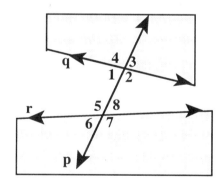

$\angle 3$, $\angle 4$, $\angle 6$, and $\angle 7$ are in the **exterior** of the two lines
cut by the transversal.

DISCOVERY

Shade the **interior** of the two lines in the figure at the bottom of the previous page.
What angles would be in the **interior**?

∠1, ∠2, ∠5, and ∠8 are in the **interior** of the two
lines q and r cut by the transversal p.
The interior angles ∠5 and ∠8 are adjacent and
supplementary.

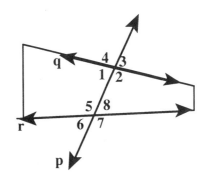

A special pair of **interior** angles are those which are on **alternate** or opposite sides of the
transversal. Can you find such a pair?

∠1 and ∠8 are on **alternate** sides of the
transversal p and in the interior of lines r and q.
∠1 is on the left side of the transversal p.
∠8 is on the right side of the transversal p.
The sides of ∠1 and ∠8 with heavy lines seem
to form the letter **Z**.
∠1 and ∠8 are called **alternate interior angles**.

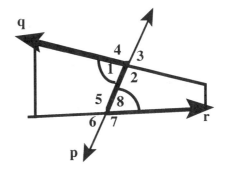

EXAMPLE 3   Name another pair of **alternate interior angles** in the figure above.
                    Shade the sides of these angles.

Solution   ∠2 and ∠5 are on **alternate**
                    sides of the transversal p.
                    The sides with heavy lines seem
                    to form a backwards **Z**.

                    ∠2 and ∠5 are **alternate**
                    interior angles.

What do you guess is meant by **alternate exterior angles**?
Can you name a pair?

EXAMPLE 4   Using the figure on page 455 that you just worked with, identify the pairs of **alternate exterior angles**.

Solution

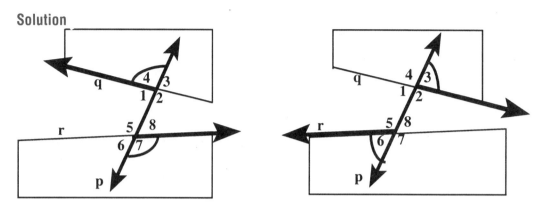

∠4 and ∠7 are **alternate exterior** angles.   ∠3 and ∠6 are **alternate exterior** angles.

There is another type of angle 304 relation illustrated at the right. Notice that ∠1 and ∠2 are in the same **corresponding** position: both **above** the lines r and q and on the **same side** of the transversal. ∠1 and ∠2 are called **corresponding angles**. There are three other pairs of corresponding angles.

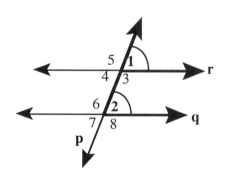

EXAMPLE 5   Using the figure above, name three other pairs of corresponding angles.

Solution

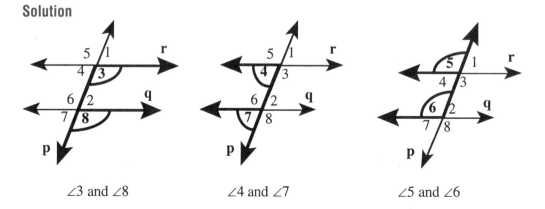

∠3 and ∠8   ∠4 and ∠7   ∠5 and ∠6

EXAMPLE 6   Name a pair of alternate interior angles formed by transversal $\overline{DB}$ to segments $\overline{AD}$ and $\overline{BC}$.

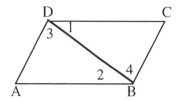

Strategy   Shade the transversal and the two segments to better visualize the alternate interior angles.

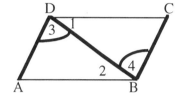

Solution $\angle 3$ and $\angle 4$ are the alternate interior angles.

EXAMPLE 7   Name a pair of corresponding angles formed by transversal r to lines t and u.

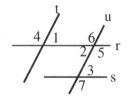

Strategy   Copy the figure. Shade the transversal r and the lines t and u to help pick out the corresponding angles.

It might also help to then turn or rotate the page so that the lines t and u are horizontal. Then you can visualize the corresponding angles as pictured in Example 5 on the previous page.

Rotate your paper so that t and u are horizontal.

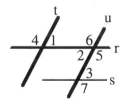 

Solution   The corresponding angles are $\angle 6$ and $\angle 4$.

SUMMARY

1. When is a line a transversal to two lines in a plane?

2. In the figure for Example 6, why is $\overline{DB}$ **NOT** a transversal to $\overline{AD}$ and $\overline{DC}$?

3. What does the word alternate mean?

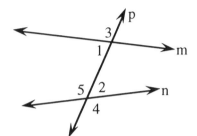

4. Which line is the transversal?
5. Is ∠3 in the exterior or the interior? Why?
6. Is ∠2 in the exterior or the interior? Why?
7. Explain why ∠1 and ∠2 are alternate interior angles.
8. Explain why ∠3 and ∠4 are alternate exterior angles.
9. Explain why ∠3 and ∠5 are corresponding angles.

Explain how to pick out each type of angle pair using q as a transversal to a and b.

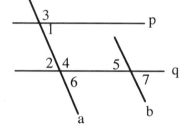

10. corresponding
11. alternate interior
12. alternate exterior

CLASSROOM PRACTICE

Identify each special type of angle pairs indicated.

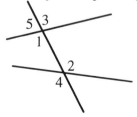
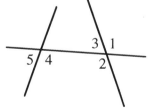
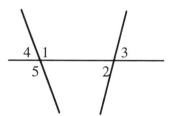

1. alternate interior
2. alternate exterior
3. corresponding

4. alternate interior
5. alternate exterior
6. corresponding

7. alternate interior
8. alternate exterior
9. corresponding

Identify alternate interior angles using:

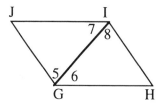

10. $\overline{GI}$ as a transversal to $\overline{JG}$ and $\overline{IH}$

11. $\overline{GI}$ as a transversal to $\overline{JI}$ and $\overline{GH}$

Using m as a transversal to r and s, identify each special type of angle pair.

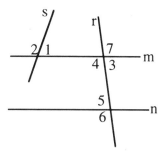

12.   alternate interior

13.   alternate exterior

14.   corresponding

Using r as a transversal to m and n, identify each special type of angle pair.

15.   alternate interior

16.   alternate exterior

17.   corresponding

WRITTEN EXERCISES

Identify each special type of angle pair.

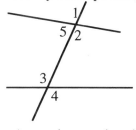
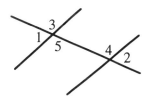

1. alternate interior	4. alternate interior	7. alternate interior
2. alternate exterior	5. alternate exterior	8. alternate exterior
3. corresponding	6. corresponding	9. corresponding

Identify alternate interior angles using $\overline{US}$ as a transversal to :

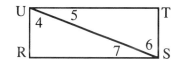

10. $\overline{RU}$ and $\overline{ST}$

11. $\overline{UT}$ and $\overline{RS}$

Using p as a transversal to g and h, identify each special type of angle pair.

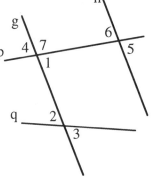

12.   alternate interior

13.   alternate exterior

14.   corresponding

Using g as a transversal to p and q, identify each special type of angle pair.

15.   alternate interior

16.   alternate exterior

17.   corresponding

REVIEW

1.   Complete the table.

     (A)   13, 7

     (B)   18, 7

     (C) $10, 2\frac{1}{5}$

     (D) $15, 8\frac{3}{4}$

n	4(n - 3) + n
6	
	23

2.   The homes of Pat, Fay, and Frank are along the same road. Pat's home is about 7 miles from Fay's home. Frank's home is about 5 miles from Pat's home. About how far apart are Fay's home and Frank's home?

     (A)   about 12 miles apart   (B)   about 2 miles apart

     (C)   either 2 miles or 12 miles apart   (D)   either 5 miles or 7 miles apart

3.   What is the next palindrome number after 7997?

OPEN-ENDED QUESTION

4.   The lengths of the sides of a rectangle are 6 and 4. One vertex of the rectangle is A(2,4). Name the coordinates of the other three vertices. Is there more than one answer? Draw all possible cases. (Assume that all sides are parallel to the axes.)

COMPUTER ACTIVITY

DISCOVERY: If two lines are cut by a transversal, what relationship must exist between any two pairs of alternate interior angles to guarantee the two lines are parallel?

Use a computer software drawing program that allows you to draw figures, label sides, duplicate figures, and flip a geometric figure about a horizontal or vertical line.

ACTIVITY

1. Draw an angle. Instruct the computer to duplicate the angle. Use the mouse to drag one of the angles so that the two angles do not overlap each other.

    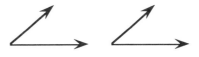

2. Label the angles as shown.
    m ∠1 = m ∠2 since ∠2 is a duplicate of ∠1.

3. Flip ∠1 about the horizontal.

4. Now flip ∠1 about the vertical.

5. Use the mouse to slide ∠1 so that
    $\overrightarrow{OB}$ and $\overrightarrow{CP}$ coincide as shown.

    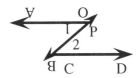

6. How is $\overrightarrow{OA}$ related to $\overrightarrow{CD}$?
    What generalization does this suggest?

10.2   Parallel Lines and Special Angle Relationships

OBJECTIVE   To apply properties of special angles formed by a transversal of parallel lines

You saw in Lesson 8.2 that parallel lines are lines in the same plane or flat surface that do not meet or intersect.

In the figure at the right,   m **is parallel to** n

m || n

Also, parallel segments are segments in the same plane which do not meet even if extended into lines.

You discovered in the computer activity of the previous page the following property.

ALTERNATE INTERIOR ANGLES PROPERTY

If a transversal intersects two lines so that **alternate interior angles** have equal measure, then the lines are **parallel**.

Given: m ∠1 = m ∠2

Conclusion: m || n

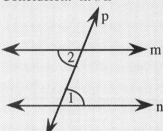

You have just seen :

If alternate interior angles are equal in measures, **then** lines are parallel.

This is an example of a conditional **statement**.

A **conditional** is a statement of the form **If .... then .... .**

An example of a **conditional** in real life is:

If you live in Indiana, **then** you live in the U.S.A.   **TRUE**

Can you write the conditional formed by switching the **if** and **then** parts? Is it true?

Conditional: **If** you live in Indiana, **then** you live in the U.S.A.   **TRUE**

Converse: **If** you live in the U.S.A., **then** you live in Indiana.   **FALSE**

In this case the **conditional** is true. But the **converse** is false!

Now let's write the converse of the **Alternate Interior Angles Property** of the previous page.

Property: **If** alternate interior angles have equal measure, **then** lines are parallel.

Converse: **If** lines are parallel, **then** alternate interior angles have equal measure.

Do you think the converse is true?

The following manipulative will help you decide whether the converse is true.

MANIPULATIVE DISCOVERY

Copy the following drawing on graph paper. Note that $\overline{AB} \parallel \overline{CD}$.

Trace ∠1 on tracing paper.

Hold your pencil point at O to hold the tracing paper in place.

Rotate the tracing paper 180° clockwise.

Do the angles **1** and **2** coincide?

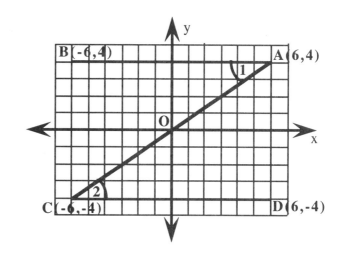

Thus, it appears that if $\overline{AB} \parallel \overline{CD}$, then _____.

The manipulative activity above suggests that the converse of the Alternate Interior Angles Property is true. It is formally stated on the next page.

CONVERSE OF ALTERNATE INTERIOR ANGLES PROPERTY

If two parallel lines are intersected by a transversal, then alternate interior angles have the same measure.

Given: m ∥ n
Conclusion;   m ∠1 = m ∠2

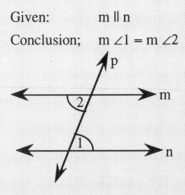

In Chapter 8 you learned to predict the results of slides, flips, and rotations of geometric figures. You just used a **rotation** to illustrate the converse of the Alternate Interior Angles Property. Another property of parallel lines is the Alternate **Exterior** Angles Property stated below.

In the exercises of this lesson, you will be asked to verify it by using a **rotation.**

ALTERNATE EXTERIOR ANGLES PROPERTY

If two parallel lines are intersected by a transversal, then alternate exterior angles have the same measure.

Given: m ∥ n
Conclusion: m ∠1 = m ∠2

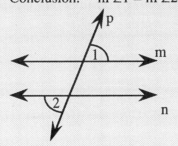

What do you think will be true about corresponding angles formed by a transversal intersecting two parallel lines? The next manipulative uses another geometric transformation, a **slide**, of Chapter 8 to help you verify conclusion.

MANIPULATIVE DISCOVERY

Note that $\overline{AB} \parallel \overline{CD}$.

Trace on tracing paper the **heavily shaded** figure, $\angle 1$.

Now **slide** this tracing of $\angle 1$ up, along the side $\overline{AE}$, keeping $\overline{AB}$ parallel to the x-axis.

$\angle 1$ coincides with $\angle 2$.

Thus, m $\angle 1$ = m $\angle 2$.

Corresponding angles have equal measure.

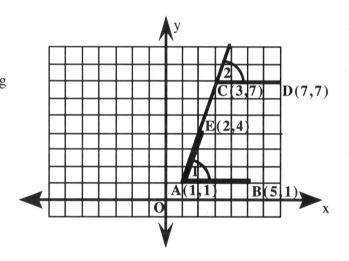

You now know that if parallel lines are intersected by a transversal, three types of special angles pairs have equal measure.

1. Given: m ∥ n: Conclusion: **Alternate interior** angles have equal measure.

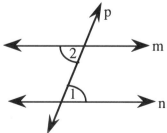

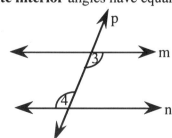

m ∠1 = m ∠2   m ∠3 = m ∠4

2. Given: m ‖ n: Conclusion: **Alternate exterior** angles have equal measure.

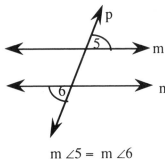

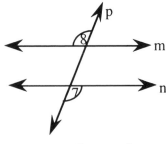

m ∠5 = m ∠6   m ∠7 = m ∠8

3. Given: m ‖ n: Conclusion: **Corresponding** angles have equal measure.

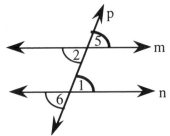

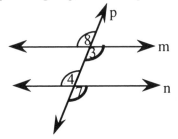

m ∠5 = m ∠1 and m ∠2 = m ∠6   m ∠7 = m ∠3 and m ∠4 = m ∠8

EXAMPLE 1   Given: a ‖ b
                     Find m ∠2.

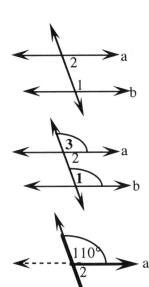

Strategy   You know three properties of angles for
                     parallel lines. Use one of them to find the
                     measure of another angle in the figure.
                     ∠3 and ∠1 are corresponding angles.
                     So, m ∠3 = m ∠1 = 110.

                     The 110° angle and ∠2 are supplementary.
                     So, m ∠2 + 110 = 180

Solution   m ∠2   = 70

EXAMPLE 2   Given: a ‖ b, m ∠1 = 115.

Find m ∠2.

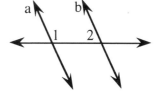

Strategy   Since a ‖ b, you can find the measure of
another angle by one of the three
properties. Then the result can be used
to find m ∠2.

m ∠1 = m ∠3 = 115.   Then use ∠3 and ∠2 are supplementary
(Alt. int. ∠s of ‖ lines have equal measure.)   to find m ∠2.

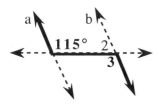

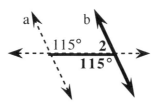

Solution   m ∠2 + 115 = 180
                                                 m ∠2   = 65

EXAMPLE 3   Given: m ∠1 = 5x + 20,

m ∠2 = 2x + 50,

a ‖ b.

Find m ∠3.

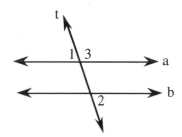

Strategy   ∠1 and ∠2 are alternate exterior angles
equal in measure since a ‖ b.
First find m ∠1.
Then use m ∠1 to find m ∠3.

m ∠1 = m ∠2

5x + 20 = 2x + 50   Set 5x + 20 = 2x + 50.

Solve. 3x + 20 = 50   Subtract 2x from each side.

3x = 30   Subtract 20 from each side.

x = 10   Divide each side by 3.

Substitute: m ∠1 = 5 · 10 + 20 = 70

Solution   m ∠3 + 70   = 180   m ∠3 + m ∠1 = 180

m ∠23   = 110

EXAMPLE 4

Given: $\overline{AB} \parallel \overline{CD}$

m $\angle 1 = 28$, m $\angle ACD = 110$.

Find m $\angle 3$.

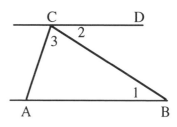

Strategy

Look for **alternate interior** angles.

m $\angle 1 = $ m $\angle 2 = 28$

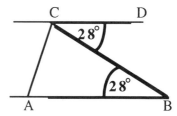

Use m $\angle ACD = 110$ and m $\angle 2 = 28$

to find m $\angle 3$.

By the Angle Addition Property

m $\angle 3 + 28 \quad = \quad 110$

m $\angle 3 \qquad = \quad 110 - 28 = 82$

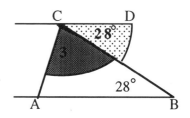

Solution

Thus, m $\angle 3 = 82$.

SUMMARY

1. What is meant by a conditional statement?

2. Is the following conditional true?

    If you are on the Wall Township Varsity High School Football Team, then you are a student of Toms River High School.

3. How do you write the converse of the conditional of Exercise 2?

4. What is the converse of the conditional of Exercise 2

    Is this converse true?

5. What do the results of Exercises 2 and 4 illustrate?

6. What are three kinds of angle relationships that exist if two parallel lines are intersected by a transversal?

7.   Given: a ∥ b,   m ∠2 = 71
      What are the steps in finding m ∠3 ?

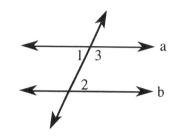

CLASSROOM PRACTICE

Consider the conditional.

If two angles are vertical, than the two angle measures are equal.

1.   Is the conditional true?
2.   Write the converse of the conditional.
3.   Is this converse true?

For each of the following exercises , assume that m ∥ n.

4.   m ∠3 = 75, m ∠2 = ?
5.   m ∠2 = 85, m ∠1 = ?
6.   m ∠4 = 65, m ∠3 = ?
7.   m ∠5 = 124, m ∠6 = ?
8.   m ∠2 = 75, m ∠6 = ?
9.   m ∠5 = 135, m ∠1 = ?

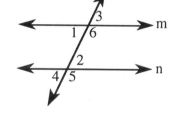

10.   m ∠6 = 123, m ∠7 = ?
11.   m ∠2 = 105, m ∠4 = ?
12.   m ∠1 = 64, m ∠8 = ?
13.   m ∠5 = 65, m ∠4 = ?
13.   m ∠7 = 115, m ∠1 = ?
14.   m ∠3 = 4x + 20, m ∠5 = 2x + 40
      Find m ∠3.
15.   m ∠7 = 3x + 60, m ∠6 = x + 100
      Find m ∠6.

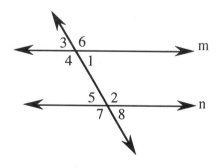

WRITTEN EXERCISES

Write the converse of each conditional. Is the converse true?

1.   If a car is a Chevrolet, then the car is a General Motors car.

2.   If an angle has a measure of 180, then the angle is a straight angle.

For each of the following exercises assume that m ‖ n.

3.   m ∠1 = 66, m ∠3 = ?

4.   m ∠7 = 112, m ∠8 = ?

5.   m ∠4 = 113, m ∠1 = ?

6.   m ∠5 = 110, m ∠3 = ?

7.   m ∠2 = 35, m ∠7 = ?

8.   m ∠1 = 75, m ∠6 = ?

9.   m ∠1 = 45, m ∠4 = ?

10.   m ∠4 = 137, m ∠5 = ?

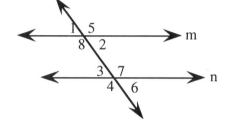

11.   m ∠3 = 3x + 20, m ∠5 = x + 40

       Find m ∠5.

12.   m ∠4 = 5x + 12, m ∠6 = 2x + 72

       Find m ∠7.

13.   m ∠2 = 6x + 40, m ∠8 = 2x + 80

       Find m ∠1.

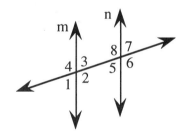

For each of the following, $\overline{AC}$ ‖ $\overline{ED}$.

14.   m ∠1 = 75, m ∠7 = ?

15.   m ∠4 = 115, m ∠3 = ?

16.   m ∠5 = 65, m ∠EBC = 120,

       m ∠2 = ?

17.   m ∠6 = 72, m ∠ABD = 100,

       m ∠2 = ?

18.   m ∠2 = 60, m ∠3 = 40,

       m ∠7 = ?

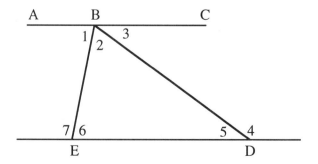

OPEN-ENDED QUESTION

19.   Complete the following data table with values of x and y.

m ∠1	x	y	x + y
30			
40			
60			
80			

Given: m ‖ n

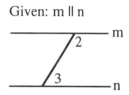

Make a generalization about the relationship of angles in the position of m ∠2 and m ∠3 if m ‖ n.

These angles are in the **interior** of the parallels. But they are not alternate interior angles. Make up an appropriate name for them.

Given: m ‖ n

REVIEW

1.   Which of the following sequence of steps transforms the equation $\frac{1}{4}x - 6 = 3$ into the equation $x = 36$?

(A)   Subtract 6 from each side and then divide each side by 4.

(B)   Multiple each side by 4 and then add 6 to each side.

(C)   Multiply each side by 4 and then subtract 6 from each side.

(D)   Multiple each side by 4 and then add 24 to each side.

2.   A football is advertised at 30% off its regular price of $50.00. Which of the following computations can be used to figure the charge to a customer?

(A)   (0.30)(50)   (B)   (0.70)(50)

(C)   (0.70)(50) + 50   (D)   50 + (0.30)(50)

3.   Martin earns $30 a week part-time. Janet earns $45 a week. After how many weeks will Jane have earned $90 more than Martin?

10.3   Sum of Angle Measures of a Triangle

OBJECTIVE   To apply the formula for the sum of the measures of the angles of a triangle

Perhaps you remember the formula for the sum of the measures of the three angles of a triangle. m ∠ A + m ∠ B + m ∠ C = ?
A parallel lines property will be applied later in the lesson to showing **why** this formula works!
Right now, let's try to discover what the formula is.

MANIPULATIVE DISCOVERY

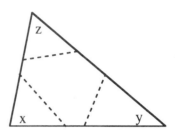

In the figure at the right x, y, and z represent the degree measures of the three angles of the triangle.
Copy the drawing.
Cut out the triangle.

Cut off the three corners of the triangle using the dashed segments as guide lines.	Rotate ∠ with measure z 180°. Slide this **z** angle between the other two as shown below.	Slide the three angles together so that they form one big angle.

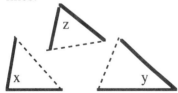
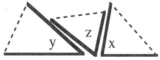
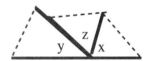

Together they form a
STRAIGHT angle.
x + y + z = 180!

This suggests that the sum of the measures
of three angles of a triangle is 180.
    x + y + z = 180

Recall that alternate interior angles formed by a transversal to two parallel lines have equal measure. This concept can now be applied to showing mathematically why the sum of the angle measures of a triangle is 180.

The three angles of △ABC at the right have degree measures x, y, and z.

We now prove that x + y + z = 180.

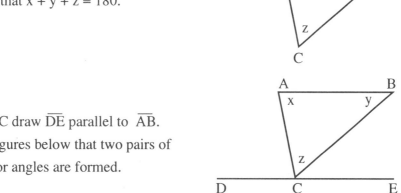

Through point C draw $\overline{DE}$ parallel to $\overline{AB}$. Notice in the figures below that two pairs of alternate interior angles are formed.

Alternate interior angles have equal measure, each **x**, if lines are parallel.

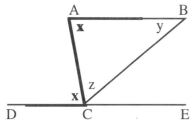

Alternate interior angles have equal measure, each **y**, if lines are parallel.

Now notice that ∠DCE is a **straight** angle. Therefore, **x + y + z = 180**.

Thus, you have now **proved** that the sum of the degree measures of a triangle is 180.

x + y + z = 180.

EXAMPLE 1   Given: △ABC is a right triangle,

                           m ∠B = 30

                     Find m ∠C.

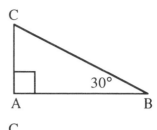

Strategy   m ∠A = 90 since △ABC is a right △.

                     Let m ∠C = x.

                     Use sum of angle measures of a

                     triangle is 180 to write an equation.

                     m ∠A + m ∠B + m ∠C =   180

                     90   + 30   + x   =   180

                           120   + x   =   180

                                     x   =   60

Solution   Thus, m ∠C = 60

EXAMPLE 2   Given: m ∠4 = 145, m ∠3 = 70

                     Find m ∠1.

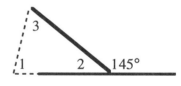

Strategy   First use ∠2 and ∠4 form a straight

                     angle to find m ∠2.

                     m ∠2 + 145   =   180

                     m ∠2   =   35

                     Now use m ∠2 = 35, m ∠3 = 70, and

                     the sum of the angle measures of a △

                     is 180 to find m ∠1.

                     m ∠1 + 35 + 70 · =   180

                     m ∠1 + 105   =   180

Solution   m ∠1   =   **75**

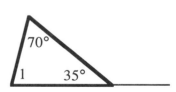

EXAMPLE 3   Given: m ∠1 = 3x + 50, m ∠2 = 2x + 20,

                    m ∠3 = 6x

               Find m ∠2.

Strategy   Use sum of angle measures of a triangle is 180 to

               write an equation.

m ∠1	+	m ∠2	+ m ∠3	=	180

Solve.

3x + 50 + 2x + 20 + 6x = 180   **Group like terms.**

(3x + 2x + 6x) + (50 + 20) = 180

11x + 70 = 180

11x = 110

x = **10**

But, the value of x is **NOT** the answer.

Use   m ∠2 = **2x** + 20 to find m ∠1.   **Substitute 10 for x.**

        m ∠2 = 2 · **10** + 20

Solution   Thus,   m ∠2 = 20 + 20 = **40**

Recall, from Lesson 3.4, that if three numbers are in the ratio 2 : 3 : 5,
they can be represented algebraically as   **2x, 3x,** and **5x.**

EXAMPLE 4   Given: m ∠1 : m ∠2 : m ∠3 = 3 : 4 : 5

               Find x.

Strategy   Write algebraic representations for each angle.

               m ∠1 = 3x,   m ∠2 = 4x,   m ∠3 = 5x

               Use sum of angle measures of a triangle is 180 to

               write an equation.

m ∠1 + m ∠2 + m ∠3 = 180

3x + 4x + 5x = 180

12x = 180

Solution   x = 15

Recall that an isosceles triangle is a triangle with
two sides of equal length.   AC = BC

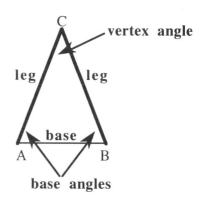

The sides of equal length are called **legs**.

$\overline{AC}$ and $\overline{BC}$ are the **legs** of the isosceles triangle.

$\overline{AB}$ is the **base**.

∠C is called the **vertex** angle.

∠A and ∠B are called the **base** angles.

What do you think must be true about the measures
of the base angles?

MANIPULATIVE DISCOVERY

Plot on a sheet of graph paper the points
A(-3,0), B(3,0), and C(0,4).
Connect the points to form △ABC.

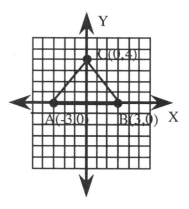

Trace the axes and the triangle on tracing paper.
Holding the portion of the tracing to the right of the
y-axis in place, fold the left side of the tracing
along the y-axis onto the right side of the tracing.

You can see that AC = BC.
So the triangle is isosceles.
What appears to be true about the measures of the
base angles, ∠A and ∠B ?

The manipulative activity above suggests an important property of isosceles triangles.
This property is stated on the next page.

ISOSCELES TRIANGLE PROPERTY

The base angles of an isosceles triangle have equal measure.

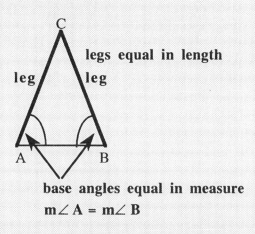

legs equal in length

base angles equal in measure
m∠ A = m∠ B

EXAMPLE 5   The measure of the vertex angle of an isosceles triangle is 40.
Find the measure of each base angle.

Strategy   Draw a diagram of the isosceles triangle.
Let x = the measure of each base angle.
Label the angle measures.

Use sum of angle measures of a Δ is 180 to
write an equation.

40 +	x	+	x	= 180
40		+ 2x		= 180 **Solve.**
		2x		= 140
		x		= 70

Solution   Thus, the measure of each base angle is 70.

SUMMARY

1.   What is the sum of the measures of the angles of any triangle?

2.   What is an isosceles triangle?

3.   What is the vertex angle of an isosceles triangle?

4.   What are the base angles of an isosceles triangle?

5.   What property exists related to the base angles of an isosceles triangle?

6.   Suppose m $\angle 1$: m $\angle 2$: m $\angle 3$ = 2 : 3 : 4. Write algebraic representations for the three angle measures.

Given: For $\triangle ABC$, m $\angle A$: m $\angle B$: m $\angle C$ = 1 : 2 : 3. To find m $\angle B$:

7.   First write algebraic representations for the three angle measure. What are they?

8.   Write what equation?

9.   What are the steps in solving the equation?

10.   Is the solution of the equation the answer to the problem?

11.   Once you have found x, how do you then find m $\angle B$?

CLASSROOM PRACTICE

1.   m $\angle 1$ = 20, m $\angle 2$ = 80, m $\angle 3$ = ?

2.   m $\angle 3$ = 55, m $\angle 2$ = 45, m $\angle 1$ = ?

3.   m $\angle 2$ = 64, m $\angle 1$ = 76, m $\angle 3$ = ?

4.   m $\angle 1$ = 42, m $\angle 2$ = 68, m $\angle 3$ = ?

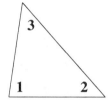

5.   m $\angle 1$ = 30, m $\angle 4$ = 105, m $\angle 3$ = ?

6.   m $\angle 3$ = 35, m $\angle 4$ = 94, m $\angle 1$ = ?

7.   m $\angle 1$ = 64, m $\angle 3$ = 37, m $\angle 4$ = ?

8.   m $\angle 3$ = 44, m $\angle 4$ = 77, m $\angle 1$ = ?

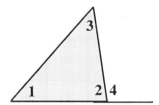

The triangle at the right is a right triangle with right angle at A.

9.   m $\angle B$ = 35, m $\angle C$ = ?

10.   m $\angle C$ = 42, m $\angle B$ = ?

11.   m $\angle B$ = 28, m $\angle C$ = ?

12.   m $\angle C$ = 2x, m $\angle B$ = x, m $\angle C$ = ?

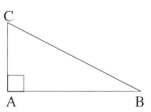

13. m ∠1 = x, m ∠2 = 2x, m ∠3 = 2x
     Find m ∠2.

14. m ∠1 = 2x + 10, m ∠2 = x + 5, m ∠3 = 2x + 15
     Find m ∠3.

15. m ∠1 : m ∠2 : m ∠3 = 2 : 1 : 2
     Find m ∠3.

16. m ∠1 : m ∠2 : m ∠3 = 3 : 5 : 2
     Find m ∠2.

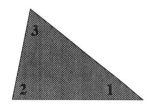

17. The measure of the vertex angle of an isosceles triangle is 20. Find the measure of each base angle.

18. The measure of the vertex angle of an isosceles triangle is 80. Find the measure of each base angle.

WRITTEN EXERCISES

1. m ∠1 = 32, m ∠2 = 78, m ∠3 = ?
2. m ∠3 = 49, m ∠2 = 38, m ∠1 = ?
3. m ∠3 = 62, m ∠1 = 77, m ∠2 = ?
4. m ∠1 = 109, m ∠2 = 68, m ∠3 = ?

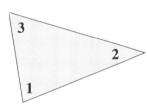

5. m ∠2 = 24, m ∠4 = 107, m ∠3 = ?
6. m ∠4 = 135, m ∠3 = 72, m ∠2 = ?
7. m ∠3 = 68, m ∠2 = 25, m ∠4 = ?
8. m ∠4 = 79, m ∠3 = 19, m ∠2 = ?

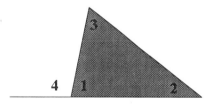

9. m ∠2 = 78, m ∠1 = ?
10. m ∠1 = 62, m ∠2 = ?
11. m ∠1 = 3x, m ∠2 = 7x
    Find m ∠2.
12. m ∠2 = 2x + 10, m ∠1 = x + 20
    Find m ∠1.

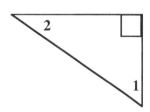

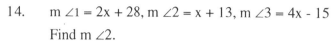

13.   m ∠1 = x, m ∠2 = x + 10, m ∠3 = x + 20
       Find m ∠2.

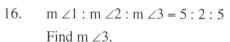

14.   m ∠1 = 2x + 28, m ∠2 = x + 13, m ∠3 = 4x - 15
       Find m ∠2.

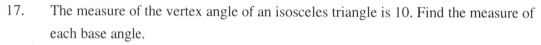

15.   m ∠1 : m ∠2 : m ∠3 = 2 : 3 : 7
       Find m ∠1.

16.   m ∠1 : m ∠2 : m ∠3 = 5 : 2 : 5
       Find m ∠3.

17.   The measure of the vertex angle of an isosceles triangle is 10. Find the measure of each base angle.

18.   The measure of the vertex angle of an isosceles triangle is 30. Find the measure of each base angle.

19.   The measure of a base angle of an isosceles triangle is 25. Find the measure of the vertex angle.

OPEN-ENDED QUESTION

20.   Complete the following data table.

m ∠4	m ∠2 + m ∠3
40	?
60	?
80	?
100	?

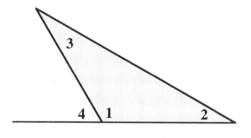

∠4 is called an **exterior angle** of the Δ.
Use the results of the data table to make
a generalization about the measure of an
exterior angle of a triangle.

REVIEW

1.   What is the next number in the following sequence?   8, 17, 35, 71, ...

2. Which point could represent the product of the numbers represented by T and V?

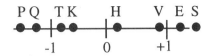

(A)   E   (B)   H

(C)   K   (D)   Q

3. Find the weight of one block if one pyramid weighs 5 pounds.

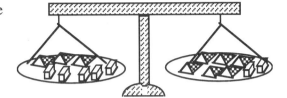

(A)   3 pounds

(B)   4 pounds

(C)   5 pounds

(D)   none of these

4. What is the units digit of the 19th term of the sequence below?

$3^1, 3^2, 3^3, 3^4, \ldots, 3^n$

(A)   1   (B)   3   (C)   7   (D)   9

5. Which inequality below would be most helpful in solving this problem?
    Bart spent an evening playing video games and drinking sodas. Each video game cost 25 cents to play, and sodas cost 60 cents each. Bart had only $8 to spend on video games and sodas. If he had 3 sodas and played as many games as he could, how many video games did he play?

(A) $0.25x + 1.80 \leq 8$ (B) $x + 1.80 \leq 8$

(C) $0.60x + 0.75 \leq 8$ (D) $3x + 0.25 \leq 8$

6. When purchasing an item, Nick gave a sales clerk a 20-dollar bill. The clerk gave him the item and change consisting of d dollar bills, q quarters, and n nickels. Which of the following expressions represents the cost in dollars of the item?

(A) $20 - (d + q + n)$ (B) $20 - d - 0.25q - 0.05n$

(C) $d + q + n$ (D) $100d + 25q + 5n$

7. An appliance store sold 40% of its TVs this week. There were 20 TVs left in stock. How many TVs did the company have in stock originally?

(A)   8   (B)   50   (C)   80   (D)   200

10.4 Discovering Properties of Special Types of Quadrilaterals by Graphing

OBJECTIVES To determine from coordinates of vertices if a quadrilateral
is a parallelogram, rectangle, square, or trapezoid
To find the lengths of sides of a rectangle or square using coordinates
To find the lengths of sides of a parallelogram using a ruler
To find measures of angles in parallelograms
To determine relationships of diagonals of a quadrilateral

The two figures at the right are called
quadrilaterals. A **quad**rilateral is a flat
geometric figure with **four** sides.

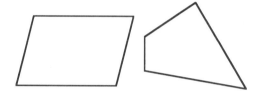

The prefix **quad** means **four**. For example,
a **quad**ruped is a **four**-egged animal.

The quadrilateral at the right has four
vertices at points P, Q, R, and S.
Two sides meet at a **vertex** of the
quadrilateral.

So, sides $\overline{RQ}$ and $\overline{RS}$ meet at **vertex R**.
Quadrilaterals are identified by their
vertices in **order** around the figure.

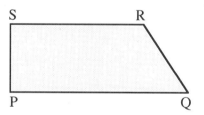

This quadrilateral can be identified as
quadrilateral PQRS, QRSP, RSPQ, SPQR,
PSRQ, SRQP, RQPS, or QPSR.

SPRQ is **NOT** a correct name for the
quadrilateral since the vertices are not
named in **order**.

S and Q are **opposite** vertices.
P and R are **opposite** vertices.

$\overline{SQ}$ and $\overline{RP}$ are called **diagonals** of the
quadrilateral. **Diagonals** connect **opposite**
vertices of a quadrilateral.

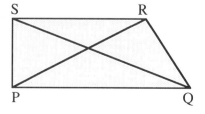

The following discovery activity is designed to pave the way for understanding the properties of a special type of quadrilateral.

MANIPULATIVE DISCOVERY

Plot the points A(-2,1), B(6,1), C(8,7), and D(0,7).

Draw the quadrilateral ABCD.

$\overline{AB}$ and $\overline{CD}$ are called **opposite** sides.

$\overline{AD}$ and $\overline{BC}$ are **opposite** sides.

Measure the length of each side to the nearest $\frac{1}{4}$ inch.

In this figure, what seems to be true about the lengths of opposite sides? What other relationship seems to exist between **opposite** sides in the quadrilateral?

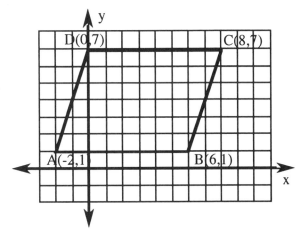

For the quadrilateral ABCD in the discovery activity above, the two pairs of opposite

sides are: (1)   **parallel:** $\overline{AB} \parallel \overline{CD}$ $\overline{AD} \parallel \overline{BC}$

              (2)   **equal in length:**   AB = CD   AD = BC

ABCD is a special type of quadrilateral called a **parallelogram**.

DEFINITION Parallelogram

A **parallelogram** is a quadrilateral in which opposite sides are **parallel.**
$\overline{AB} \parallel \overline{CD}, \overline{AD} \parallel \overline{BC}$

The sides are also **equal in length.**
AB = CD, AD = BC

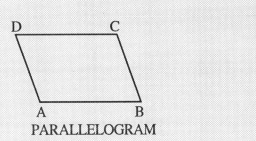

PARALLELOGRAM

EXAMPLE 1   Plot the points A(3,2), B(11,2), C(11,7), and D(3,7).

Draw the quadrilateral ABCD.

Find the length in units of each side.

Is ABCD a parallelogram?

What makes ABCD a special type of parallelogram?

Solution

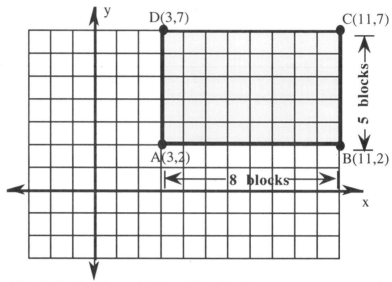

AB = DC = 8 units and BC = AD = 5 units.

From the drawing, $\overline{AB}$ || $\overline{CD}$ and $\overline{AD}$ || $\overline{BC}$.

Therefore, ABCD is a parallelogram since two pairs of sides are parallel.

Note that m ∠ A = m ∠ B = m ∠ C = m ∠ D = **90**.

So, ABCD is a special type of parallelogram since it has **4 right angles.**

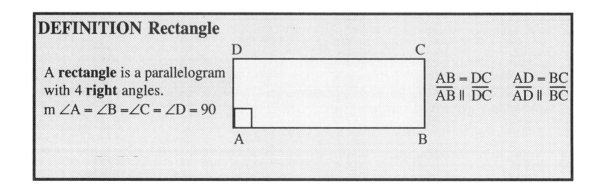

DEFINITION Rectangle

A **rectangle** is a parallelogram with 4 **right** angles.
m ∠A = ∠B =∠C = ∠D = 90

$$\frac{AB = DC}{AB \parallel DC} \quad \frac{AD = BC}{AD \parallel BC}$$

EXAMPLE 2   Plot the points A(-1,-1), B(4,-1), C(4,4), and D(-1,4).

Draw the quadrilateral ABCD.

Find the length in units (by counting blocks) of each side.

Is ABCD a rectangle? Why?

What makes ABCD look like a special type of rectangle

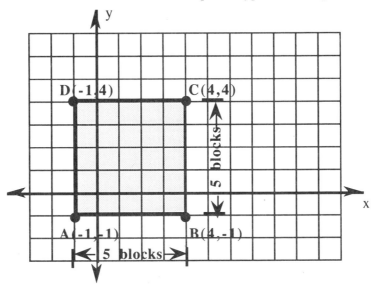

Solution   AB = BC = CD = DA = **5**.

Opposite sides are **parallel**.

So, ABCD is a parallelogram.

All four angles are **right** angles.

So, ABCD is a special type of parallelogram, a **rectangle**.

ABCD is a special type of rectangle since all four sides have the same length.

DEFINITION Square

A **square** is a rectangle with all four sides equal in length.
AB = BC = CD = DA

AB ∥ DC   AD ∥ BC
m ∠A = ∠B = ∠C = ∠D = 90

There is one special type of quadrilateral that is **NOT** a parallelogram.

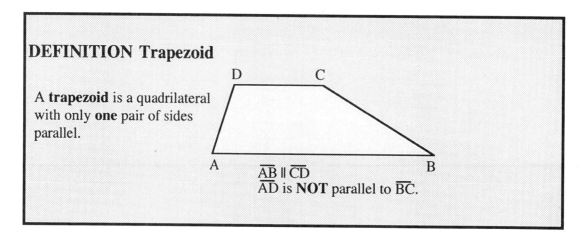

DEFINITION Trapezoid

A **trapezoid** is a quadrilateral with only **one** pair of sides parallel.

$\overline{AB} \parallel \overline{CD}$
$\overline{AD}$ is **NOT** parallel to $\overline{BC}$.

Below is a summary of the characteristics of the 4 special types of quadrilaterals illustrated in this lesson.

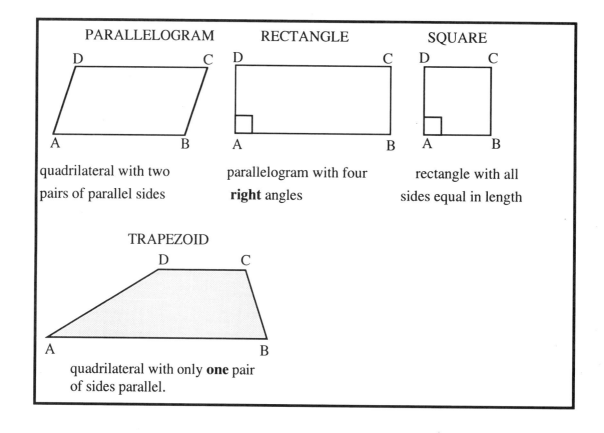

PARALLELOGRAM

quadrilateral with two pairs of parallel sides

RECTANGLE

parallelogram with four **right** angles

SQUARE

rectangle with all sides equal in length

TRAPEZOID

quadrilateral with only **one** pair of sides parallel.

EXAMPLE 3   Identify the special type of quadrilateral.

Solution   parallelogram and rectangle

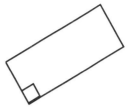

Recall a special property of angle relationships for parallel lines.

If parallel lines are cut by a transversal, then alternate interior angles have equal measure.

The next example applies this idea to finding the measure of an angle in a parallelogram.

EXAMPLE 4   Given: ABCD is a parallelogram
                  Find m ∠1.

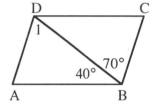

Strategy   Since ABCD is a parallelogram,

$\overline{AB} \parallel \overline{DC}$ and $\overline{AD} \parallel \overline{BC}$.

So, alternate interior angles have equal
measure. Determine which alternate
interior angles to use.
Shade the sides of ∠**1**.

Shade the side parallel to

$\overline{AD}$, a side of ∠**1**.

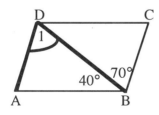

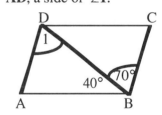

The alternate interior angles
are ∠**1** and the **70°** angle.

Solution   So, m ∠ 1 = **70**.

SUMMARY

1.   What is a quadrilateral?

2.   How do you decide how to label the
     quadrilateral at the right?

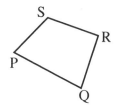

3.   Is PRSQ a correct name for the
     quadrilateral? Why?

4.   What is a parallelogram?

5.   What are two special types of parallelograms?

6.   How does a rectangle differ from a square?

7.   Is a trapezoid a special type of parallelogram? Explain why.

CLASSROOM PRACTICE

Plot the points F(1,2), H(9,2), W(6,6), and P(-2,6).

Draw the quadrilateral FHWP and use the figure to answer exercises 1-4.

1.   Use a ruler to measure, to the nearest $\frac{1}{4}$ inch, the length of each side.

2.   Which sides are parallel?

3.   Is FHWP a parallelogram? Why?

4.   Is FHWP a rectangle? Why?

Plot the points T(-2,1), G(4,1), A(4,4), and F(-2,4).

Draw the quadrilateral TGAF and use the figure to answer exercises 5-8.

5.   Find the length, in units, of each side.

6.   Is TGAF a parallelogram? Why?

7.   Is TGAF a square? Why?

8.   What special kind of parallelogram is TGAF? Why?

Plot the points A(1,1), H(12,1), T(9,5), and M(4,5).

Draw the quadrilateral AHTM and use the figure to answer exercises 9-12.

9.   Use a ruler to measure, to the nearest $\frac{1}{4}$ inch, the length of each side.

10.   Which sides are parallel?

11.   Is AHTM a parallelogram? Why?

12.   What special kind of quadrilateral is AHTM? Why?

Plot the points A(2,1), B(6,4), C(3,8), D(-1,5).

Draw the quadrilateral ABCD and use the figure to answer exercises 13-16.

13.   Use a ruler to measure, to the nearest $\frac{1}{4}$ inch, the length of each side.

14.   Is ABCD a parallelogram? Why?

15.   What appears to be true about the angle measures?

16.   What special kind of parallelogram does the figure appear to be? Why?

Given: STUV is a parallelogram

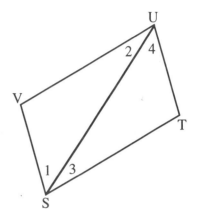

17.   m $\angle$ 1 = 38, m $\angle$ 3 = 26

        Find m $\angle$ 4.

18.   m $\angle$ 4 = 62, m $\angle$ 2 = 29

        Find m $\angle$ 3.

19.   m $\angle$ 3 = 19, m $\angle$ 1 = 72

        Find m $\angle$ 2.

20.   m $\angle$ 2 = 44, m $\angle$ 4 = 17

        Find m $\angle$ 1.

WRITTEN EXERCISES

Plot the points F(-2,-3), H(4,-3), W(10,5), and P(4,5).

Draw the quadrilateral FHWP and use the figure to answer exercises 1-4.

1.   Use a ruler to measure, to the nearest $\frac{1}{4}$ inch, the length of each side.

2.   Which sides are parallel?

3.   Is FHWP a parallelogram? Why?

4.   Is FHWP a rectangle? Why?

Plot the points Q(-2,3), R(6,3), W(6,11), and G(-2,11).

Draw the quadrilateral QRWG and use the figure to answer exercises 5-8.

5.   Find the length, in units, of each side.

6.   Is QRWG a parallelogram? Why?

7.   What appears to be true about the angle measures?

8.   What special kind of parallelogram is QRWG? Why?

Plot the points K(-4,2), L(8,-3), M(13,9), and N(1,14).

Draw the quadrilateral KLMN and use the figure to answer exercises 9-12.

9.   Use a ruler to measure, to the nearest $\frac{1}{4}$ inch, the length of each side.

10.   Is KLMN a parallelogram? Why?

11.   What appears to be true about the angle measures?

12.   What special kind of quadrilateral does KLMN appear to be? Why?

Plot the points A(2,1), B(12,1), C(10,8), D(5,8).

Draw the quadrilateral ABCD and use the figure to answer exercises 13-16.

13.   Use a ruler to measure, to the nearest $\frac{1}{4}$ inch, the length of each side.

14.   Which sides are parallel?

15.   Is ABCD a parallelogram? Why?

16.   What special kind of quadrilateral is ABCD? Why?

Given: TSVU is a parallelogram:

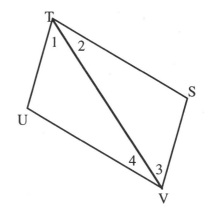

17.   m ∠ 4 = 44, m ∠ 3 = 39
      Find m ∠ 2.

18.   m ∠ 1 = 72, m ∠ 2 = 10
      Find m ∠ 3.

19.   m ∠ 3 = 17 m ∠ 4 = 55
      Find m ∠ 2.

20.   m ∠ 2 = 44, m ∠ 1 = 27
      Find m ∠ 4.

OPEN-ENDED QUESTION

21.   Plot the points A(1,2), B(10,2), C(12,7), and D(3,7).

      Draw ABCD and verify that it is a parallelogram. Draw the diagonals,

      $\overline{AC}$ and $\overline{BD}$. Use a ruler to determine if the diagonals of a parallelogram are always equal in length. Is there ever a parallelogram with diagonals equal in length? If so, draw one on graph paper and give the coordinates of the four vertices.

REVIEW

1. There are four different figures in the spiral below. If they are labeled S, T, U, and V in the order in which they first appear (beginning at **Start** and going clockwise), what letters represent the missing figures?

   (A) VU

   (B) ST

   (C) TV

   (D) UV

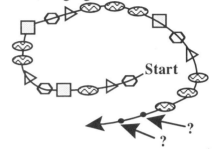

2. Which of the figures below cannot be folded to form a closed box?

   (A)   (B)   (C)   (D)

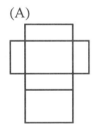 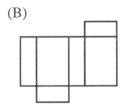 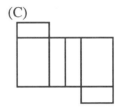 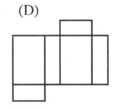

3. The fare for a taxi ride consists of $5.00 for the first mile and a charge of $1.25 for each additional half-mile. At this rate, what is the cost of a taxi ride of 6 miles?

   (A) $11.25   (B) $12.50   (C) $17.50   (D) $30

4. Solve the proportion $\frac{x}{4} = \frac{2}{3}$.

   (A) 6   (B) $2\frac{2}{3}$ (C) $\frac{3}{8}$ (D) 5

5. At a football game Saretha sells sodas at $0.75 each to raise money for booster club activities. At the end of the game she counts the money collected. She counts it 4 times getting 4 different results. Which of the following could be the correct total?

   (A) $142.35   (B) $215.50   (C) $335   (D) $337.50

10.5   Similar Geometric Figures

OBJECTIVES   To graph a figure similar to a figure with given coordinates

To verify by measurements with a ruler and protractor that figures are similar

To use proportions to solve similar figures problems

To identify similar triangles formed by transversals to parallel lines

Recall that geometric figures are **congruent** if they have the same **shape** and **size**. Many important applications involve geometric figures that are **similar.** **Similar** figures have the same **shape** but not necessarily the same size.

For example, a scale model car has the same shape as the real car it models. A Lionel electric train is said to be built to scale. What does this mean?

Suppose you have a 3" by 5" photo of a friend. If you have the photo enlarged to a 9" by 15" photo, the two are **similar.** They have the same **shape**. What do you think this means?

DISCOVERY

The drawings below show an original face and four other faces. Faces (A) and (B) have the same shape as the original. Can you explain why? But faces (C) and (D) are **NOT** the same shape as the original. Can you explain why?

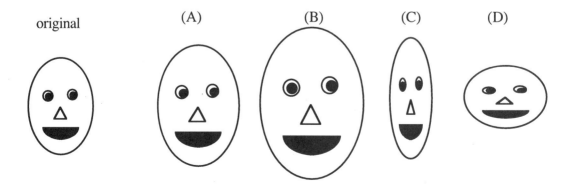

The smaller figure represents the front of a house. The larger figure is a **magnification** of the first.

Notice that corresponding angles have the same measure.

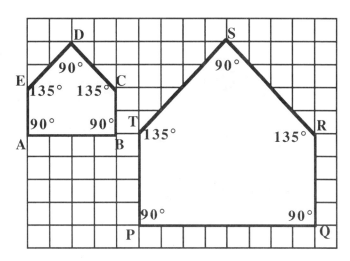

If you copy these drawings and measure the sides of each figure, you will discover a common ratio.

AB = 1"   BC = $\frac{1}{2}$"   CD = $\frac{3}{4}$"   DE = $\frac{3}{4}$"   EA = $\frac{1}{2}$"

PQ = 2"   QR = 1"   RS = $1\frac{1}{2}$"   ST = $1\frac{1}{2}$"   TP = 1"

PQ is **twice** EA   QR is **twice** BC   RS is **twice** CD   ST is **twice** DE   TP is **twice** EA

The two figures are said to be **SIMILAR**.

1. Their corresponding sides are all in the **same** ratio, **1: 2**
2. Their corresponding angles are **equal** in measure.

EXAMPLE 1   Plot the points A(2,1), B(6,1), and C(6,8).

Draw   △ABC.

Multiply both coordinates of each vertex of △ABC by 2.

Graph the resulting triangle.

How do the lengths of the sides of this triangle compare with the lengths of the sides of △ABC?

How do the angle measures of this triangle compare with the angle measures of △ABC?

Does it have the same shape as △ABC?

(solution on next page)

Strategy   First plot the points A, B, and C. Draw △ABC.

Graph the result of multilplying both coordinates of each point by 2.

A(2,1)   B(6,1)   C(6,8)

$\downarrow$ $\downarrow$ $\downarrow$

(2 · **2**, 1 · **2**)   (6 · **2**, 1 · **2**)   (6 · **2**, 8 · **2**)

P(4,2)   Q(12,2)   R(12,16)

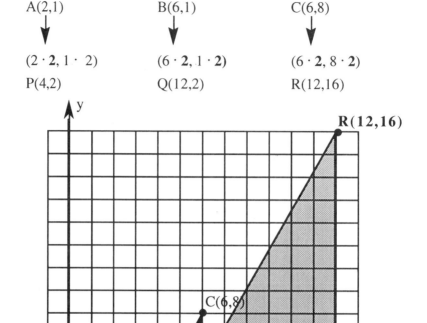

Measure sides and angles on your graph paper for the two triangles.
(side lengths to nearest $\frac{1}{4}$", angle measures to nearest degree)

AB = 1"   BC = $1\frac{3}{4}$"   AC = 2"

PQ = 2"   QR = $3\frac{1}{2}$"   PR = 4"

TWICE AB   **TWICE BC**   **TWICE AC**

m ∠A = m ∠P = 60   m ∠B = m ∠Q = 90   m ∠C = m ∠R = 30

Solution   Thus, the two triangles have the same shape: they are **similar**.

In Example 1 on the previous page, you saw that the corresponding side lengths of ΔPQR are **twice** those of ΔABC.

The corresponding side lengths are **proportional** (in the **same ratio**) but **not** equal.

The two triangles are **similar** but **not** congruent.

Similar figures have the same **shape** but **not** the same size.

The symbol for **is similar to** is ~.

You can write   ΔABC   ~   ΔPQR, which is read as

                         ΔABC **is similar to** ΔPQR.

The symbol ~ looks like the symbol for **is congruent to** (≅) without the =.

DEFINITION Similar Figures

Geometric figures are similar if :

1. corresponding angles have equal measure and
2. corresponding sides are **proportional (have the same ratio)**.

Recall the property for proportions..

$$\text{If } \frac{a}{b} = \frac{c}{d} \text{, then}$$

$$a \cdot d = b \cdot c \qquad \textbf{Cross multiply.}$$

For example, $\text{If } \frac{3}{5} = \frac{6}{10} \text{, then}$

$$3 \cdot 10 = 5 \cdot 6 \qquad \textbf{Cross multiply.}$$

$$30 = 30 \qquad \textbf{True}$$

In the next example you will use this property of proportions to determine whether two rectangles are similar.

EXAMPLE 2   For each figure, are the two rectangles similar? Show why or why not.

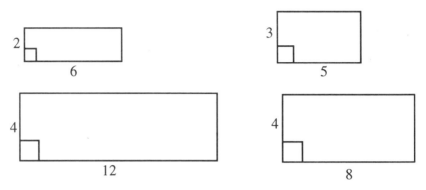

Strategy

1. In each case corresponding angles are equal in measure.

All the angles are right angles since both figures are rectangles.

2. Now check for proportionality of sides.

Write a proportion for each figure.

$$\frac{2}{4} \overset{?}{=} \frac{6}{12} \qquad\qquad \frac{3}{4} \overset{?}{=} \frac{5}{8}$$

$$2 \cdot 12 \overset{?}{=} 4 \cdot 6 \qquad\qquad 3 \cdot 8 \overset{?}{=} 4 \cdot 5 \quad \textbf{Cross multiply.}$$

$$24 = 24 \qquad\qquad\quad 24 \neq 20$$

Corresponding sides   Corresponding sides
are proportional.   are **NOT** proportional.

Rectangles are similar.   Rectangles are **NOT** similar.

CONDITIONS NECESSARY FOR FIGURES TO BE SIMILAR

For **triangles**, it can be proved that two **triangles** are **similar** if **either** of the two conditions below is true.

1. corresponding angles have equal measure, **OR**

2. corresponding sides are **proportional (have the same ratio).**

For other geometric figures, **BOTH** conditions must be true if the figures are to be similar.

EXAMPLE 3   Find x for the similar right triangles.

Strategy   Write a proportion. Solve it.

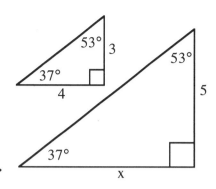

$$\frac{3}{5} = \frac{4}{x}$$

$$3 \cdot x = 5 \cdot 4 \text{ **Cross multiply.**}$$

$$3x = 20$$

Solution $x = 6\frac{2}{3}$

Notice that for Example 3 above, other proportions could have produced the same result.

$$\frac{5}{3} = \frac{x}{4}$$ $$\frac{3}{4} = \frac{5}{x}$$ $$\frac{4}{3} = \frac{x}{5}$$

$$20 = 3x$$ $$3x = 20$$ $$20 = 3x$$

$$6\frac{2}{3} = x$$ $$x = 6\frac{2}{3}$$ $$6\frac{2}{3} = x$$

The result is the same for each proportion: $x = 6\frac{2}{3}$

The last two proportions above suggest an important property for similar right triangles which will be applied in the next lesson on **Slopes of Lines**.

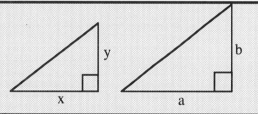

If two right triangles are similar, then

$\frac{y}{x} = \frac{b}{a}$ Ratio of leg lengths is the same.

Parallel segments can produce similar triangles.

Recall first the Alternate Interior Angles Property.

If $\overline{AB}$ ∥ $\overline{CD}$, then m ∠ 1 = m ∠ 2 by the **Alternate Interior Angles Property**.

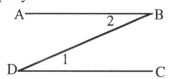

EXAMPLE 4

Given: ABCD is a trapezoid.
Identify any similar triangles. Indicate why they are similar.

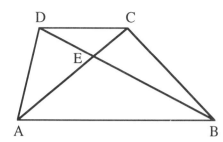

Strategy

Since ABCD is a trapezoid, $\overline{\textbf{AB}} \parallel \overline{\textbf{CD}}$.
Shade the triangles containing the parallel segments.
Draw these triangles separately.
Look for 3 pairs of angles that have equal measure.

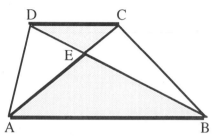

1. m ∠ D = m ∠ B by alternate interior angles property

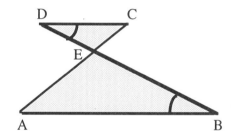

2. m ∠ A = m ∠ C by alternate interior angles property

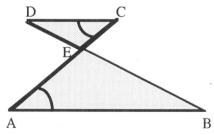

3. m ∠ 1 = m ∠ 2 since **vertical angles** have equal measure.

Solution

So, ΔDEC ~ ΔBEA since **3** pairs of corresponding **angles** have **equal** measure.

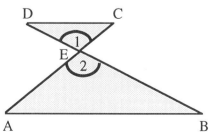

SUMMARY

1. What two conditions are necessary for geometric figures other than triangles to be similar?

2. If two triangles are similar, then corresponding sides are _____ and corresponding angles have ____ _____.
    Do you need both of these conditions to guarantee similarity of triangles?

3. How do you determine if these rectangles are similar?

4. How do you find x if the two triangles are similar?

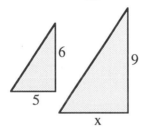

5. Suppose you are given the vertices of △ABC are A(3,1), B(6,1), and C(4,7). If you draw △ABC, how can you then draw a triangle whose sides are twice the length of those of △ABC?
    These two triangles will be ____.

6. Given: $\overline{RS} \parallel \overline{PT}$
    How can you show the two triangles are similar?

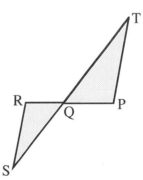

7. How do you solve the proportion $\frac{3}{4} = \frac{x}{7}$?

8. What is the symbol for "is similar to" ?

CLASSROOM PRACTICE

Plot the points A(1,3), B(5,3), C(5,6), and D(1,6). Draw rectangle ABCD.

Use this figure you just drew to answer exercises 1-3.

1.   Find the length of each side of ABCD.

2.   Multiply both coordinates of each of the four vertices of ABCD by 3.
      Graph the resulting rectangle. Find the lengths of the sides of this new rectangle.

3.   Show that the two rectangles are similar.

Plot the points P(1,2), Q(7,2), and R(1,6). Draw ΔPQR. (Use for Exercises 4-6.)

4.   Use a ruler to find to the nearest $\frac{1}{4}$ inch the length of each side.

5.   Multiply both coordinates of each of the three vertices of ΔPQR by 2.
      Graph the resulting triangle. Find the lengths of the sides of this new triangle.

6.   Show two ways that the two triangles are similar.

Determine whether the rectangles are similar. Show why or why not.

7.

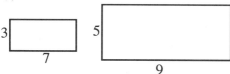

8.

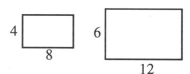

9.   Find x for the similar triangles.

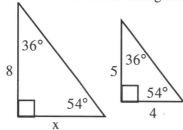

10.   Find x for the similar rectangles.

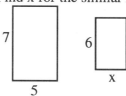

11.   Given: $\overline{AB} \parallel \overline{CD}$

        Find m ∠ 1, m ∠ 2, m ∠ B, m ∠ A.

        Is ΔDEC ~ ΔBEA?

        Why?

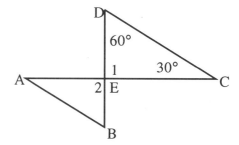

WRITTEN EXERCISES

Plot the points A(1,4), B(6,4), C(6,10), and D(1,10). Draw rectangle ABCD.
Use this figure to answer exercises 1-3

1. Find the length of each side of ABCD.

2. Multiply both coordinates of each of the four vertices of ABCD by 2.
   Graph the resulting rectangle. Find the lengths of the sides of this new rectangle.

3. Show that the two rectangles are similar.

Plot the points P(1,1), Q(6,1), and R(2,7). Draw ΔPQR. (Use figure for Exercises 4-6.)

4. Use a ruler to find to the nearest $\frac{1}{4}$ inch the length of each side.

5. Multiply both coordinates of each of the three vertices of ΔPQR by 2.
   Graph the resulting triangle. Find the lengths of the sides of this new triangle.

6. Show two ways that the two triangles are similar.

Determine whether the rectangles are similar. Show why or why not.

7.   8.

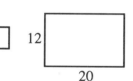

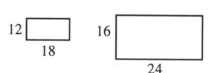

9. Find x for the similar triangles.   10. Find x for the similar rectangles.

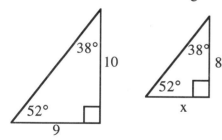

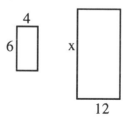

11. Given: segments m and n are parallel. Are the two triangles similar? Explain why.

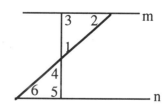

Use the similar triangles at the right to answer exercises 13-14.

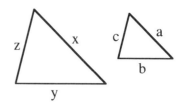

12.   a = 6, b = 8, x = 10, y = ?

13.   z = 5, y =7, b = 4, c = ?

Given: ABCD is a trapezoid.

14.   Find m ∠1 .

15.   Find m ∠2.

16.   Find m ∠3.

17.   Find m ∠4.

18.   Is ΔDEC ~ ΔBEA? Why?

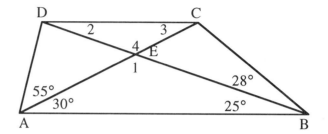

OPEN-ENDED QUESTION

19.   You have seen that two triangles are similar if the measures of the **three** angles of one triangle equal the measures of the **three** corresponding angles of the other triangle. Use the following to discover another way to show triangles similar.

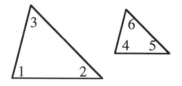

m ∠1 = 70, m ∠2 = 40, m ∠4 = 70, m ∠5 = 40. Find m ∠3 and m ∠6.

m ∠1 = 65, m ∠2 = 35, m ∠4 = 65, m ∠5 = 35. Find m ∠3 and m ∠6.

m ∠1 = 80, m ∠2 = 45, m ∠4 = 80, m ∠5 = 45. Find m ∠3 and m ∠6.

The results above suggest that if the measures of two angles of one triangle equal the measures of two angles of a second triangle, then _____.

From the results above, is it necessary to show three pairs of angles equal in measure to show triangles similar? Why?

Review: Chapters 1-10

For each of the following exercises assume that m ‖ n.

1.   m ∠ 3 = 85, m ∠ 5 = ?

2.   m ∠ 4 = 108, m ∠ 7 = ?

3.   m ∠ 5 = 78, m ∠ 2 = ?

4.   m ∠ 3 = 5x - 10, m ∠ 5 = 2x + 11

      Find m ∠ 3.

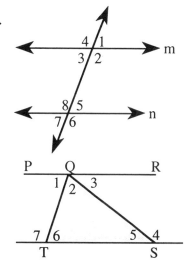

For each of the following, $\overline{PR}$ ‖ $\overline{TS}$.

5.   m ∠ 4 = 112, m ∠ 2 = 27, m ∠ 6 = ?

6.   m ∠ TQR = 115, m ∠ 5 = 45, m ∠ 2 = ?

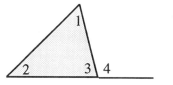

7.   m ∠ 4 = 112, m ∠ 2 = 77, m ∠ 1 = ?

8.   m ∠ 3 = x, m ∠ 1 = 2x + 10, m ∠ 2 = 3x + 20

      Find m ∠ 4.

9.   m ∠ 3 = x, m ∠ 1 = 2x + 20, m ∠ 2 = 3x + 10

      Find m ∠ 2.

Plot the points A(3,2), B(7,5), C(4,9), and D(0,6).

10.   Use a ruler to measure, to the nearest $\frac{1}{4}$ inch, the length of each side.

11.   Is ABCD a parallelogram? Why?

12.   What appears to be true about the angle measures?

13.   What special kind of parallelogram does ABCD appear to be?

ABCD is a parallelogram.

14.   m ∠ 3 = 32, m ∠ 2 = 29, m ∠ 1 = ?

15.   m ∠ 1 = 46, m ∠ 4 = 37, m ∠ 2 = ?

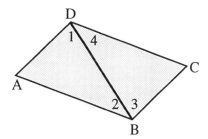

16.   The measure of the vertex angle of an isosceles triangle is 32.

       Find the measure of each base angle.

Plot the points P(2,2), Q(7,2), and R(3,8). Draw $\triangle$PQR.

17.   Use a ruler to measure, to the nearest $\frac{1}{4}$ inch, the length of each side.

18.   Multiply both coordinates of each of the three vertices of $\triangle$PQR by 2.

         Graph the resulting triangle. Find the lengths of the sides of this triangle.

19.   Are the triangles similar or congruent? why?

Use the similar triangles at the right to
answer Exercises 20-21.

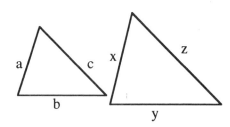

20.   a = 3, b = 4, x = 5, y = ?
21.   z = 4, y = 7, b = 3, c = ?

Given: ABCD is a trapezoid

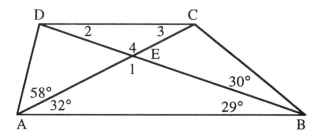

22.   Find m $\angle$ 1
23.   Find m $\angle$ 3
24.   Is $\triangle$AEB ~ $\triangle$CED? Why?

25.   Monica has indicated that she wants to withdraw money from her bank's
         automatic teller. The computer screen displays **"ENTER MULTIPLES OF 20"**.
         Which entry below would not be acceptable to the computer?

         (A)   160   (B)   130   (C)   200   (D)   440

26.   Compare the following.

         I   This month, Acme Appliances sold $\frac{2}{3}$ as many stereos as last month.

         II   Last month, Acme Appliances' stereo sales were 150% of this
               month's sales.

         III   This month, Acme Appliances sold 60 stereos, and last month it sold
               40 stereos.

         Which statements above are equivalent to one another?

         (A)   I and II only   (B)   I and III only

         (C)   II and III only   (D)   I, II, and III

27. The arrangements at the right show the first 3 terms of a pattern. How many squares would be in the arrangement representing the seventh term of this pattern?

1 st term   2 nd term   3 rd term

(A) 28   (B) 56   (C) 84   (D) 131

28. The average price of a home in Rumson is $350,000. The average price of a home in Neptune is $170,000. In both cities the average home price is 6 times the average income. About how much more is the average income in Rumson than in Neptune?

(A) $20,000 (B) $30,000
(C) $80,000 (D) $86,000

29. If x = -4, which of the following does **NOT** equal 16?

(A) x^2 (B) $-x^2$ (C) $(-x)^2$ (D) $-4x$

30. PQ = g and PR = h
Find QR.

(A) g + h   (B) g - g   (C) gh   (D) h - g

31. Examine the pattern **mathmathmathmath ...**
If this pattern keeps repeating, what symbol will be in the 113 th position?

(A) a   (B) h   (C) m   (D) t

32. What is the weight of one of the blocks if each pyramid weighs 2 pounds and the scale is balanced?

(A) 2   (B) 3
(C) 8   (D) 16

33. Which of these choices would you write in the blank to make a true statement?

$$3.2^3 \underline{\quad} 1.6^8$$

(A) >   (B) =   (C) <   (D) is twice

34.   Five different shapes appear in the spiral at the right. They are labeled P, Q, R, S, and T in the order in which they first appear at start. What letters represent the two missing figures in the order in which they appear going clockwise in this spiral?

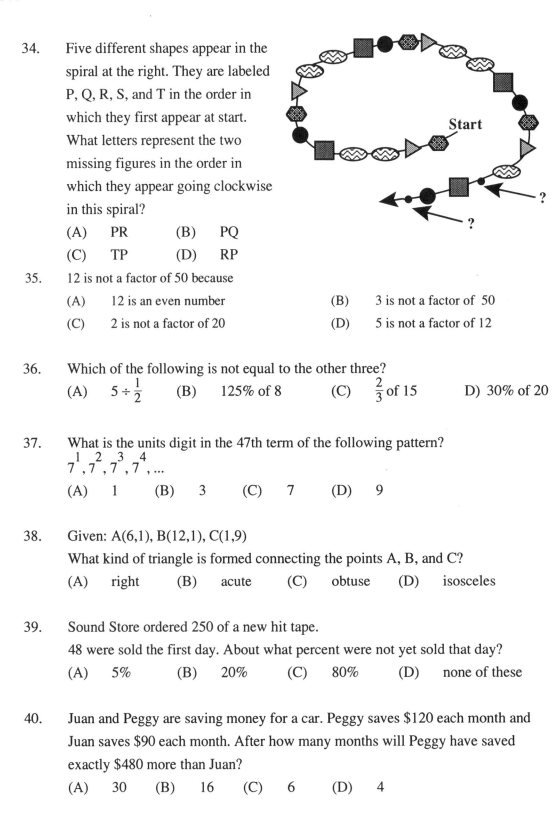

(A)   PR   (B)   PQ
(C)   TP   (D)   RP

35.   12 is not a factor of 50 because

(A)   12 is an even number   (B)   3 is not a factor of 50

(C)   2 is not a factor of 20   (D)   5 is not a factor of 12

36.   Which of the following is not equal to the other three?
(A) $5 \div \frac{1}{2}$ (B)   125% of 8   (C) $\frac{2}{3}$ of 15   D) 30% of 20

37.   What is the units digit in the 47th term of the following pattern?
$7^1, 7^2, 7^3, 7^4, ...$
(A)   1   (B)   3   (C)   7   (D)   9

38.   Given: A(6,1), B(12,1), C(1,9)
What kind of triangle is formed connecting the points A, B, and C?
(A)   right   (B)   acute   (C)   obtuse   (D)   isosceles

39.   Sound Store ordered 250 of a new hit tape.
48 were sold the first day. About what percent were not yet sold that day?
(A)   5%   (B)   20%   (C)   80%   (D)   none of these

40.   Juan and Peggy are saving money for a car. Peggy saves $120 each month and Juan saves $90 each month. After how many months will Peggy have saved exactly $480 more than Juan?
(A)   30   (B)   16   (C)   6   (D)   4

41. A particular plant starts as a single stem. At the beginning of the second year
     it grows four branches and therefore has five tips growing. Each year, every
     branch does the same thing. That is, it grows four branches and continues to
     grow itself. How many tips are on that plant in the fifth year if no tip or
     branch has been destroyed?

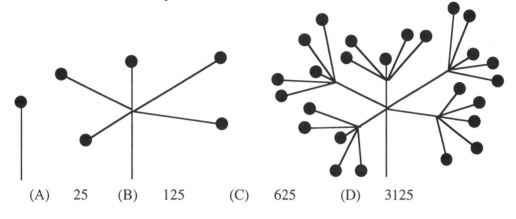

     (A)   25   (B)   125   (C)   625   (D)   3125

42. Performing which set of transformations on the
     heavily shaded figure will **NOT** result in
     the lightly shaded figure being completely
     covered by the heavily shaded figure?

     (A)   translation 2 units to the right followed
            by reflection in the x-axis

     (B)   reflection in the x-axis followed by
            reflection in the y-axis

     (C)   translation 6 units to the right followed by reflection in the x-axis

     (D)   rotation of 180° about the origin

43. This chart shows $8,000,000,000
     in all major retail car sales.
     Ford sales were about what
     percent of General Motors sales?

     (A)   123%   (B)   80%
     (C)   285%   (D)   2.2%

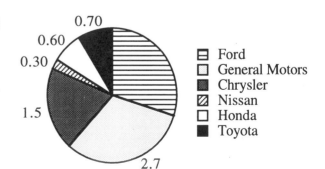

44.   Which spinner below would give you the best probability of spinning a Q?

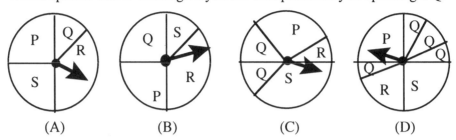

      (A)   (B)   (C)   (D)

45.   The general partners in a small company, Muriel, Consuela, and Dennison, share
      its profits in the ratio 3:4:5, respectively. If the total profits of the business came
      to $240,000 this year, what was Consuela's share?
      (A) $20,000   (B) $60,000
      (C) $80,000   (D) $100,000

46.   If 5y - 7 = 6 + 14y, then y =
      (A) $\frac{13}{9}$ (B) $\frac{1}{9}$ (C) $-\frac{1}{19}$ (D) $-\frac{13}{9}$

47.   A car traveled 5 miles in 10 minutes. Find its average speed for that trip.
      (A)   50 mph   (B)   30 mph   (C)   2.0 mph   (D)   5 mph

OPEN ENDED QUESTION

48.   The yearly salaries of all the employees in a small computer software designing
      company are given below.
         Company Executive Officer: $100,000
         Director: $70,000
         Research Analysts: $50,000, $48,000, $46,000, $46,000
         Programmers: $38,000, $38,000, $38,000, $26,000
         Secretaries: $21,000, $20,000, $13,000
      Find the mean, median, and mode of the salaries.
      How is each of these statistics affected if the top salary is excluded?
      What statistic would best represent a typical salary in this company? Explain.

Chapter

11

Graphing Lines

11.1   Slope of a Line

OBJECTIVES To find the slope of a non-vertical line or segment

If the x-axis represents level ground and the
segments $\overline{AB}$ and $\overline{AC}$ represent paths up a
hill, $\overline{AC}$ would be more difficult to climb than
$\overline{AB}$. The reason is that $\overline{AC}$ has a steeper
slope than $\overline{AB}$.

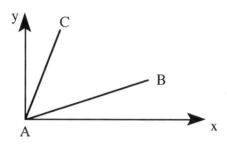

Here's how to describe the slope of a line or segment in mathematical terms.
We borrow a carpenter's description for the slope of the roof of a house.

If the roof rises 3 units for every 4 units of
horizontal run, a carpenter expresses the **slope**
of the roof as **rise** to **run**.
At the right, the slope is $\dfrac{3}{4}$ $\dfrac{\text{rise}}{\text{run}}$.

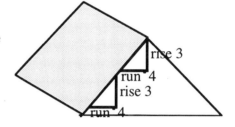

If you know the coordinates of two points of a segment, you can describe the slope of the segment
in terms of **rise over run**, as shown below.

Given the points P(2,1) and Q(6,7), you can
find the slope of the segment joining them as
follows.

First, plot the points P and Q.

Then draw a line segment between them.
Sketching the right triangle helps you visualize
the **rise** and **run**.

So the slope, by counting blocks, is
$$\frac{6}{4} = \frac{3}{2} \quad \frac{\text{rise}}{\text{run}}.$$

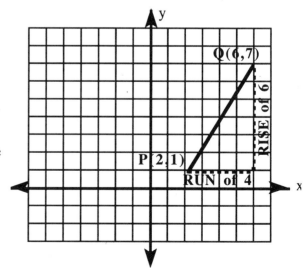

The slope of $\overline{PQ}$ can be found without actually graphing points and drawing a triangle.

Notice for the illustration of the previous page, the slope of $\overline{PQ}$ can be expressed as:

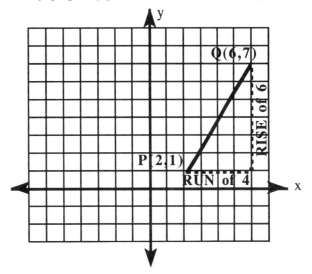

difference of y-coordinates
------
difference of x-coordinates.

$$\frac{7-1}{6-2} = \frac{6}{4} = \frac{3}{2}$$

This suggests that the slope of a non-vertical line segment can be found directly from the coordinates of the endpoints of the segment.

EXAMPLE 1   Find the slope of the line using points B and C.   **B(0,2), C(3,4)**

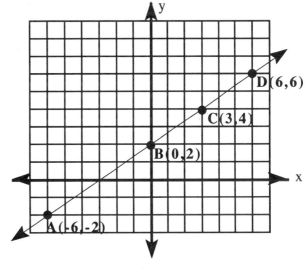

Strategy   Use slope =

diff. of y-coord.
------
diff. of x-coord.

Solution $\dfrac{4-2}{3-0} = \dfrac{2}{3}$

What happens if you use other points to find the slope of the line in Example 1 above?
For example, try C(3,4), D(6,6)   or   A(-6,-2), D(6,6).

$$\text{slope of } \overline{CD} = \frac{6-4}{6-3} = \frac{2}{3} \qquad\qquad \text{slope of } \overline{AD} = \frac{6-(-2)}{6-(-6)} = \frac{8}{12} = \frac{2}{3}$$

This illustrates that the slope of a line is the **same** for any segment of the line.
Thus, the slope of the line of Example 1 is $\frac{2}{3}$, no matter what two points are used.

On the previous page you saw that the slope of a line is the **same** for any two points on the line. This can be justified by **similar triangles** as shown below.

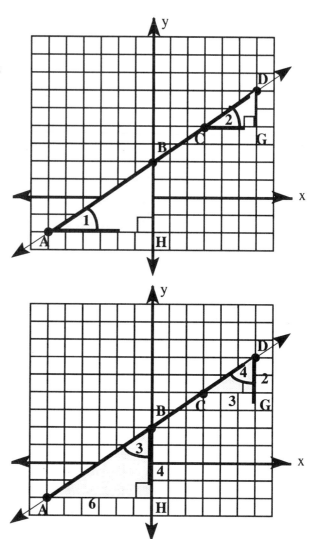

Recall that triangles are **similar** if the measures of their corresponding angles are the **same.**

1. ∠G and ∠H are right angles.
    m ∠ G = m ∠ H = 90.

2. $\overline{AH}$ ∥ $\overline{CG}$
    Therefore m ∠ 1 = m ∠ 2.
    (Corresponding angles of parallels are equal in measure.)

3. $\overline{BH}$ ∥ $\overline{DG}$
    Therefore m ∠ 3 = m ∠ 4.
    (Corresponding angles of parallels are equal in measure.)

3 pairs of angles equal in measure
Therefore, ΔAHB ~ ΔCGD.
Now, since the triangles are **similar,** the sides are **proportional.**
Corresponding legs of the right triangles are in the same ratio.

$$\frac{BH}{HA} = \frac{DG}{GC}$$

$$\frac{4}{6} = \frac{2}{3}$$

slope of $\overline{AB}$ = slope of $\overline{CD}$

> **DEFINITION   Slope of a Non-Vertical Line or Line Segment**
>
> $$\textbf{slope} = \frac{\text{the difference of the y-coordinates}}{\text{the difference of the x-coordinates}}$$

EXAMPLE 2   Find the slope of $\overline{AB}$ for A(2,4) and B(11,7).

Strategy   You can use the ratio $\dfrac{\textbf{diff. of y-coord.}}{\textbf{diff. of x-coord.}}$ in two ways.

First way   Second way

$\dfrac{\text{y-coord. of B - y-coord. of A}}{\text{x-coord. of B - x-coord. of A}}$ $\dfrac{\text{y-coord. of A - y-coord. of B}}{\text{x-coord. of A - x-coord. of B}}$

$\dfrac{7-4}{11-2} = \dfrac{3}{9} = \dfrac{1}{3}$ $\dfrac{4-7}{2-11} = \dfrac{-3}{-9} = \dfrac{3}{9} = \dfrac{1}{3}$

Both ways give the same slope.

Thus, the slope of $\overline{AB}$ is $\dfrac{1}{3}$.

The slope of a line segment can be a negative number. This is illustrated in Example 3. First recall from algebra that an expression like 6 - (-3) becomes 6 + 3, or 9.

Example 3   Find the slope of $\overline{CD}$ for C(1,7) and D(11,2).

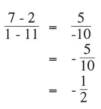

$$\frac{7-2}{1-11} = \frac{5}{-10}$$
$$= -\frac{5}{10}$$
$$= -\frac{1}{2}$$

Slope is **negative**.

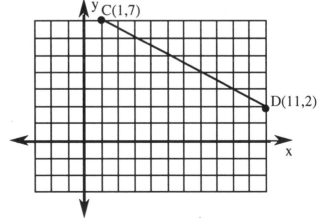

Solution   Thus, the slope of

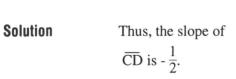

$\overline{CD}$ is $-\dfrac{1}{2}$.

You have seen that the slope of a non-vertical line segment can be either positive or negative. The slope of a non-vertical line segment can also be zero.
This is illustrated in Example 4 below.

EXAMPLE 4   Find the slope of $\overline{CD}$ for C(1,7) and D(11,2).

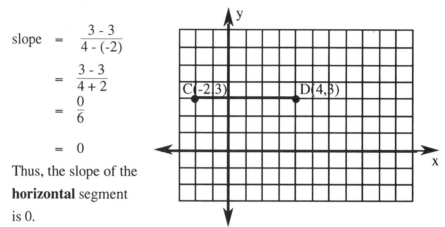

$$\text{slope} \; = \; \frac{3-3}{4-(-2)}$$

$$= \; \frac{3-3}{4+2}$$

$$= \; \frac{0}{6}$$

$$= \; 0$$

Solution   Thus, the slope of the **horizontal** segment is 0.

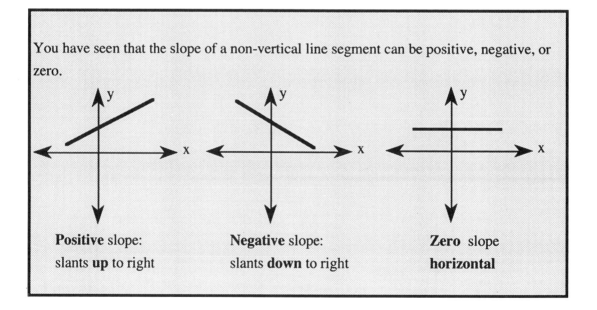

You have seen that the slope of a non-vertical line segment can be positive, negative, or zero.

Positive slope: slants **up** to right

Negative slope: slants **down** to right

Zero slope **horizontal**

SUMMARY

1.   How do you find the slope of a line segment if you are given the coordinates of two points on the line segment?

2.   Describe the slant of a line segment with positive slope.

3.   Describe the slant of a line segment with negative slope.

4.   Describe the slant of a line segment with zero slope.

CLASSROOM PRACTICE

Find the slope of $\overline{AB}$ for the given coordinates of points A and B.

1.	A(1, 1), B(5, 4)	2.	A(5, 7), B(9, 8)	3.	A(3, 6), B(6, 8)
4.	A(5, 2), B(4, 7)	5.	A(4, 3), B(1, 9)	6.	A(4, 6), B(6, 5)
7.	A(4, 5), B(10, 5)	8.	A(2, 5), B(1, 7)	9.	A(3, 3), B(7, 8)
10.	A(4, 6), B(2, 8)	11.	A(8, 4), B(2, 7)	12.	A(4, 9), B(3, 9)
13.	A(-5, 3), B(7, 3)	14.	A(-4, 2), B(2, 4)	15.	A(-3, 1), B(5, 3)

WRITTEN EXERCISES

Find the slope of $\overline{CD}$ for the given coordinates of points C and D.

1.	C(5, 7), D(11, 11)	2.	C(2, 3), D(12, 8)	3.	C(8, 5), D(20, 13)
4.	C(15, 6), D(2, 10)	5.	C(7, 9), D(9, 11)	6.	C(14, 12), D(6, 6)
7.	C(13, 5), D(3, 15)	8.	C(11, 14), D(5, 18)	9.	C(8, 12), D(4,12)
10.	C(-4, 2), C(11, 12)	11.	C(-3, -5), D(-12, 1)	12.	C(-4, 6), D(11, 9)

OPEN-ENDED QUESTION

13.   Using graph paper, draw two line segments that are parallel. Write the
      coordinates of two points on each segment. Find the slope of each segment.
      Repeat the instructions above for another pair of parallel line segments.
      Make a generalization about the slope of segments that are parallel.

REVIEW

1.   What geometric figure is formed by rotating this
      plane figure about the labeled side?

      (A)   horizontal cylinder   (B)   vertical cylinder

      (C)   horizontal cone   (D)   vertical cone

2. Performing which set of transformations on
    the lightly shaded triangle will **NOT** result in
    the lightly shaded triangle completely covering
    the heavily shaded triangle?

    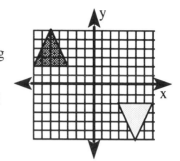

    (A)   translation 10 units to the left followed
           by reflection in the x-axis
    (B)   rotation of 180° about the origin
    (C)   reflection in the x-axis followed by
           reflection in the y-axis
    (D)   translation 6 units to the left followed
           by reflection in the x-axis

3. When purchasing an item, Wanda gave the clerk a 10-dollar bill. He gave her the
    item and change consisting of d dollars, q quarters, and n nickels. Which of the
    following expressions represents the cost of the item?

    (A)   10 - (d + q + n)   (B)   10 - (d + 0.25q + 0.05n)
    (C)   10 - (100d + 0.25q + 0.05n)   (D)   10 - (100d + 0.25q + 0.05n)

4. At the right are three views of a
    die. Which number is opposite 5?

    (A)   1   (B)   3
    (C)   4   (D)   6

     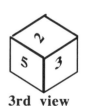

    1st view   2nd view   3rd view

5. The pentagon in figure (a) is 6 cm
    on a side and is rolled to the right
    along a line. Which of the
    following distances could it have
    rolled so that the shaded circle
    would be in the position shown in
    figure (b)?

    figure (a)   figure (b)

    (A)   18 cm   (B)   24 cm   (C)   42 cm   (D)   48 cm

11.2   Graphing a Line

OBJECTIVES   To graph a line given an equation of the line

To determine whether the graph of a line is the result of a slide of a line with a given equation

To write an equation of a line given its graph

To choose an equation that describes a set of points

You have learned to graph a point like A(2,7).

An equation like $y = 2x + 3$ describes a relationship between x and y.

You can use the equation to make a table of values for x and y.

Then this table can be use to graph a set of points which is called the graph of the equation. This is illustrated in the next example.

EXAMPLE 1   Draw the graph of $y = 2x + 3$ by using a data table of values for x and y.

Strategy   Choose any three numbers for x, say **0, 2,** and **4**.

Substitute these values for **x** in the equation $y = 2x + 3$

to find each y value.

Produce this table in the form shown below.

x	2x + 3	y		x	y	
0	2(0) + 3	3	→	0	3	→ (0,3)
2	2(2) + 3	7	→	2	7	→ (2,7)
4	2(4) + 3	11	→	4	11	→ (4,11)

Write as ordered pairs.

Now plot the points (0,3), (2,7), and (4,11) on graph paper and draw a line through them.

(continued on next page)

Label the points A, B, and C as shown in the graph at the right.

Draw a line through the three points.

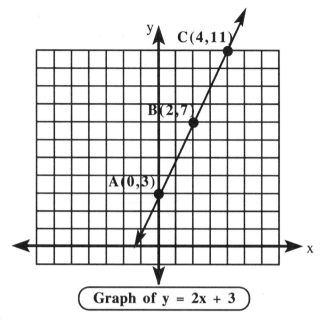

Graph of y = 2x + 3

Solution   Thus, the graph of y = 2x + 3 is the line containing the three points.

The numbers **2** and **3** in the equation y = 2x + 3 play an important role in developing a short cut for graphing an equation of a line.

EXAMPLE 2   Where does the graph of y = 2x + 3 of Example 1 above **intercept** or cross the y-axis?

Solution   The graph of y = 2x + **3** intercepts the y-axis at **3**.

EXAMPLE 3   What is the slope of the graph of the equation y = 2x + 3?

Strategy   Find the slope of $\overline{AB}$ or $\overline{BC}$.

Use slope = $\dfrac{\textbf{difference of y-coordinates}}{\textbf{difference of x-coordinates}}$.

slope of $\overline{BC}$ slope of $\overline{AB}$

$\dfrac{11-7}{4-2} = \dfrac{4}{2} = \dfrac{2}{1}$ or **2** $\dfrac{7-3}{2-0} = \dfrac{4}{2} = \dfrac{2}{1}$ or **2**

Solution   Thus, the slope of the graph of y = **2**x + 3 is $= \dfrac{2}{1}$ or **2**

Notice the two patterns suggested by Examples 2 and 3 from the previous page.

For the graph of $y = 2x + $**3**, the graph **intercepts** or crosses the y-axis at **3**.

For the graph of $y = $**2**$x + 3$, the **slope** of the line is **2** or $\frac{2}{1}$.

$$y = \mathbf{2}x + \mathbf{3}$$

slope   y-intercept   (crosses y-axis at 3)

STANDARD EQUATION OF A LINE

For any equation of the form $y = \mathbf{m}x + \mathbf{b}$, its graph is a line with

slope **m** and y-intercept **b**.

EXAMPLE 4   For the equation $y = \frac{3}{4}x - 6$, the graph of the equation is a line

with y-intercept ?   and slope ?

$$y = \frac{3}{4}x - \mathbf{6}$$

slope: $\frac{3}{4}$ y-intercept: **- 6**

Solution

The patterns you have just worked with can be used to draw the graph of an equation of a line

EXAMPLE 5   Graph $y = \frac{2}{5}x + 1$ using the slope and y-intercept.

Strategy   **1.** First determine from the equation the slope and y-intercept.

$$y = \frac{2}{5}x + \mathbf{1}$$

slope: $\frac{2}{5}$ y-intercept: **1**   **(continued on next page)**

2. The y-intercept of

$y = \frac{2}{5}x + 1$ is **1**.

Put a dot at **1** on the y-axis.

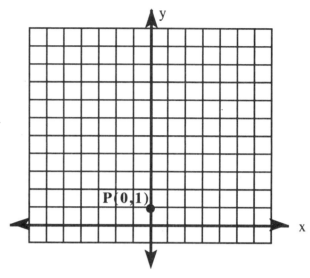

3. Use the slope of

$y = \frac{2}{5}x + 1$ is $\frac{2}{5}$ to

plot a second point. From (0,1) move up 2 and right 5. Put a dot at Q(5,3).

4. Draw a line through the two points P and Q.

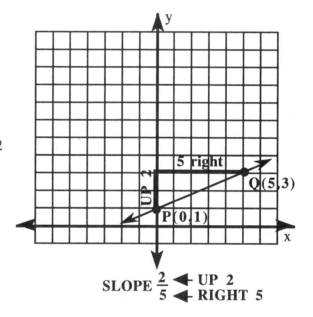

Solution   The line through the points P(0,1) and Q(5,3) is the graph of

$y = \frac{2}{5}x + 1$.

Sometimes you will have to rewrite the equation of a line so that you can easily recognize the slope and y-intercept. You will see this in the first part of the next example.

EXAMPLE 6   Graph y = 3x and y = 3x + 7 on the same graph paper.

What relationship seems to exist between the two graphs?

Strategy

(1)   First graph y = 3x. Rewrite

y = 3x as   y = $\frac{3}{1}$ x + **0.**

slope   y-intercept

Put a dot at **0** on the y-axis.

Use the slope = $\frac{3}{1}$ to plot a second
point.

Draw a line through the two points

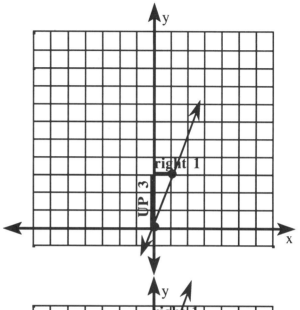

(2)   Now graph y = 3x + 7.

y = $\frac{3}{1}$ x + **7.**

slope   y-intercept

Put a dot at **7** on the y-axis.

Use the slope = $\frac{3}{1}$ to plot a second
point.

Draw a line through the two points.

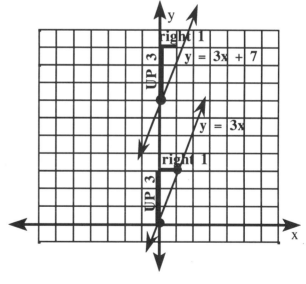

Solution   The two lines are parallel.

If you have drawn the graph of y = 3x, you can think of graphing y = 3x + 7 in terms of a
slide or **translation**. This is discussed on the next page.

Graphing y = 3x + 7 is the same as graphing y = 3x and **sliding** it **7** units up.

You can see this if you draw the two graphs on the same sheet of graph paper.

Trace the axes and the graph of y = 3x on tracing paper.

Slide the tracing of y = 3x up **7** units. The graphs are the same!

The results of Example 6 suggest the following property.

If the slopes of two lines are the same, then the lines are parallel.

EXAMPLE 7   Write an equation that describes the set of points graphed below.

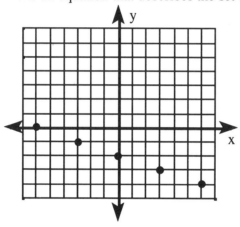

Strategy   Draw a line through the set of points. Find an equation of the line.
                   This equation will then be an equation describing the set of points.

The y-intercept is **-2.**

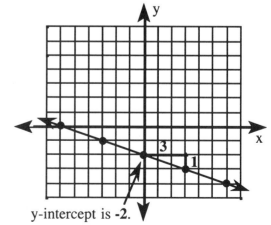

The line slants **down.**
The slope is **negative.**
The slope is $-\frac{1}{3}$.

So, an equation is

Solution $y = -\frac{1}{3}x$ **-2.**

slope   y-intercept

SUMMARY

1. What role do the numbers 3 and -5 in the equation $y = 3x - 5$ play in graphing the equation of the line?

2. What does **m** represent in $y = \mathbf{m}x + b$, the standard equation of a line?

3   What does **b** represent in $y = mx + \mathbf{b}$, the standard equation of a line?

4. How can you rewrite $y = x$ so that it will be in the $y = mx + b$ format?

    HINT: What number is understood to be in front of x?

5. What are the steps in graphing $y = \frac{3}{4}x + 7$?

6. The graph of $y = 2x + 5$ can be thought of as **sliding** the graph of $y = 2x$ _____?

CLASSROOM PRACTICE

Give the slope and y-intercept of each equation.

1. $y = \frac{4}{5}x + 6$ 2. $y = \frac{1}{2}x - 4$ 3. $y = \frac{3}{4}x + 8$

4. $y = 2x - 5$ 5. $y = 3x + 1$ 6. $y = x$

7. $y = -\frac{1}{2}x + 8$ 8. $y = -\frac{2}{3}x - 6$ 9. $y = -3x + 4$

10. Which graph below is the graph of   11. Which graph below is the graph of

    $y = \frac{3}{4}x + 1$ $y = -\frac{2}{3}x + 4$

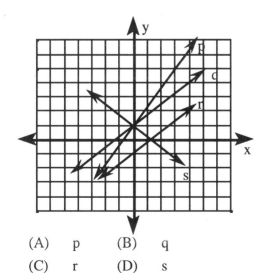

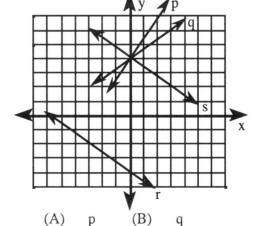

(A)   p   (B)   q   (A)   p   (B)   q
(C)   r   (D)   s   (C)   r   (D)   s

Graph each equation using slope and y-intercept.

12. $y = \frac{2}{3}x + 6$ 13. $y = \frac{3}{4}x - 2$ 14. $y = -\frac{1}{2}x + 5$

Write an equation for each set of points graphed below.

15.   16.

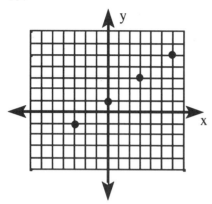   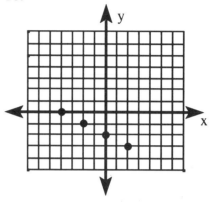

17. The graph of $y = \frac{1}{3}x$ is shown at the right.

Which statement below is true about the graph of $y = \frac{1}{3}x + 4$?

(A)   It intersects the graph of $y = \frac{1}{3}x$
        at the origin.

(B)   It is perpendicular to the graph
        of $y = \frac{1}{3}x$.

(C)   It is a translation (**slide**) of the
        graph of $y = \frac{1}{3}x$ 4 units up.

(D)   It is a translation (**slide**) of the
        graph of $y = \frac{1}{3}x$ 4 units to the right.

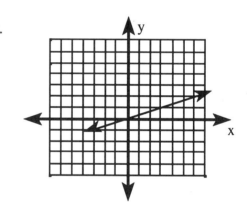

WRITTEN EXERCISES

Give the slope and y-intercept of each equation.

1. $y = \frac{5}{6}x + 2$ 2. $y = \frac{2}{3}x - 8$ 3. $y = -\frac{5}{4}x + 3$

Graph each equation using slope and y-intercept.

4. $y = \frac{2}{3}x + 7$ 5. $y = \frac{4}{5}x - 1$ 6. $y = \frac{1}{3}x - 5$

7. $y = 3x - 2$ 8. $y = 2x - 4$ 9. $y = 2x - 7$

10. $y = -\frac{5}{2}x + 1$ 11. $y = -\frac{3}{5}x - 2$ 12. $y = -\frac{1}{6}x + 5$

13. Which graph below is the graph of   14. Which graph below is the graph of
     $y = \frac{2}{3}x + 5$ $y = -\frac{3}{4}x + 2$

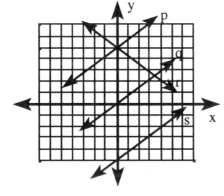   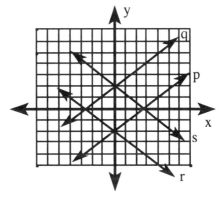

(A)   p   (B)   q   (A)   p   (B)   q
(C)   r   (D)   s   (C)   r   (D)   s

Write an equation for each set of points graphed below.

15.   16.

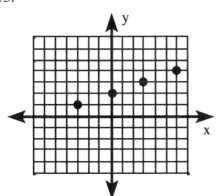   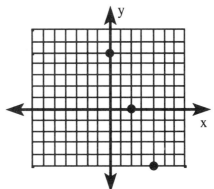

17. Graph the line with y-intercept 5 and parallel to the graph of $y = \frac{1}{2}x + 4$.

18. The graph of $y = \frac{3}{4}x - 3$ can be drawn by **sliding** the graph of $y = \frac{3}{4}x$

     __ units _____.

19.   Draw the graph of y = 2x - 4. Which of the statements below are true about the graph of y = 2x + 6?

       I   It is parallel to the graph of y = 2x + 7.

       II   It is a slide 6 units up of the graph of y = 2x - 4.

       III It is a slide 10 units up of the graph of y = 2x - 4.

       (A)   I only   (B)   II only   (C)   I and II   (D)   I and III

OPEN ENDED QUESTION

20.   Write an equation of the line through the point (3,7) and parallel to the graph of

       $y = \frac{2}{3} x$. Write a clear description of how you derived your answer.

REVIEW

1.   A medium sized bus can transport no more than 35 students as passengers. If each bus makes only one trip, find the smallest number of buses needed to transport 112 students to a football game.

       (A)   4   (B)   3.2   (C)   3   (D)   2

2.   Which of these statements could you write in the blank to make a true statement?

                      4.7×10^{-1} _____ 3.2×10^{-1}

       (A)   >   (B)   <   (C)   =   (D)   none of these

3.   One car traveled 12 miles in 15 minutes. Find its average speed for the trip.

       (A)   1.25 miles per hour   (B)   48 miles per hour

       (C)   80 miles per hour   (D)   180 miles per hour

4.   While solving a problem a group of students determined that the whole numbers a and b must satisfy the equation 3a + 7b = 36.

       Marge said that the equation tells us something about the value of b. In fact,

       (A)   b must be odd.   (B)   b must be a prime.

       (C)   b must be divisible by 7.   (D)   b must be a multiple of 3.

5.   20% more than 40 is what number?

11.3   Linear Relationships in Data Tables

OBJECTIVE   To find the missing value in a data table that indicates a linear
relationship between two variables

Recall from Example 1 of the last lesson that a
data table can represent the coordinates of
points on a line.

Since the graph is a **line** we say there is a
linear relationship between x and y.

x	y
0	3	→ (0,3)
2	7	→ (2,7)
4	11	→ (4,11)

Write as ordered pairs.

You can use the data table to find the **slope**
of the line.

x	y
0	3
2	7
4	11

OR

x	y
0	3
2	7
4	11

Recall that the slope of a line is

difference of y-coordinates
difference of x-coordinates.

$$\frac{7-3}{2-0} = \frac{4}{2} = \frac{1}{2}$$ **SAME** $$\frac{11-7}{4-2} = \frac{4}{2} = \frac{1}{2}$$

Sometimes, letters other than
x and y may be used in a data
table to represent the
coordinates of points.

p	q
2	7
9	10

r	c
1	4
6	7

It helps to think of slope as

difference of **2nd** coordinates
difference of **1st** coordinates.

$$\text{slope} = \frac{\text{diff. of } \textbf{q}\text{-coord.}}{\text{diff. of } \textbf{p}\text{-coord.}}$$

$$= \frac{10-7}{9-2} = \frac{3}{7}$$

or $$= \frac{7-10}{2-9} = \frac{-3}{-7} = \frac{3}{7}$$

$$\text{slope} = \frac{\text{diff. of } \textbf{c}\text{-coord}}{\text{diff. of } \textbf{r}\text{-coord.}}$$

$$= \frac{7-4}{6-1} = \frac{3}{5}$$

or $$= \frac{4-7}{1-6} = \frac{-3}{-5} = \frac{3}{5}$$

Sometimes you will be given a data table that represents a **linear** relationship like the one
you just saw. This means that the numbers of the table represent the coordinates of points
on a line. This is illustrated in the next example.

EXAMPLE 1   The table at the right indicates
a linear relationship between a
and b.
According to this pattern, find
the number that belongs in the
box in the table.

a	b
1	3
3	7
6	13
7	□
9	19

Strategy   Since this is a **line**ar relationship the values of a and b represent coordinates
of points on a line.

Let **b** represent the missing value that belongs in the box.

You need an equation involving **b** so that you can solve for b.

Use the idea of **slope** to write an equation involving **b**.

Step 1
Find the slope using
any two rows other
than the one with the
variable **b**.

$$\frac{13 - 7}{6 - 3} = \frac{6}{3} = \frac{2}{1}$$

a	b
1	3
3	7
6	13
7	b
9	19

Step 2
Find the slope using
the row with the
variable **b** and **any**
other row.

$$\frac{b - 13}{7 - 6} = \frac{b - 13}{1}$$

a	b
1	3
3	7
6	13
7	b
9	19

Step 3   Set the two resulting **slopes equal**. (The slope of a line is the same for
any two points. on the line.)

$$\frac{2}{1} = \frac{b - 13}{1}$$ **A proportion**

$$2 \cdot 1 = 1(b - 13)$$ **Cross multiply.**

$$2 = b - 13$$

$$15 = b$$ **Add 13 to each side.**

Solution   Thus, 15 is the number that belongs in the box.

Scientists record data from experiments with the hope of eventually finding patterns that will enable them to predict future results.

For example, in testing the effectiveness of a new antibacterial spray, Janet, a chemist, might record the number of bacteria after the spray has been used for different periods of time.

She might use this data to predict the number of bacteria expected after a given number of hours. This process is illustrated in the next example.

Assume in the example below that the data describes a **linear** relationship.

EXAMPLE 2   Suppose that Janet observes that once an antibacterial spray is used, after 4 hours there are 80 bacteria.

After 6 hours there are 70 bacteria.

After 10 hours there are 50 bacteria.

Make a data table describing these results.

Use the data table to predict the number of bacteria after 14 hours.

Strategy   **1.**   First make a data table to display the given data.

h	b
4	80
6	70
10	50
14	b

Use **h** for number of **h**ours.

Use **b** for number of **b**acteria.

Now proceed as in Example 1 to write an equation to find **b.**

2.   Find the slope using any two rows other than the one with the variable **b.**

h	b
4	80
6	70
10	50
14	b

SLOPE 1 $\dfrac{70 - 80}{6 - 4} = \dfrac{-10}{2}$

$= \dfrac{-5}{1}$

3.   Find the slope using the row with the variable **b** and any other row.

h	b
4	80
6	70
10	50
14	b

SLOPE 2 $\dfrac{b - 50}{14 - 10} = \dfrac{b - 50}{4}$

4.   Set the two slopes equal. Solve the proportion for **b.**

$\dfrac{-5}{1} = \dfrac{b - 50}{4}$ **(continued on next page)**

$$\frac{-5}{1} = \frac{b - 50}{4} \qquad \textbf{Solve the proportion.}$$

$$-5 \cdot 4 = 1(b - 50) \qquad \textbf{Cross multiply.}$$

$$-20 = b - 50$$

$$-20 + 50 = b \qquad \textbf{Add 50 to each side.}$$

$$30 = b$$

Solution   Thus, there are 30 bacteria after 14 hours.

Frequently in real-life applications the data relationship is **NOT** linear.

These types of problems are studied in more advanced mathematics courses.

SUMMARY

The table at the right indicates a linear relationship between
the variables r and s.

r	s
1	6
3	8
7	☐
10	15

1.   What is the first step in finding the number that
      belongs in the box?
      How can this be done two different ways?

2.   What is the second step if you let b = the number
      missing from the box?

3.   What proportion can you now write?

4.   How do you solve this proportion?

CLASSROOM PRACTICE

Each table below indicates a linear relationship between the variables.

Find the number that belongs in the box in each table.

1.

r	s
0	3
2	7
4	☐
5	13

2.

x	y
3	2
4	4
6	☐
7	10

3.

a	b
2	5
3	☐
4	11
5	14

4.

x	y
1	2
2	6
5	☐
7	26

5.

a	b
0	1
4	□
6	4
12	7

6.

p	q
3	1
6	7
8	□
10	15

7.

c	d
0	1
3	□
6	3
9	4

8.

r	s
0	□
6	5
9	7
12	9

For the problems below assume that there is a linear relationship for the given data.

9. The monthly cost of owning a car is dependent upon the number of miles driven. Natasha keeps a record of her cost of driving a car. Suppose the cost for driving 100 miles is $10, the cost for driving 200 miles is $15, and the cost of driving 1,000 miles is $55. Make a data table describing these results.
   Use the data table to predict the cost of driving 1,600 miles.

10. When a diabetic takes long-acting insulin, there is a linear relationship between the insulin level and time. Suppose that the for t = 1 hour, the insulin level is 140, for 2 hours the insulin level is 180, for 3 hours the insulin level is 220.
    Make a data table showing the relationship of insulin level to time.
    Use the data table to find the insulin level for 4 hours.

WRITTEN EXERCISES

Each table below indicates a linear relationship between the variables.
Find the number that belongs in the box in each table.

1.

r	s
3	8
4	11
6	□
7	20

2.

a	b
0	5
2	□
3	11
5	15

3.

x	y
4	15
5	19
6	□
8	31

4.

p	q
0	1
2	-3
4	□
5	-9

5.

r	s
0	5
3	7
6	□
9	11

6

a	b
0	-3
4	0
5	□
8	3

7.

x	y
0	8
2	7
4	□
6	5

8.

m	n
0	2
3	□
6	0
9	-1

9.   The number of chirps that a cricket makes in a minute is a function of the temperature. As a result, it is possible to use a cricket as a thermometer! The following data is collected: 40 chirps in 50 minutes, 60 chirps in 55 minutes, 120 chirps in 70 minutes. Make a data table describing these results. Use the data table to predict the number of chirps in 140 minutes.

OPEN-ENDED QUESTION: Applying the Graphing Calculator

10.   The population of ants at an anthill is tallied at the end of each month. The following data is collected: 8,000 ants at the end of 2 months, 9,500 ants at the end of 3 months, 10,000 ants at the end of 4 months, 11,000 ants at the end of 5 months, 13,000 ants at the end of 6 months, and 13,500 ants at the end of 7 months. Make a data table for these results.

Use a graphing calculator to graph the points corresponding to this data.

Is the set of data really linear? That is, are all the points on a line?

Pick 3 points which appear to lie in line with each other.

Are the other points almost on this line? Make a new data table for those 3 points.

Use this data table to approximate the number of ants at the end of 8 months.

REVIEW

1.   The formula for changing temperature from Celsius to Fahrenheit is $F = \frac{9}{5}C + 32$. If the temperature of something is $25°$ C, find the temperature in degrees Fahrenheit .

2.   Which of the following is **NOT** equal to the other three?

(A)   150% of 16   (B)   16 increased by $\frac{1}{2}$ of 16

(C) $16 \div \frac{2}{3}$ (D) $1\frac{1}{4} \cdot 16$

3.   The number of Gloucester City High School students who gave to the Diabetes Fund this year was 215. This figure is 120% of last year's. figure. This means that:

(A)   215 more students gave this year than last year.

(B)   The number of donators this year is 1.20 times 215.

(C)   The number of donators increased from last year to this year.

(D)   The amount of donations increased from last year to this year.

11.4   Using Line Graphs to Compare Data

OBJECTIVE   To interpret data displayed by line graphs

You have graphed lines. Line graphs are frequently used to compare two sets of data as shown in the example below.

EXAMPLE 1   Which car takes the longer amount of time to go from 0 to 30 mph.? About how much longer does this car take?

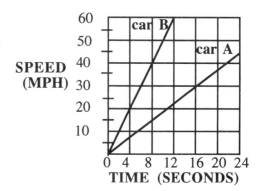

Strategy

Start at 30 on the speed axis and move horizontally to the right to the line for Car B. Then move down to the time axis. The number appears to be halfway between 4 and 8.

$$\frac{4+8}{2} = \frac{12}{2} = \mathbf{6}$$

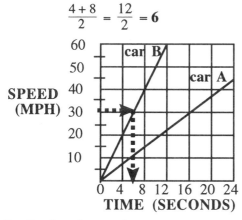

Car B takes **6** seconds.

Start at 30 on the speed axis and move horizontally to the right to the line for Car A. Then move down to the time axis. to **16**.

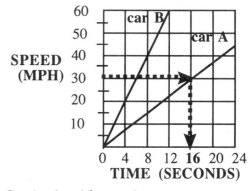

Car A takes **16** seconds.

Solution   Therefore, Car A takes **10** second more than Car B. **(16 - 6 = 10.)**

EXAMPLE 2   At 12 seconds, the speed of
Car B is what percent of the
speed of Car A?

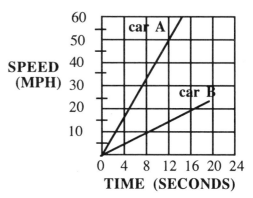

Strategy   Use the graph to find the
speed of each car at 12
seconds.

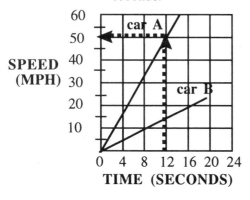

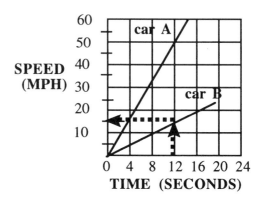

Car A: 50 mph   Car B: 15 mph

Write an equation involving percent.

The speed of Car B is what percent of the speed of Car A?

$$15 = x \qquad\qquad\qquad 50$$

$$15 = 50x$$

$$\frac{15}{50} = \frac{50x}{50}$$

$$0.30 = x$$

Solution   Thus, Car B's speed is 30% of Car A's speed.

EXAMPLE 3   Find the average of the speeds of the two cars of Example 2 at 12
seconds?

Solution   Average $= \dfrac{50 + 15}{2} = \dfrac{65}{2} = 32\tfrac{1}{2}$ mph

SUMMARY

In a five-hour period the towns of Trenton and Asbury Park got as much rainfall in a bad storm as indicated in the chart at the right.

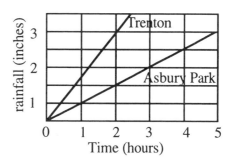

1. How do you read from the chart the amount of rainfall Trenton got in 2 hours?

2. How do you find the number of hours it took for $2\frac{1}{2}$ inches of rain to fall in Asbury Park?

3. How do you find the average number of inches of rain that fell in 2 hours for the two cities?

CLASSROOM PRACTICE

The chart at the right shows the amount of money saved by two students from their part time paychecks over a five-week period of time.

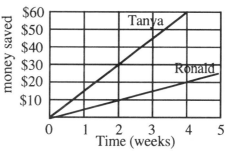

1. How much did Tanya save at the end of two weeks?

2. How much did Ronald save at the end of two weeks?

3. How long did it take Ronald to save $15?

4. How long did it take Tanya to save $45?

5. How much more did Tanya save than Ronald by the end of two weeks?

6. How much less did Ronald save than Tanya by the end of the first week?

7. Ronald's savings was what percent of Tanya's savings at the end of 4 weeks?

8. Find the average of the two students' savings at the end of 3 weeks.

9. After how many weeks were their combined savings $40?

Use the chart at the right to answer exercises 10-16.

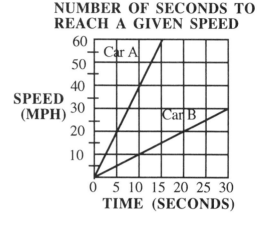

NUMBER OF SECONDS TO REACH A GIVEN SPEED

10. What is the speed of Car B at 30 seconds?

11. Estimate the speed of Car B at 15 seconds.

12. How long did it take Car A to reach a speed of 20 mph?

13. About how long did it take Car B to reach a speed of 15 mph?

14. Which car was going faster after 5 seconds? About how much faster?

15. At ten seconds, the speed of Car B was what percent of the speed of Car A?

16. Find the average of the speeds of the two cars at 15 seconds.

WRITTEN EXERCISES

The chart at the right compares the sales of two clerks in the cosmetics department of a mall store over a five day period of time.

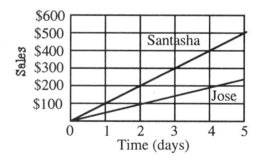

1. Find Jose's sales at the end of 4 days.

2. Find Santasha's sales at the end of 3 days.

3. After how many days did Jose's sales come to $150?

4. At the end of 3 days, whose sales were greater and by how much?

5. At the end of 4 days Jose's sales were what percent of Santasha's sales?

6. Find the average of their sales at the end of 3 days.

The chart at the right shows the amounts of money two workers saved out of their salaries over a period of 60 weeks.

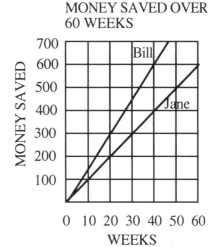

MONEY SAVED OVER 60 WEEKS

7. What were Bill's savings at the end of 30 weeks?

8. Find Jane's savings at the end of 50 weeks.

9. How many weeks did it take Bill to save $600?

10. How many weeks did it take Jane to save $450?

11. How many weeks did it take Bill to save $150?

12. At the end of 40 weeks, Jane's savings as what percent of Bill's?

13. Find the average of the two savings at the end of 30 weeks.

OPEN-ENDED QUESTION

14. Draw the graphs of each of the following on the same set of axes.
    $y = 2x + 1$ and $y = 3x + 5$. When $x = 2$, how much greater is the y-value of the graph of $y = 3x + 5$ than the y-value of the graph of $y = 2x + 1$?
    Write an explanation of each of the steps you used in solving this problem?

REVIEW

1. Find the slope and y-intercept of the graph of the equation $y = \frac{2}{3} x - 4$.

2. Graph the equation $y = \frac{1}{2} x + 4$.

3. The measure of the vertex angle of an isosceles triangle is 40. Find the measure of each base angle.

4.   The table at the right indicates a linear relationship between x and y. According to the pattern, find the value of the number that belongs in the box.

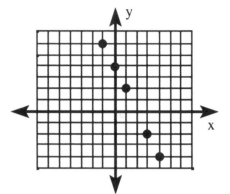

x	y
2	6
□	10
5	12

(A)   3   (B)   4   (C)   5   (D)   6

5.   Which is the correct equation for the set of points graphed at the right?

(A)   y = 2x + 4

(B)   y = 2x - 4

(C)   y = -2x + 4

(D)   y = -2x

6.   The graph of $y = \frac{1}{2}x - 2$ is shown at the right. Which of the statements below are true about the graph of $y = \frac{1}{2}x + 5$?

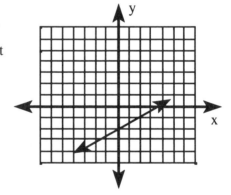

I   It is parallel to the graph of $y = \frac{1}{2}x - 2$

II   It is a slide of the graph of $y = \frac{1}{2}x - 2$ five units up.

III   It is a slide of the graph of $y = \frac{1}{2}x - 2$ seven units up.

(A)   I and II   (B)   I only   (C)   III only   (D)   I and III

7.   Solve 4x - 2 = 2x + 8

(A)   5   (B)   3   (C) $1\frac{2}{3}$ (D)   1

11.5   Increasing, Decreasing, Constant Functions

OBJECTIVE   To determine from a graph whether a function is increasing, decreasing, or constant

In the last lesson, you saw that a line graph can be used to show the relationship between two sets of data such as money saved and the time it takes to save it.

In this lesson, you will learn to determine from a graph whether a pattern is increasing, dsecreasing, or staying the same.

EXAMPLE 1   The graph shows the amount of savings of a worker after a given number of weeks.

As the time increases, what happens to the savings?

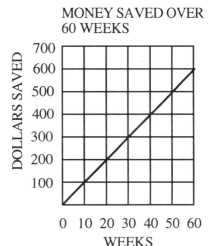

Strategy   Use sample data to draw a conclusion.

At 10 weeks the savings are $100.

At 20 weeks the savings are $200.

At 30 weeks the savings are $300.

At 50 weeks the savings are $500.

Solution   Notice from the results above that as the time increases the savings **increase**.

$100, $200, $300, $400

increasing or getting **bigger**

DISCOVERY

From the graph of Example 1, how could you predict that the savings are increasing even if you were given no numbers?

Let's take another look at the results of Example 1.

Notice in the graph below that at 20 weeks the savings are $200. The length of the first dashed segment corresponds to $200 in savings. The length of the second dashed segment corresponds to $400, the savings at 40 weeks. This second dashed segment is **longer** than the first. The savings **increased** as time **increased** from 20 to 40.

This graph is the same as the one at the left with two deletions. The numbers on the axes and the grid lines are not shown. The dashed segments representing savings **increase** as you move to the right along the time axis.

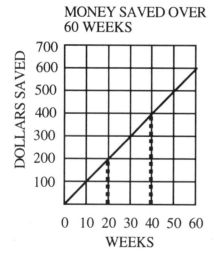

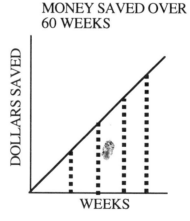

Therefore, the savings **increase** as time increases. The dashed segments are getting **longer** as you look from left to right.

The next examples show how to use the idea above to predict a pattern from a rough sketch of a graph without numbers or grid lines.

EXAMPLE 2   Using this graph, what
happens to the temperature

(1)   from a to b?

(2)   from b to c?

(3)   from c to d?

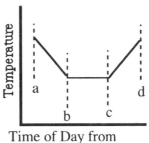

Time of Day from
6:00 P.M to 6:00 A.M.

Strategy   Draw dashed segments in each region. Determine what happens
to their lengths as you go from left to right.

Temperature from a to b   Temperature from b to c   Temperature from c to d

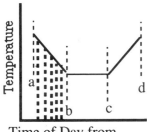   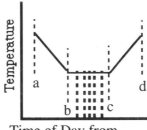   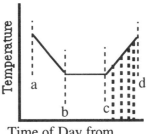

Time of Day from   Time of Day from   Time of Day from
6:00 P.M to 6:00 A.M.   6:00 P.M to 6:00 A.M.   6:00 P.M to 6:00 A.M.

Dashed segments are   Dashed segments are the   Dashed segments are
getting **shorter** from left to   **same** length from left to   getting **longer** from left to
right.   right.   right.

Solution

Thus, the temperature is   Thus, the temperature is   Thus, the temperature is
decreasing from a to b.   **not** changing from b to c. **increasing** from c to d.
                              The temperature is said to
                              be **constant**.

A line graph does not have to be straight.

The next example involves a curved line graph.

Thus, in mathematics we can also think of **curved** lines.

EXAMPLE 3   The graph at the right represents
                     Mustafa's auto trip from Santa
                     Fe to Denver.
                     Which of the following is most
                     likely to have happened from
                     time a to time b?

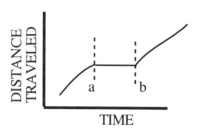

(A)   He was driving slowly.

(B)   He stopped a few times for a red traffic light.

(C)   He was driving fast on the parkway.

(D)   He stopped for lunch.

Strategy   From the graph, what is true about the distances traveled?
                     The dashed segments represent
                     the distances traveled between
                     times a and b.
                     Note that these distances are
                     constant, do **not** change. If the
                     distance traveled between time a
                     and time b does **not** change,
                     then he must **NOT** be moving.

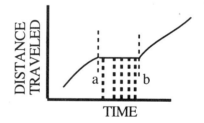

Now let's look at the multiple-choice possibilities.

(A) and (C) indicate he was moving. If so, his distance traveled should be **changing**.

Choice (B) says he stopped only a few times. If so, he was **moving** the rest of the time.

Solution   Now look at choice (D). If he stopped for lunch, his car was **NOT** moving. His distance traveled was **NOT** changing.

                     Thus, he stopped for lunch. Choice **D** is the correct choice.

The next examples illustrate some interesting patterns such as taxi cab and postal rates.
Graphs of such patterns will be seen to look like **steps** and are therefore called **step
graphs** or **step functions**.

Suppose a taxicab company has the following rate schedule.

$2.00 for up to 1 mile

$3.50 for 1 mile or more up to 2 miles

$5.00 for 2 miles or more up to 3 miles

$7.00 for 3 miles or more up to 4 miles

No rides for more than 4 miles

Notice the pattern indicated by the dashed segments in the **graph** of this data.

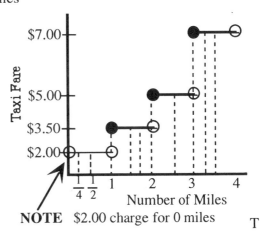

The fare is the **same** for
$\frac{1}{4}$ mile, $\frac{1}{2}$ mile, and $\frac{3}{4}$ mile: **$2.00**

The fare is the **same** for
1 miles, $1\frac{1}{2}$ miles, and $1\frac{3}{4}$ miles: **$3.50**

The fare is the same for
2 mules and $2\frac{1}{2}$ miles: **$5.00**

The fare is the **same** for
3 miles, $3\frac{1}{4}$ miles, and $3\frac{1}{2}$ miles.   **$7.00**

his graph is called a **step** graph.
It looks like **steps** of a staircase.
Also, the taxi rate is said to increase by **steps.**

EXAMPLE 4   Suppose the Post Office increases the cost of first-class mailing to 35 cents for the first ounce or fractional part of an ounce and 28 cents for each additional ounce or fractional part of an ounce. Which graph below best represents the cost of mailing a first-class letter depending upon its weight in ounces?

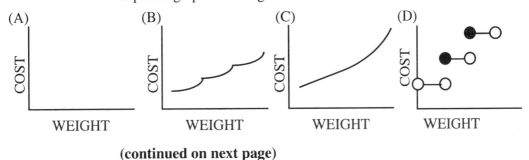

(continued on next page)

Strategy   The pattern is like that of the **step** graph above Example 4 of the
                      previous page: the same charge for up to 1 ounce, then an additional
                      28 cents for from 1 to 2 ounces, an additional 28 cents for the next
                      step, etc.

Solution   Thus, the correct choice is (D).

In the next example you will be asked to draw your own graph describing the relationship
between two sets of data. The rough graph will differ from person to person. The shape is
not important. Therefore, the graph might be a straight or curved line in a variety of
shapes. The important idea is whether or not it accurately displays if data is increasing,
decreasing, or staying the same.

EXAMPLE 5   A large chunk of ice is attached to the roof of a moving truck.
                      It is dislodged by a sudden gust of wind, blown upward from the roof
                      of the truck, flies through the air, and lands on the highway.
                      Graph the height of the chunk of ice during this period of time.

Strategy   Before you try to draw the graph think about what is happening to the
                      ice on the roof of the truck.

As the truck moves, the height   The wind breaks the ice   Then the ice begins to fall
of the ice above the road does   loose and lifts it up.   so that its height above
not change. The height is   The height is now   the road now **decreases**
constant.   **increasing**.   until it hits the road.

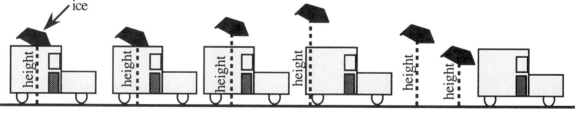

Solution

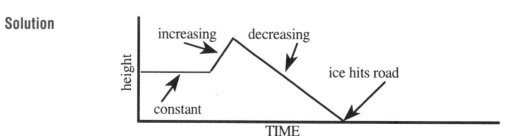

SUMMARY

1. What relationship is shown in the graph at the right?
2. Describe how to determine whether the temperature is increasing, decreasing, or remains constant between p and q.
3. Describe how to determine whether the temperature is increasing, decreasing, or remains constant between q and r.

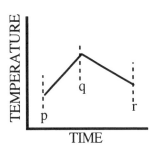

4. Suppose a portion of a graph shows a relationship that is **constant**. What will this portion of the graph look like?

Tell how to draw a graph of the speed related to time between a and b if the speed is:

5. decreasing
6. increasing
7. constant

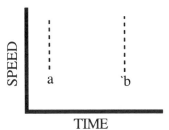

CLASSROOM PRACTICE

For each graph indicate whether the speed is decreasing, increasing, or constant.

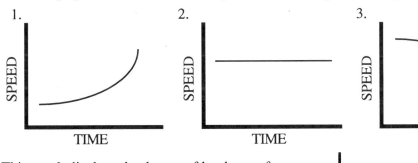

This graph displays the degree of loudness of a stereo over a given time interval. Describe what is happening to the loudness over the indicated time.

4. from a to b
5. from b to c
6. from c to d

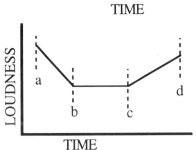

7. The graph at the right represents Joan's first day of driving on a cross-country trip. Which of the following is most likely to have happened between times r and s?

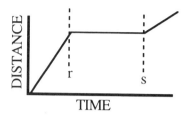

DISTANCE

TIME

(A)   Joan increased her speed.

(B)   Joan stopped several times for traffic lights.

(C)   Joan returned to the last motel to get something she forgot.

(D)   Joan stopped for lunch.

This graph represents Mr. Burke's speed on the Pennsylvania Turnpike.

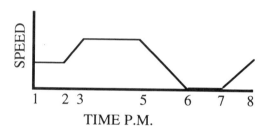

SPEED

TIME P.M.

8. During which time intervals is his speed increasing?

9. During which time intervals is his speed constant?

10. During which time interval was he slowing down to prepare to stop for dinner?

11. What happened between 6 P.M. and 7 P.M.? Explain your conclusion.

12. Sketch a numberless graph of the rising and setting of the sun in relation to the horizon. Label the axes as **height** and **time**.

WRITTEN EXERCISES

For each graph indicate whether the speed is decreasing, increasing, or constant.

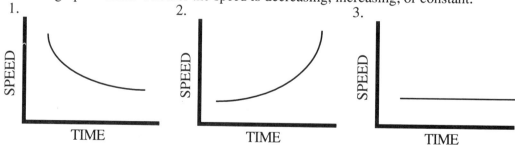

1.   2.   3.

SPEED   SPEED   SPEED

TIME   TIME   TIME

4. Draw a numberless graph that shows temperature steadily decreasing at night.

This graph displays the speed of a car on the turnpike for indicated time intervals. In which time interval is each of the following happening?

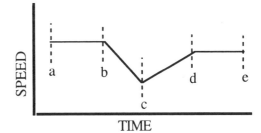

5.   The car is on cruise control.

6.   The driver is accelerating.

7.   The driver is slowing down.

8.   The number of bags of hard rolls on the shelves of a deli is related to the time of day. Suppose the shelves are full when the deli opens. Some customers buy rolls early in the morning and many more buy rolls around lunch time. Right after lunch the shelves are refilled.

      Draw a rough graph indicating the number of bags of rolls on the shelves from the time of the store's opening until shortly after lunch.

9.   Think of pairs of positive factors of 48.

      Consider the graph of all possible pairs of such factors:

      (2,24), (3,16), (4,12),   ... ,(12,4), (16,3). Which of the following most likely represents such a graph?

      HINT: As the first numbers increases, 3, 4, ... , 12, 16 the second numbers 24, 16, 12, ..., 4, 3 __crease? So the graph must be a __creasing relation.

(A)   (B)   (C)   (D)

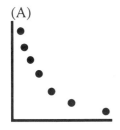   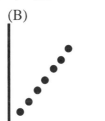   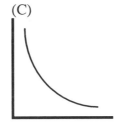   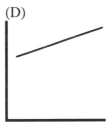

OPEN-ENDED QUESTION

10.   John belongs to a weight-loss club. Each member contributes money to a fund for a prize that goes to the person with the greatest weight loss after 6 weeks. Charges are: $10 for loss of less than a pound, $5.00 for loss of 1 pound or more up to 2 pounds, $3.00 for loss of 2 pounds or more up to 4 pounds, only $1.00 for loss of 4 pounds or more. Draw a numberless graph representing these rules. Explain how this graph represents the data.

REVIEW   CHAPTERS 1-11

Find the slope of $\overline{AB}$ for the given coordinates of the points A and B.

1.   A(4, 3), B(8, 5)   2. A(5, 6), B(10, 6)   3. A(8, 3), B(2, 7)

4.   Give the slope and y-intercept of $y = \frac{2}{3}x - 9$.

5.   Graph the equation $y = -\frac{3}{4}x + 5$.

6.   Which graph is the graph of
      $-\frac{1}{2}x - 3$: p, q, r, or s?

7.   Write an equation for the set of
      points graphed at the right.

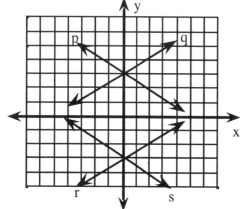

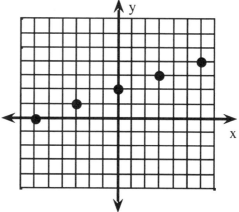

8.   The graph of $y = \frac{4}{5}x + 6$ can be drawn by **sliding** the graph of $y = \frac{4}{5}x$

      _____ units _____.

9.   Draw the graph of $y = 3x - 4$. Which of the statements below are true about the
      graph of $y = 3x + 2$?

         I   It is a slide 2 units up of the graph of $y = 3x - 4$.

         II   It is parallel to the graph of $y = 3x - 4$.

         III   It is a slide 6 units up of the graph of $y = 3x - 4$.

      (A)   I only   (B)   II and III only

      (C)   I and III ony   (D)   I only

10. The graph of $y = \frac{2}{3}x$ is shown at the right. Which statement is true about the graph of $y = \frac{2}{3}x + 5$?

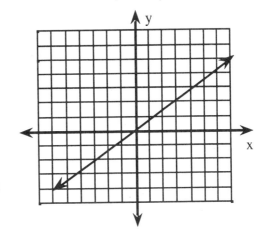

   (A) It is perpendicular to the graph of $y = \frac{2}{3}x$.

   (B) It is a translation of the graph of $y = \frac{2}{3}x$ five units to the right.

   (C) It intersects the graph of $y = \frac{2}{3}x$ at the origin.

   (D) It is a translation of the graph of $y = \frac{2}{3}x$ five units up.

11. The table at the right indicates a linear relationship between x and y. Find the number that belongs in the box.

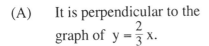

x	y
1	1
4	7
6	☐
8	15

The chart at the right shows the amount of money saved by two workers.

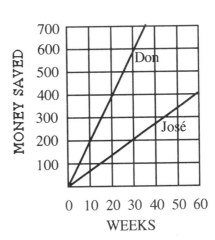

12. About how much money did José save after 50 weeks?

13. Find the average of the two savings after 30 weeks.

14. After 30 weeks, José's savings is what percent of Don's savings?

15. Malcolm graphed all possible combinations of the numbers of correct and incorrect responses that a student could make on a 20-question true-false test. Which graph below MOST LIKELY resembles Malcolm's graph?

(A)

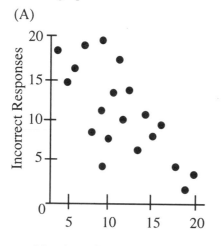

(B)

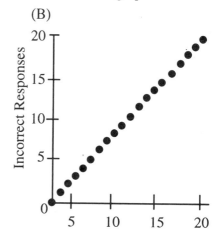

(C)

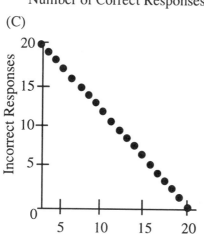

(D)

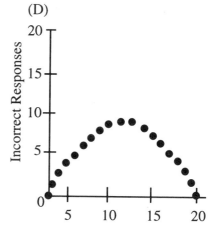

16. This graph corresponds to Mr. Johnson's trip from one town to another. What was most likely happening between time a and time b?

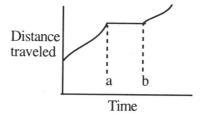

(A) Mr. Johnson stopped for a meal.	(B) He was moving slowly.
(C) He stopped at several traffic lights.	(C) He was traveling fast.

17.   Consider the number 36. Some pairs of matching positive integer factors of 36
       are (2, 18), (3, 12), (4, 9), (6, 6), ... (12, 3), (18, 2). Suppose someone graphs all
       possible pairs of matching positive integer factors of a given positive integer.
       Which of the following most likely represents such a graph?

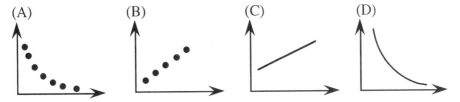

(A)   (B)   (C)   (D)

For exercises 18-19, which interval at
the right pictures the described rate
of speed of a racing car?

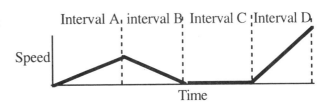

18.   Rate of speed decreasing steadily   19.   Pit stop for repairs

For each of the following exercises assume that m ‖ n.

20.   m ∠ 3 = 75, m ∠ 5 = ?

21.   m ∠ 4 = 112, m ∠ 7 = ?

22.   m ∠ 3 = 7x - 13, m ∠ 5 = 5x + 15
       Find m ∠ 3.

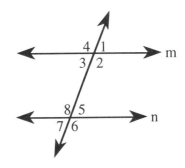

For each of the following, $\overline{PR}$ ‖ $\overline{TS}$.

23.   m ∠ 5 = 34, m ∠ 6 = 82, m ∠ 2 = ?

24.   m ∠ 4 = 118, m ∠ 2 = 27, m ∠ 6 = ?

25.   m ∠ TQR = 125, m ∠ 5 = 40, m ∠ 2 = ?

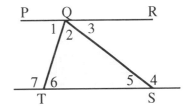

Plot the points A(4, 4), B(8, 7), C(5, 11), and D(1, 8).

26.   Use a ruler to measure, to the nearest $\frac{1}{4}$ inch, the length of each side.

27.   Is ABCD a parallelogram? Why?

28.   What appears to be true about the angle measures?

29.   What special kind of parallelogram does ABCD appear to be?

30.   ABCD is a parallelogram.

       m $\angle$ 3 = 38, m $\angle$ 2 = 27, m $\angle$ 1 = ?

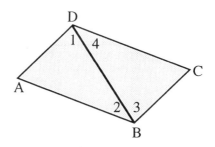

31.   The measure of the vertex angle of an isosceles triangle is 28.
       Find the measure of each base angle.

Plot the points P(1, 1), Q(6, 1), and R(2, 7). Draw $\triangle$PQR.

32.   Use a ruler to measure, to the nearest $\frac{1}{4}$ inch, the length of each side.

33.   Multiply both coordinates of each of the three vertices of $\triangle$PQR by 2.
       Graph the resulting triangle. Find the lengths of the sides of this triangle.

34.   Are the triangles similar or congruent? Why?

Use the similar triangles at the right to
answer Exercises 35-36.

35.   a = 2, b = 4, x = 7, y = ?

36.   z = 2, y = 5, b = 3, c = ?

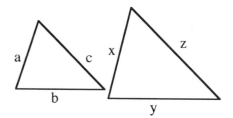

37.   The average price of a home in Hightown is $330,000. The average price of a
       home in Lowtown is $172,000. In both cities the average home price is 5 times
       the average yearly income. About how much more is the average income in
       Hightown than in Lowtown?

       (A) $22,000   (B) $32,000
       (C) $100,000   (D) $158,000

Given: PQRS is a trapezoid

38.   Find m ∠ 1
39.   Find m ∠ 2
40.   Is   Δ PQT ~ Δ RST? Why?

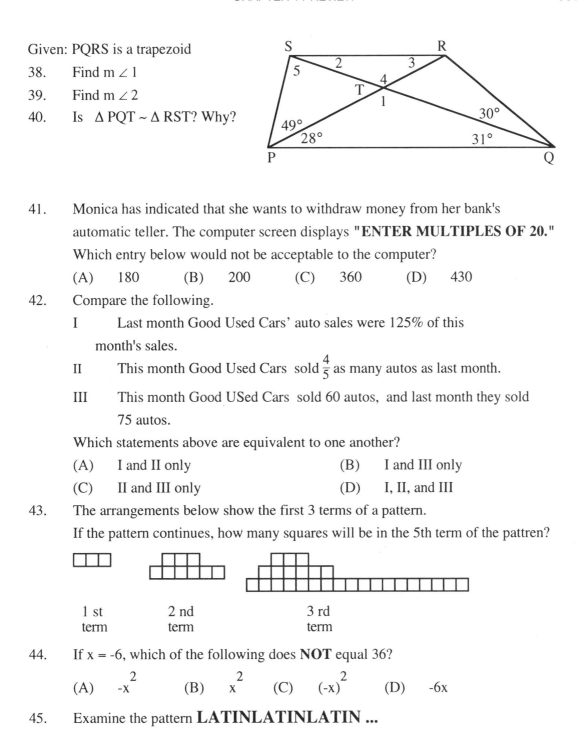

41.   Monica has indicated that she wants to withdraw money from her bank's
       automatic teller. The computer screen displays **"ENTER MULTIPLES OF 20."**
       Which entry below would not be acceptable to the computer?

       (A)   180   (B)   200   (C)   360   (D)   430

42.   Compare the following.

       I   Last month Good Used Cars' auto sales were 125% of this
              month's sales.

       II   This month Good Used Cars sold $\frac{4}{5}$ as many autos as last month.

       III   This month Good USed Cars sold 60 autos, and last month they sold
              75 autos.

       Which statements above are equivalent to one another?

       (A)   I and II only   (B)   I and III only

       (C)   II and III only   (D)   I, II, and III

43.   The arrangements below show the first 3 terms of a pattern.

       If the pattern continues, how many squares will be in the 5th term of the pattren?

       1 st   2 nd   3 rd
       term   term   term

44.   If x = -6, which of the following does **NOT** equal 36?

       (A) $-x^2$ (B) x^2 (C) $(-x)^2$ (D) $-6x$

45.   Examine the pattern **LATINLATINLATIN ...**

       If this pattern keeps repeating, what symbol will be in the 103rd position?

       (A)   T   (B)   A   (C)   I   (D)   L

46.   PQ = a and QR = b. Find PR.

P   Q   R

(A)   ab   (B)   a - b   (C)   a + b   (D)   b - a

47.   Which of these choices would you write in the blank to make a true statement?

$$1.9^8 \underline{\quad} 3.8^4$$

(A)   >   (B)   =   (C)   <   (D)   is half

48.   There are 4 different figures in the spiral below. If they are labeled P, Q, R, and S in the order in which they first appear (beginning at **Start** and going clockwise), what letters represent the missing figures?

(A)   RQ

(B)   PQ

(C)   QR

(D)   SQ

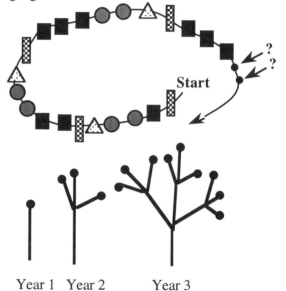

49.   A shrub starts as a single stem in Year 1. At the start of Year 2, it grows 2 branches and therefore has three tips growing. Each year every branch does the same thing. That is, it grows 2 branches and continues to grow itself. How many tips are on the shrub in the 7th year if no branch has died?

Year 1   Year 2   Year 3

This graph shows the foreign language choices of 300 students.

50.   How many chose Japanese?

51.   The number choosing French is what % of the total?

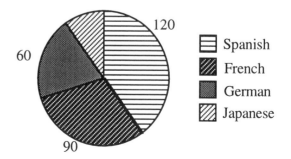

52.   Performing which set of transformations on the lightly
       shaded triangle will **NOT** result in the lightly shaded
       triangle completely covering the heavily shaded triangle?

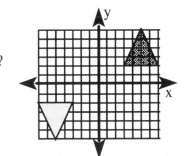

       (A)   translation 10 units to the right followed by
              reflection in the x-axis

       (B)   translation 3 units to the right followed by
              reflection in the x-axis

       (C)   rotation of 180° about the origin

       (D)   reflection in the x-axis followed by reflection in
              the y-axis

53.   Which spinner below would give you the best probability of spinning a K?

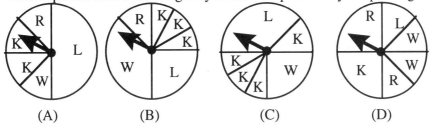

       (A)   (B)   (C)   (D)

54. $\overrightarrow{OA} \perp \overrightarrow{OB}$, m $\angle 1$: m $\angle 2 = 2 : 7$.
       Find m $\angle 1$.

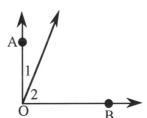

55.   Solve $\frac{3}{4}$ x - 8 = 16

56.   Bill's average for 3 tests is 65. What must he get on the fourth test to
       raise his average to 70?

57.   The perimeter of a rectangle is 60 in. The length is 10 in. Find the area.

OPEN-ENDED QUESTION

58.   A bag of 12 marbles contains 3 red marbles and 2 green marbles. The rest are
       blue. One marble is selected at random. Write an explanation of how you would
       find the probability of selecting a blue marble.

Chapter

▶ **12**

Area and Volume

12.1   Units of Measure

OBJECTIVES   To determine the appropriate unit of measure for a quantity

To convert units of measure to like units of measure

To combine units of measure

When finding perimeters, areas, or volumes it is necessary to decide what unit of measure is most practical.

For example, we don't talk about the distance between two cities in terms of inches. We use miles. On the other hand, we use inches for the scale of a road map.

You probably don't have trouble with inches, feet, and miles. But you may have trouble choosing appropriate units of measure in the metric system.

You need to know the meaning of metric measurements in terms of real-life situations.

Let's first consider length.

The basic unit of metric length is the **meter**.

1 meter is approximately 39.37 inches, or a little more than **1 yard**.

| 1 yard |
| 1 meter |

Use it to measure the length of a room.

The abbreviation for meter is **m**.

Other metric measures of length are as follows.

| 1 **kilo**meter | (1 km) | = 1000 meters (1000 m) | Use to measure **distance** between **cities**. **Large** distance   (**kilo** indicates **large**) |

1 **centi**meter   (1 cm)   = $\frac{1}{100}$ meter   Use to measure length of a paper clip.

1 cm is a little less than $\frac{1}{2}$ inch   **Small** distances

1 **milli**meter   (1 mm)   = $\frac{1}{1000}$ meter   Use to measure size of head of a pin. **Very small** distances (**milli** indicates **very small**)

EXAMPLE 1   What unit of measure would be most appropriate to measure each of the following?

                                                                    Solution

(a)   length of a sheet of paper   centimeter   (cm)

(b)   length of a room   meter   (m)

(c)   thickness of a sheet of paper   millimeter   (mm)

(d)   distance between two cities   kilometer   (km)

Two other units of metric measurement are **gram** for **weight** and **liter** for **volume**.

The three metric units are summarized below.

Length	**Weight**	**Volume**
basic unit: **meter** (**m**)	basic unit: **gram** (**g**)	basic unit: **liter** (**L**)
1 meter is a little over **1 yard** length of a room: in meters	1 gram is the approximate weight of one paper clip.	1 liter is a little over 1 quart.
kilometer: (**km**) distance between two cities: in kilometers	**kilogram** (**kg**) 1 kilogram is a little over 2 pounds.	**kiloliter** (**kL**) 1 kiloliter is 1,000 liters.
centimeter: (**cm**) length of sheet of paper: in centimeters		
millimeter (**mm**) (**very tiny**): measures thickness of sheet of paper	**milligram** (**mg**) (**very tiny**) e.g. measure for medicine dose: pills or aspirin	**milliliter** (**mL**) (**very tiny**) e.g. liquid medicine

Suppose two measurements are given in different units, such as meters and kilometers. The next example shows how to combine such mixed measurements to get a **total**.

EXAMPLE 2   Jason ran 3 km 700 m on Saturday and 7 km 800 m on Tuesday.
How far did he run altogether on the two days?

Strategy   3 km + 700 m + 7 km + 800 m

3 km + 7 km   +   (700 m + 800 m)   **Combine like terms.**

10 km   +   1500 m

10 km   +   (**1000 m** + 500 m)

$\boxed{10 \text{ km} \quad + \quad \textbf{1 km}}$ + 500 m   **1000 m = 1 km**

11 km   + 500 m

Solution   Thus, Jason ran 11 km 500 m altogether.

EXAMPLE 3   A boxer weighs 80 kg. He must lose weight to make a certain weight
category. He loses 4 kg 160 g. Find his new weight.

Strategy   Because he **loses** weight, you know to **subtract**.

Rewrite 80 kg

Think:

80 =	79	+ 1	Use **1 kg** = 1000 g	
80 kg	79 kg	**1 kg**	79 kg	**1000 g**
-4 kg 160 g	- 4 kg	160 g	- 4 kg	160 g
			75 kg	840 g

Solution   The boxer's new weight is 75 kg 840 g.

Notice the same role of **prefixes** in different metric measurements.

Many metric measurements involve conversions based on **1000** units.

1 **kilo**gram   =   1 kg = **1000** g

1 **kilo**meter   =   1 km = **1000** m   A **kilo** is very **large**.

1 **kilo**liter   =   1 kL = **1000** L

1000 millimeters = **1000** mm = 1 m

1000 milligrams = **1000** mg = 1 g   A **milli** is very **small**.

1000 milliliters   = **1000** mL = 1 L

Notice the following pattern for metric measurements.

For 1360 g	For 3895 m	For 2680 mL
$1360 \div 1000 = 1.360$	$3895 \div 1000 = 3.895$	$2680 \div 1000 = 2.680$
So, 1**360** g = 1.**360** kg	3**895** m = 3.**895** km	2**680** mL = 2.**680** L

EXAMPLE 4   Three bottles of medicine have the following volumes:

940 mL, 790 mL, and 976 mL.

Find the total volume in liters if all the medicine is poured into a single

bottle.

$$
\begin{array}{r}
940 \text{ mL} \\
790 \text{ mL} \\
+ \quad 976 \text{ mL} \\
\hline
2706 \text{ mL}
\end{array}
$$

Solution   2**706** mL = 2.**706** L   **1000 mL = 1 L**

Let's now take a look at another important unit of measure, that of **time**.

1 hour	=	60 minutes		1 minute	=	60 seconds
1 h	=	60 min		1 min	=	60 sec

EXAMPLE 5   Jane is on the swim team. Her goal is to swim for a total of 12 hours this

weekend. She swam for 4 h 35 min on Friday and 5 h 40 min on

Saturday.

How long must she swim on Sunday to meet her 12-hour goal?

Strategy   First find the **total** time spent so far swimming on Friday and Saturday.

$$
\begin{array}{ll}
\quad 4 \text{ h} \quad 35 \text{ min} \\
+ \ 5 \text{ h} \quad 40 \text{ min} \\
\hline
\quad 9 \text{ h} \quad 75 \text{ min}
\end{array}
$$ **Add to find total.**

9 h   **60 min**   + 15 min   **Rewrite 75 min as 60 min + 15 min**

9 h   **1 h**   + 15 min

10 h   15 min

(continued on next page)

Now find how much time Jane has to swim to make her goal.

12 h		11 h	60 min	**Rewrite 12 h as 11 h 60 min**
-10 h	15 min	-10 h	15 min	
		1 h	45 min	

Solution   Thus, Jane must swim 1 hour and 45 minutes on Sunday.

The idea of combining like units of measure is now applied to a perimeter problem. Perimeters can be in terms of metric or standard units. The next problem applies the formula for the perimeter of a rectangle.

Also recall the Distributive Property. For example,   **2**(3x + 5)

$$= \ \mathbf{2} \cdot 3x + \mathbf{2} \cdot 5$$
$$= \ \ \ 6x \ + \ 10$$

EXAMPLE 6   How much fencing would be needed to enclose the backyard with dimensions indicated at the right?

9 ft 7 in.

15 ft 10 in.

Strategy   Use the perimeter formula for a rectangle:

P = 2L + 2W.

Note, first that 15 ft 10 in. means 15 ft + 10 in.

P = **2**(15 ft   +   10 in.) +   **2**(9 ft   +   7 in.)

P = 30 ft   +   20 in. +   18 ft   +   14 in.   **Distribute the 2.**

P = | 30 ft + 18 ft | + | 20 in. + 14 in. | **Group like terms.**

P =   48 ft   +   34 in.

Use **12 in. = 1 ft** to rewrite 34 in. as feet and inches.

P = 48 ft + | 34 in. |

P = 48 ft + | (**12 in. + 12 in. + 10 in.**) |

P = 48 ft + (**1 ft** + **1 ft**   + 10 in.)

P = 48 ft +   **2 ft**   + 10 in.

P =   50 ft   + 10 in.

Solution   Thus, 50 ft 10 in. of fencing are needed to enclose the back yard.

SUMMARY

1.   A meter is about how many yards?
2.   About how many pounds is a kilogram?
3.   A liter is a little over how many quarts?

What metric unit of measure would be most appropriate to measure each of the following?

4.   distance between two cities
5.   length and width of the cover of this book
6.   thickness of a sheet of paper
7.   weight of a football

8.   How do you subtract 6 kg 120 g from 200 kg?

How do you rewrite each of the following?

9.   50 km 2400 m?   10.   5 h 80 min   11.   5 yd 7 ft

12.   4323 m = ? km

CLASSROOM PRACTICE

What metric unit of measure would be most appropriate to measure each of the following?

1.   distance between two exits on a parkway
2.   amount of soda in a large Pepsi bottle
3.   thickness of a needle point
4.   length of a pencil
5.   height of a room
6.   a person's weight
7.   weight of a fly

8.   Wanda ran 8 km 500 m on Tuesday and 4 km 800 m on Thursday. How far did she run altogether on the two days?

9.   Tina weighs 65 kg 400 g. She gains 4 kg 700 g. Find her new weight.

10.   Jim weighed 80 kg 200 g. He lost 3 kg 500 g. Find his new weight.

11.   Jon ran 8 km 600 m on Monday and 6 km 500 m on Tuesday.

      How far did he run altogether on the two days?

12.   Express 2345 g as kg.

13.   Express 3245 m as km.

14.   Express 4573 mL as L.

15.   Three bottles of medicine have the following volumes:

      730 mL, 845 mL, and 425 mL

      Find the total volume in liters if they are poured into one bottle.

16.   Natasha wants to work 16 hours this week. She works 6 h 30 min on Monday and

      5 h 40 min on Thursday. How long must she work on Friday to work a total of 16

      hours?

17.   José wants to practice swimming a total of 9 hours this week. He practices

      3 h 30 min on Wednesday and 2 h 40 min on Thursday. How much time

      must he spend swimming Saturday to accomplish his goal of a total of 9 hours for

      the week?

Find the perimeter of each rectangle.

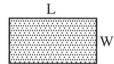

18.   L = 4 ft 8 in, W = 2 ft 9 in

19.   L = 8 yd 2 ft, W = 5 yd 2 ft   (3 ft = 1 yd)

20.   L = 7 km 500 m, W = 6 km 700 m.

WRITTEN EXERCISES

What metric unit of measure would be most appropriate to measure each of the
following?

1.   length of a stick of gum

2.   weight of a dog

3.   amount of milk in the largest container sold in most convenience stores

4.   length of a leg of an ant

5.   distance from the Charlotte airport to downtown Charlotte

6.   weight of a needle

7.   length and width of a high school gym

8.   Greg ran 9 km 400 m on Tuesday and 6 km 900 m on Thursday. How far did he run altogether on the two days?

9.   Sonya weighs 55 kg 500 g. She gains 2 kg 600 g. Find her new weight.

10.   Ron weighed 90 kg 100 g. He lost 4 kg 300 g. Find his new weight.

11.   Lou ran 7 km 300 m on Monday and 8 km 900 m on Tuesday. How far did he run altogether on the two days?

12.   Express 4345 g as kg.

13.   Express 5412 m as km.

14.   Express 3500 mL as L.

15.   Three bottles of medicine have the following volumes:

      390 mL, 945 mL, and 352 mL

      Find the total volume in liters if they are poured into one bottle.

16.   Carl wants to work 20 hours this week. He works 7 h 20 min on Monday and 6 h 50 min on Thursday. How long must he work on Friday to work a total of 20 hours?

17.   Abdul wants to practice swimming a total of 10 hours this week. He practices 2 h 30 min on Wednesday and 4 h 50 min on Thursday. How much time must he spend swimming Saturday to accomplish his goal of a total of 10 hours for the week?

Find the perimeter of each rectangle.

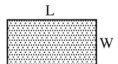

18.   L = 7 ft 9 in., W = 2 ft 5 in.

19.   L = 10 yd 2 ft, W = 8 yd 1 ft   (3 ft = 1 yd)

20.   L = 9 km 600 m, W = 7 km 800 m.

OPEN-ENDED QUESTION

21.   Explain in detail in your own words how to find the following difference.
      Do not just give the answer. Explain how you can subtract since 600 is larger than 400.

          7 km 400 m
      -3 km 600 m

REVIEW

1. The pentagon in figure (a) is 3 cm on a side and rolled to the right along the line. Which of the following distances could it have rolled so that the shaded circle would be in the position shown in figure (b)?

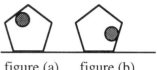

figure (a)   figure (b)

   (A)   30 cm   (B)   27 cm   (C)   21 cm   (D)   15 cm

2. Which spinner below would give the best probability of spinning an R?

 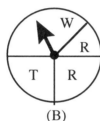 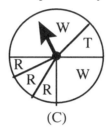 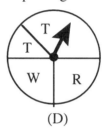

   (A)   (B)   (C)   (D)

3. Jane tossed the die at the right 7 times. The first two times the die landed with 2 dots on the upper face. The last time it landed with 4 dots on the upper face. What is the probability that it will land with 2 dots showing up on the next toss of the die?

   (A) $\frac{4}{7}$ (B) $\frac{2}{7}$ (C) $\frac{1}{6}$ (D) $\frac{1}{7}$

4. The table at the right indicates a linear relationship between the variables. Find the number that belongs in the box.

   (A)   7   (B)   6   (C)   5   (D)   4

a	b
0	3
2	7
☐	11
8	19

5. What is the next term in the sequence 2, 8, 26, 80, ... ?

12.2   Areas of Parallelograms and Triangles

OBJECTIVES   To find the area of a parallelogram

To find the area of a triangle

To solve problems about areas of triangles and parallelograms

In the parallelogram at the right, $\overline{DE}$ is a

perpendicular from D to side $\overline{AB}$.

The little **box** at E is a way of telling you this.

$\overline{DE}$ is an **altitude** or **height** of the parallelogram.

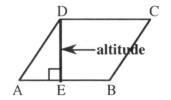

In the parallelogram below, $\overline{DE}$ is an altitude or height from D to opposite side $\overline{AB}$.

Notice that the total area is composed of the area of the triangle and the shaded region (a trapezoid).

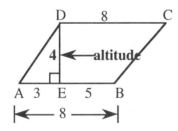

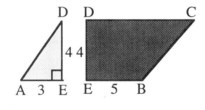

You know how to find the area of a rectangle. Copy the triangle on tracing paper.

Slide the triangle to the opposite side of the trapezoid so that $\overline{AD}$ and $\overline{BC}$ coincide.

The area of the original parallelogram ABCD is the same as the area of this **rectangle.**

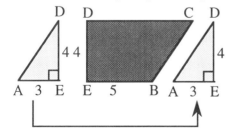

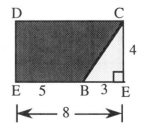

The area of the rectangle is $A = 4 \cdot 8 = 32$.

So, the area of the original parallelogram must also be 32.

Notice the pattern from the previous page.

The **A**rea of the parallelogram is the length of the **altitude** (or **height**) times the length of the side to which it is drawn:

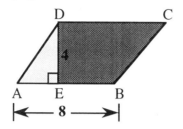

$$A = \quad 4 \quad \cdot \quad 8$$

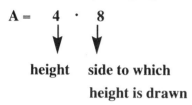

height   side to which height is drawn

This suggests the following formula.

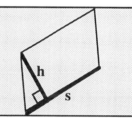

AREA OF PARALLELOGRAM

A = length of **h**eight time length of **s**ide to which height is drawn.
A = **h** · **s**

As seen above, the height (or altitude) of a parallelogram is not always vertical.

A **height** of a parallelogram is any segment from a vertex **perpendicular** **t**o the **opposite** side.

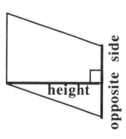

EXAMPLE 1   Find the area of the parallelogram. The lengths of the sides are given in centimeters.

(continued on next page)

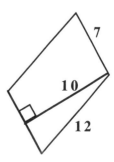

Strategy   Shade the height and the opposite to which
it is drawn.
Opposite sides are equal in length, each 7.
A = 7 . 10 = 70
Now express the area in terms of square
centimeters.

Thus, the area is 70 cm^2.

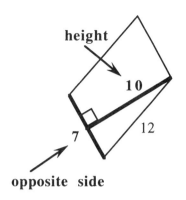

opposite side

EXAMPLE 2   The area of a parallelogram is 44 ft^2.
The length of an altitude is 5 ft. Find the length of a side to which the
altitude is drawn.

Strategy   Use the formula   A = hs
                                  44 = 5 · s   **A = 44, h = 5**
                Solve: 44 = 5s
                                  $8\frac{4}{5}$ = s   **Divide each side by 5.**

Solution   Thus, the length of a side to which the altitude is drawn is $8\frac{4}{5}$ ft.

DISCOVERY

In the parallelogram at the right, $\overline{DB}$ is called a
diagonal. It joins two opposite vertices, D and B. The
diagonal divides the parallelogram into two triangles.

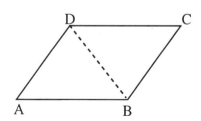

What do you think is the relationship between the two
triangles?
If you know area of the parallelogram is 48 in^2, what
must be the area of a triangle?

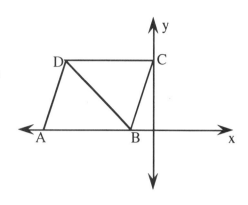

Transformations can be used to show the relationship of the two triangles formed by the diagonal $\overline{BD}$ of the parallelogram ABCD. Use tracing paper to trace △ DBC. Then **flip** △ DBC about the y-axis. **Flip** the result about the x-axis. These two **flips** are illustrated below. Draw the **flip** of △ DBC about the y-axis.

Draw the **flip** of the resulting △ about the x-axis. Label the **flip** △ PQR.

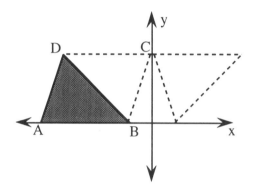

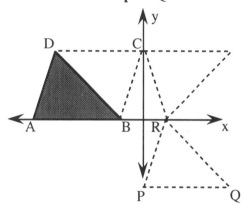

It is now easy to see that the resulting △ PQR is **congruent** to △ ABD. You can verify this by sliding △ PQR to exactly cover △ ABD.

Therefore, the diagonal $\overline{BD}$ of the parallelogram forms **two congruent** triangles.

The **area** of **one** of these triangles must be $\frac{1}{2}$ the area of the parallelogram.

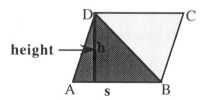

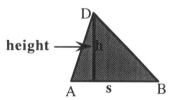

Area of **parallelogram**: **hs**   Area of **triangle**: $\frac{1}{2}$ **hs**

This suggests the following formula, on the next page, for the area of a triangle.

AREA OF A TRIANGLE

$A = \frac{1}{2}hs$

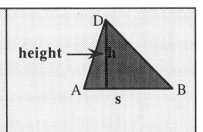

Notice below that a triangle has three different heights (altitudes).

In each case the area is $\frac{1}{2}$ of the length of the height times the length of the side to which

it is drawn.

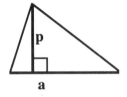

$A = \frac{1}{2}\mathbf{pa}$

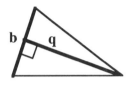

$A = \frac{1}{2}\mathbf{qb}$

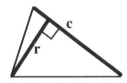

$A = \frac{1}{2}\mathbf{rc}$

EXAMPLE 3   Find the area of the triangle.

The sides are measured in meters.

Strategy   The answer will reflect the units of measure.

The area will be written in terms of square meters, m^2.

Shade the height and the side to which it is drawn.

Use the area formula.

$A = \frac{1}{2} \cdot$ height $\cdot$ side to which it is drawn

$A = \frac{1}{2} \cdot \; \mathbf{5} \quad \cdot \quad \mathbf{12}$

$A = \frac{1}{2} \cdot \quad 60 = 30$

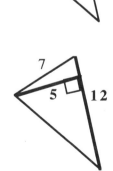

Solution   Thus, the area of the triangle is $30 \; m^2$.

In the next example you will see that for a right triangle either of the two perpendicular

sides can be treated as a height of the triangle.

EXAMPLE 4   Find the area of the triangle.

The sides are measured in feet.

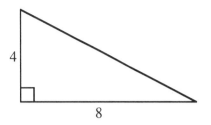

Strategy   You can use either 4 or 8 as a height.

Use the formula $A = \frac{1}{2}$ hs.

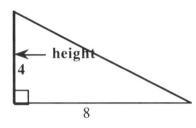

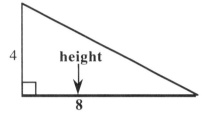

$h = 4, s = 8$ $s = 4, h = 8$

$A = \frac{1}{2} h \cdot s$ $A = \frac{1}{2} h \cdot s$

$A = \frac{1}{2} \cdot 4 \cdot 8$ $A = \frac{1}{2} \cdot 8 \cdot 4$

$A = \quad 2 \cdot 8 = 16$ $A = \quad 4 \cdot 4 = 16$

Solution   Thus, the area of the triangle is **16 ft^2**.

The area is the **same** whether you use 4 or 8 as the height.

With larger numerical values, you might want to use a calculator to compute the area of a triangle. In this case, use **0.5** instead of $\frac{1}{2}$ in the area formula.

EXAMPLE 5   Find the area of a triangle with a side of length 47 cm and a height to that side of length 19 cm.

Strategy   Use $A = 0.5$ hs

$A = 0.5 \cdot 19 \cdot 47$

Enter 0.5   Enter **x**   Enter 19   Enter **x**   Enter 47   Enter =
Read the answer: **446.5.**

Solution   Thus, the area of the triangle is 446.5 cm^2.

EXAMPLE 6   Given: Area of a triangle is 48 cm^2, length of a side is 13 cm.

Find h to the nearest tenth of a cm.

Strategy   Use the formula.

$$A \ = \ \tfrac{1}{2}\,hs.$$

$$48 \ = \ \tfrac{1}{2} \cdot h \cdot 13 \quad \textbf{A = 48, s = 13}$$

$$48 \ = \ \tfrac{1}{2} \cdot 13 \cdot h \quad \textbf{Multiplication can be done in any order.}$$

$$48 \ = \ 6.5h$$

$$7.3846154 \ = \ h \qquad \textbf{Divide each side by 6.5.}$$

Solution   Thus, h = 7.4 cm, to the nearest tenth of a cm.

SUMMARY

1.   What is another name for **altitude?**

2.   What is the formula for the area of a parallelogram?

3.   What is the height of a triangle?   How many heights does a triangle have?

4.   What is the formula for the area of a triangle?

5.   How do you find the area of the
triangle at the right?

6.   Explain how to solve the following problem.

The area of a triangle is 97 m^2 and a side is 11 m. Find, to the nearest tenth of a

meter, the length of a height drawn to that side.

CLASSROOM PRACTICE

Find the area of each parallelogram. Lengths of the sides and heights are given in inches.

1.

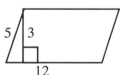

2.

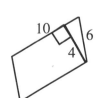

3.

4.

5.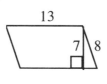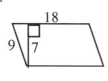

6.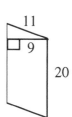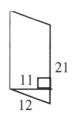

7.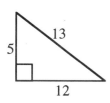

8.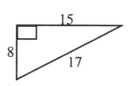

9.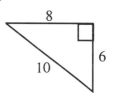

Find the area of each triangle. The lengths of the sides and heights are given in inches.

10.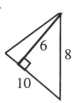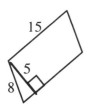

11.

12.

13.

14.

15.

16.   The area of a parallelogram is 56 in^2. The length of an altitude is 6 in.
       Find the length of a side to which the altitude is drawn.

17.   The area of a triangle is 57 m^2. The length of a side is 7 m. Find, to
       the nearest tenth of a meter, the length of a height to that side.

WRITTEN EXERCISES

Find the area of each parallelogram. Lengths of the sides and heights are given in meters.

1.
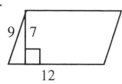

2.
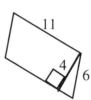

3.

4.

5.

6.

7.

8.
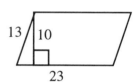

9.
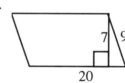

Find the area of each triangle. The lengths of the sides and heights are given in inches.

10.
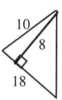

11.
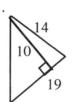

12.

13.
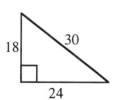

14.
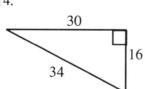

15.
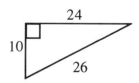

16.   The area of a parallelogram is 50 in^2. The length of an altitude is 8 in.
        Find the length of a side to which the altitude is drawn.

17.   The area of a triangle is 97 m^2. The length of a side is 11 m. Find, to the
        nearest tenth of a meter, the length of a height to that side.

18.   The area of a triangle is 139 m^2. The length of a side is 15 m. Find, to
        the nearest tenth of a meter, the length of a height to that side.

19.   Choose the correct symbol to
        produce a true statement: <, >, =.
        area of triangle __ area of
        parallelogram

20.   Use graph paper to draw a
        rectangle with the same area as
        the triangle. Give the coordinates
        of the vertices of the rectangle.
        Is there more than one answer?

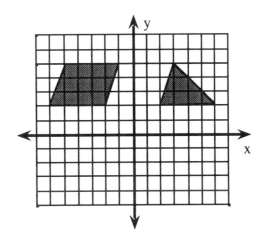

OPEN-ENDED QUESTION

21.   The area of a triangle is 60 m^2. The length of a side is 10 m. The height drawn to
        that side is the same as the height of a rectangle with area 36 m^2.

        Find the perimeter of the rectangle.

REVIEW

Simplify (Ex. 1-4)

1. $3x + 2(4x - 1)$ 2. $\frac{3}{4}$ of 24   3. $-4(-2)^3$ 4. $-18 \div -3$

5.   A car rental agency owns 200 cars. At the moment, 40 are rented.
     What percent of all the cars are **NOT** now rented?

12.3   Square Root and the Pythagorean Property

OBJECTIVES To find the square root of a number

To apply the Pythagorean Property

In arithmetic, **addition** can be **undone** by **subtraction**.

For example, $2 + 5 = 7$ $7 - 5 = 2$.

We see that **adding 5** to 2 can be **undone** by **subtracting 5** from 7.

Addition and subtraction are **inverse operations** of each other.

The word *inverse* means *opposite*.

Likewise, multiplication and division are **inverse operations** of each other.

An important example of an **inverse operation** is the **inverse** of **squaring** a number.

Remember: 6 **squared**, or 6^2, is $6 \cdot 6 = 36$.

The two numbers being multiplied are the **same**.

The **inverse** of **squaring** is finding the **square root**.

The symbol for **square root** is $\sqrt{}$.

$\sqrt{36} = 6$, since 6 is the positive number which when **squared** is 36.

Other examples of square root are: $\sqrt{49} = 7$, since $7^2 = 7 \cdot 7 = 49$,

$\sqrt{64} = 8$, since $8^2 = 8 \cdot 8 = 64$.

EXAMPLE 1   Simplify $\sqrt{81}$.

Solution $\sqrt{81} = 9$, since $9^2 = 9 \cdot 9 = 81$.

An application of **square root** to geometry is illustrated below.

Suppose that each side of the square at the right is of length **a = 5**.

Then the area of the square is A = **a · a = a^2 = 5^2 = 25.**

Thus to get the area, you **square** the length of a side.

Think, area is 25:   **a^2 = 25.**

                               a = $\sqrt{25}$

                               a = 5   **(a must be positive since lengths of**

                                                       segments are positive.)

If there is no **exact** square root, then use a calculator as shown below.

    a = $\sqrt{65}$

    a = 8.0622577   **Enter 65. Press the $\sqrt{\ }$ key.**

EXAMPLE 2   Chang got an answer of about 4.90 when he entered 24 on his calculator and pressed the $\sqrt{\ }$ key. As usual, he stopped to think whether the calculator answer was reasonable.

Which of the following is the most likely explanation for him to believe that his calculator answer is or is not reasonable?

(A)   It is not reasonable, because the answer should be a whole number.

(B)   It is reasonable, because 4 squared is 16 while 5 squared is 25.

(C)   It is not reasonable, because the answer should be only slightly more than 4.

(D)   It is reasonable, because 4 and 24 are both even numbers.

Strategy   Estimate $\sqrt{24}$. Find positive numbers whose squares are close to 24.

                     3^2 = 9,   4^2 = 16,   5^2 = 25

                            24 is between 16 and 25.

So, $\sqrt{24}$ must be between **4** and **5**. This suggests (B) is the solution.

(continued on next page)

Checking the other answers:

(A) is not possible since there is no whole number between 4 and 5.

(C) is not possible since a number slightly more than 4 when squared is close to 16, **not** 24.

(D) is irrelevant. For example, **6**.23 is certainly not the square root of 24 even though **6** and **24** are both even numbers

Solution   Therefore, (B) is the solution.

EXAMPLE 3   Which of these is the closest approximation to $\sqrt{3000}$?

(A)   50   (B)   60   (C)   54.1   (D)   54.7

Strategy   You could square each multiple-choice answer to see which result is closest to 3000.

It is faster to use a calculator to find $\sqrt{3000}$.

Then determine which multiple choice answer is closest to $\sqrt{3000}$.

Enter 3000. Press the $\sqrt{}$ key: Read 54.772256.

Solution   The closest multiple choice answer is **(D)**, 54.7.

We now take another look at applying square root to geometry.
The application will involve finding the lengths of sides of a right triangle.

This triangle is a right triangle.
The **longest side** of the triangle, c, is called
the **hypotenuse**.

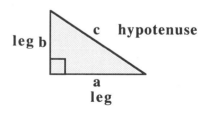

The other two sides of the triangle, a and b,
are called the **legs**.
The **legs** form the **right angle.**

PYTHAGOREAN PROPERTY

In any right triangle, the **sum** of the **squares** of the lengths of the **legs** equals the **square** of the length of the **hypotenuse**.

$$\text{leg}^2 + \text{leg}^2 = \text{hypotenuse}^2$$
$$a^2 + b^2 = c^2$$

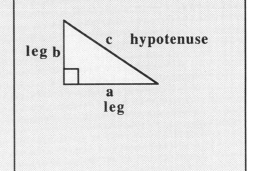

EXAMPLE 4   For this right triangle, p = 7.0, s = 6.0.

Find g, to the nearest tenth.

Strategy

$$\text{leg}^2 + \text{leg}^2 = \text{hypotenuse}^2$$
$$g^2 + s^2 = p^2$$
$$g^2 + 6^2 = 7^2 \qquad s = 6,\ p = 7$$
$$g^2 + 36 = 49$$
$$g^2 = 13$$
$$g = \sqrt{13}$$
$$g = 3.6055513$$

Solution   Thus, g = 3.6, rounded to the nearest tenth.

EXAMPLE 5   Find the perimeter of the quadrilateral ABCD.

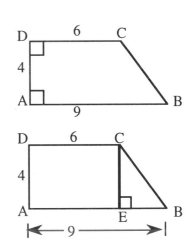

Strategy   The perimeter is the sum of the lengths of all the sides. You need to find the missing length BC.

From C draw $\overline{CE}$ perpendicular to $\overline{AB}$. The quadrilateral is now separated into a **rectangle** and **right triangle**.

(continued on next page)

CE = 4 and EB = 9 - 6 = 3.

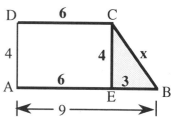

Use the Pythagorean Property to find x.

$$4^2 + 3^2 = x^2$$
$$16 + 9 = x^2$$
$$25 = x^2$$
$$\sqrt{25} = x$$
$$5 = x$$

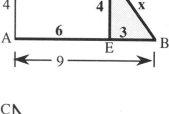

So, **BC = 5**

Now find the perimeter of ABCD.

AB	+	BC	+	CD	+	DA		
9	+	**5**	+	6	+	4	=	24

Solution   Thus, the perimeter of ABCD is 24.

EXAMPLE 6   Given: a = 6, m = 5.

Find, to the nearest tenth of a unit, the
perimeter and area of the right triangle.

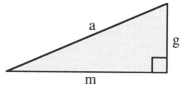

Strategy   You need the value of **g** to find the
perimeter and area.

Use the Pythagorean Property to find **g**.

$$m^2 + g^2 = a^2$$
$$5^2 + g^2 = 6^2 \qquad\qquad \mathbf{m = 5, a = 6}$$
$$25 + g^2 = 36$$
$$g^2 = 11 \qquad\qquad \textbf{Subtract 25 from each side.}$$
$$g = 3.3166248$$

(continued on next page)

Find the perimeter.

$P = a + m + g$

$P = 6 + 5 + 3.3166248$

$ = 14.3166248$

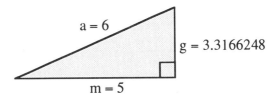

$a = 6$

$g = 3.3166248$

$m = 5$

Solution 1

> **The perimeter is therefore 14.3, to the nearest tenth of a unit.**

Strategy

> Now find the area.
>
> $A = \dfrac{1}{2} mg$
>
> $A = \dfrac{1}{2} \cdot 5 \cdot 3.3166248$
>
> $A = 0.5 \cdot 5 \cdot 3.3166248$
>
> Use a calculator.
>
> Enter 0.5   Enter **X**   Enter 5   Enter **X**   Enter 3.3166248 Enter =
>
> Read 8.291562.

Solution 2

> **The area is therefore 8.3, to the nearest tenth of a unit.**

It is important to remember the **Pythagorean Property** as :

$$\text{leg}^2 + \text{leg}^2 = \text{hypotenuse}^2.$$

Do **NOT** think in terms of $a^2 + b^2 = c^2$!

$$\text{leg}^2 + \text{leg}^2 = \text{hypotenuse}^2.$$

$$b^2 + c^2 = a^2$$

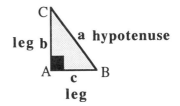

C

leg b   a hypotenuse

A   c   B

leg

SUMMARY

1.   What is meant by the square root of a number?

2. $\sqrt{25} = ?$ How do you show that your answer is correct?

3.   How do you find $\sqrt{78}$ using a calculator?

4.   To estimate $\sqrt{61}$, you find two positive numbers whose squares are close to 61. Thus $\sqrt{61}$ is between ___ and ___ .

5. What is a fast way to determine which number below is the closest approximation to $\sqrt{4506}$?

    (A)   23   (B)   47   (C)   59   (D)   65

6. How do you determine from a drawing of a right triangle which sides are the legs and which side is the hypotenuse?

7. What is the Pythagorean Property?

8. How do you solve $x^2 + 7 = 19$ for the positive value of x? How do you use the calculator to complete the solution?

8. Identify the legs and hypotenuse of the right triangle. Use the Pythagorean Property to write an equation.

CLASSROOM PRACTICE

Simplify each.

1. $\sqrt{16}$ 2. $\sqrt{100}$

Simplify using a calculator.

        3. $\sqrt{175}$ 4. $\sqrt{2564}$ 5. $\sqrt{96}$

6. Which of the following is a good estimate of $\sqrt{72}$? Explain why in terms of the answer being between two numbers.

    (A)   36   (B)   7.5   (C)   8.5   (D)   9.5

7. Which of the following is a good estimate of $\sqrt{44}$? Explain why in terms of the answer being between two numbers.

    (A)   5.6   (B)   7.6   (C)   2.2   (D)   6.6

8. Which of these is the closest approximation to $\sqrt{1546}$?

    (A)   29.4   (B)   39.3   (C)   77.1   (D)   44.4

Find the length, to the nearest tenth of a unit, of the indicated side.

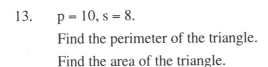

9. g = 5, s = 9, p =?

10. s = 9, g = 7, p = ?

11. p = 7, s = 5, g = ?

12. p = 8, g = 4, s = ?

13. p = 10, s = 8.

   Find the perimeter of the triangle.

   Find the area of the triangle.

14. p = 8, s = 7.

   Find, to the nearest tenth of a unit, the

   perimeter and area of the triangle.

For the given area of the square, find the length of a side to the nearest tenth of a unit,.

15.. area = 138 cm^2

16. area = 249 ft^2

17. Which of the numbers below is **NOT** equal to the other three?

   (A)   2.1 x 10^2 (B)   210%   (C) $\frac{21}{10}$ (D) $\sqrt{4.41}$

18. Which of these choices would you write in the blank to make a true statement?

$$\sqrt{\frac{324}{729}} \ \_\_\_\_ \ \tfrac{1}{3} \text{ of } 2$$

   (A)   <   (B)   >   (C)   =   (D)   Cannot be determined

   HINT: Use a calculator to evaluate $\sqrt{\frac{324}{729}}$.

   Enter 324   Enter ÷ 729   Enter =   Enter $\sqrt{\ \ }$

WRITTEN EXERCISES

1. Simplify $\sqrt{25}$

2. Simplify $\sqrt{144}$

Simplify using a calculator.

3. $\sqrt{143}$ 4. $\sqrt{5263}$ 5. $\sqrt{89}$

6.   Which of the following is a good estimate of $\sqrt{66}$? Explain why in terms of the answer being between two numbers.

(A)   33   (B)   7.8   (C)   8   (D)   9.4

7.   Which of the following is a good estimate of $\sqrt{93}$? Explain why in terms of the answer being between two numbers.

(A)   9.6   (B)   3.1   (C)   46.5   (D)   10.1

8.   Which of these is the closest approximation to $\sqrt{3247}$?

(A)   163.1   (B)   181.2   (C)   57.0   (D)   570.8

Find the length, to the nearest tenth of a unit, of the indicated side.

9. $g = 4, s = 10, p =?$

10. $s = 11, g = 8, p = ?$

11. $p = 6, s = 4, g = ?$

12. $p = 10, g = 5, s = ?$

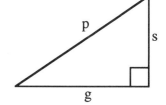

13. $p = 13, s = 12.$

Find the perimeter of the triangle.

Find the area of the triangle.

14. $p = 9, s = 6.$

Find, to the nearest tenth of a unit, the perimeter and area of the triangle.

For the given area of the square, find the length of a side to the nearest tenth of a unit.

15..   area = 147 cm^2

16.   area = 3156 ft^2

17.   Which of the numbers below is **NOT equal** to the other three?

(A) 0.024×10^2 (B) $\sqrt{5.76}$ (C)   24   (D)   240%

18.   Which of these choices would you write in the blank to make a true statement?

$$\sqrt{\frac{1089}{1936}} \ \underline{\quad\quad} \ \frac{1}{4} \text{ of } 3$$

(A)   <   (B)   >   (C)   =   (D)   Cannot be determined

Find the perimeter of each quadrilateral.

19.   20.

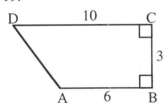

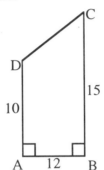

This figure is a rectangle.

21.   DB = 17, AB = 15.

Find the perimeter of the rectangle.

22.   AD = 5.0 in., DB = 8.0 in.

Find, to the nearest tenth of an

inch, the perimeter of the rectangle.

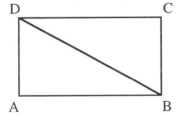

OPEN-ENDED QUESTION

23.   Given : A(1, 2), B(11, 2), C(11, 10), D(7, 10)

Plot the points on graph paper and draw the quadrilateral ABCD.

Find the perimeter of ABCD.

Find the area of ABCD.

REVIEW

1.   What is the next term in the sequence 5, 21, 85, 341, ... ?

2. What symbols are missing from
    the positions x and y in the pattern
    at the right?

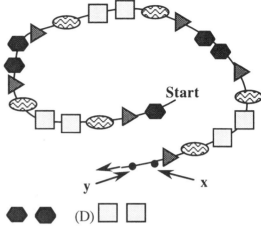

Start

y   x

(A)   (B)   (C)   (D)
    x   y   x   y   x   y   x   y

3. A medium sized bus can transport no more than 35 students as passengers.
    If each bus makes no more than one trip, find the smallest number of buses
    needed to transport 143 students to a field hockey game.

4. What is the next number in the pattern 5, 5, 10, 15, 25, 40, 65, ...?

5. Which of the following is **NOT** equal to the others?
    (A) $8 \div \frac{1}{4}$ (B) $4\sqrt{64}$ (C) $\frac{2}{3}$ of 48   (D) $100 \cdot 3.2$

6. If x = -4, which of the following does not equal 16?
    (A) $-x^2$ (B) $(-x)(-x)$ (C) $(-x)^2$ (D) x^2

7. The length of a rectangle is L ft. The width is 3 ft less than its length.
    Write and simplify an expression for the perimeter of the rectangle.

8. Akmal's test average test average for four tests in math is 85.
    What must he get on the next test to raise his average to 87 for the five tests?

Use these quiz scores to answer exercises 9-13:
100, 80, 90, 85, 90, 80, 20

9.   What is the mean?   10.   What is the mode?
11. What is the median?   12.   What is the range?
13. Which measure of central tendency best describes the data? Explain why.

12.4   Complex Geometric Figures

OBJECTIVES   To find the area of a complex geometric figure

To apply formulas for circumference and area of a circle

Frequently, a complex geometric figure involves both a circle and a rectangle or square. Let's briefly review some properties of a circle.

At the right is a diagram of a circle.
O is called the **center** of the circle.

We now review two formulas for circles.

Area: A = π · r²   (π **is approximately 3.14**)

Circumference (perimeter): C = 2 · π · r

R or $\overline{OA}$ is a **radius** of the circle.

$\overline{OB}$ and $\overline{OC}$ are also **radii**.

$\overline{BC}$ is a **diameter** of the circle.

Note at the right that if a radius has length 3, then a diameter has length 6.

diameter length is twice radius length, or
radius length is $\frac{1}{2}$ **diameter length**

EXAMPLE 1   Find the circumference of a circle with diameter 38 in.

Strategy   Since the diameter length is 38, the radius length is $\frac{1}{2}$ of 38, or 19.

Use **C = 2 · π · r** and π = 3.14.

C = 2 · 3.14 · 19

C =   6.28 · 19 = 119.32

Solution   Thus, the circumference is 119.32 in.

EXAMPLE 2 Find the area of a circle with radius 19 in.

Strategy Use $A = \pi \cdot r^2$ and $\pi = 3.14$.

$A = 3.14 \cdot 19^2$

Use a calculator.

Enter 3.14   Enter **X**   Enter 19   Enter x^2 Enter =

Read 1133.54.

Solution Thus, the area is 1133.54 in^2.

The next example involves a circle inside a square.

EXAMPLE 3 The figure at the right shows a circle of radius 6 inside a square. In terms of π, what is the area of the shaded region inside the square and outside the circle?

Strategy **1.** First find the length of a side of the square (special type of rectangle).

2. Since the radius is 6, the diameter (distance across circle) is 12. From the drawing, this 12 is also the length of a side of the square.

3. Find the area of the circle: $A = \pi r^2$

$A = \pi \cdot 6 \cdot 6 = \pi \cdot 36 = 36\pi$

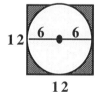

4. Find the area of the square. $A = 12 \cdot 12 = 144$

Find the shaded area: area of square - area of circle

Solution Thus, the shaded area is   **144 - 36π**

The next example is similar to the one above.

It involves a rectangle inside a rectangle: a picture glued onto a piece of cardboard.

It also applies a real=life problem of finding a cost.

EXAMPLE 4   Sasha has a 6" by 14" picture. She glues this picture to a mat board so that there is a 2" border all the way around her picture.

The cost of the mat board is $0.03 per square inch. Find the cost of the mat board.

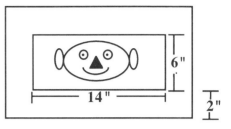

Strategy   The cost is in terms of **square inches**.

This tells you to find the **area** of the mat board.

1. Since area = ab, you must first find the **length** and **width** of the mat board.

To see this, imagine the picture separate from the mat board.

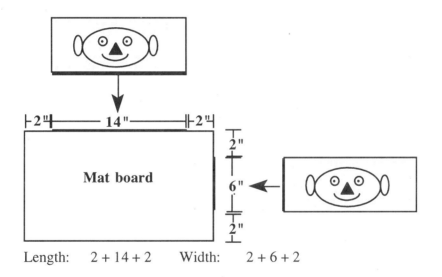

Length: 2 + 14 + 2   Width: 2 + 6 + 2

2. Length: **18**   Width: **10**

Area of mat board: **18 · 10**

3. So, the area of the mat board is **180 square inches**.

Use the cost is $0.03 per **square inch** to find the cost of the mat board.

Cost: cost per square inch times number of square inches is total cost

$0.03   180   = $5.40

Solution   Thus, the cost of the mat board is $5.40.

Sometimes, the area of a geometric figure can be more easily found by breaking it up into triangles and rectangles. This is illustrated in the next example.

EXAMPLE 5   Find the area of the shaded figure.

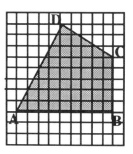

Strategy   This is an irregular figure.

But, it is made up of one rectangle and two triangles.

You know how to find the area of a triangle or rectangle.

Separate the shaded figure into two triangles and one rectangle.

Find the area of each.

Then find the total area.

Area of triangle 1

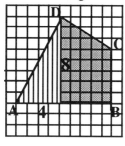

Area of triangle 2

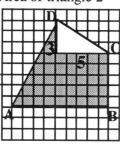

Area of square or rectangle

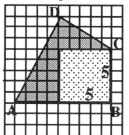

$$A = \frac{1}{2} \cdot 8 \cdot 4 = \mathbf{16}$$ $$A = \frac{1}{2} \cdot 3 \cdot 5 = \frac{1}{2} \cdot 15 = 7\frac{1}{2}$$ $$A = 5 \cdot 5 = \mathbf{25}$$

The area of the shaded region is the sum of the areas of the three figures:

$$\mathbf{16 + 7\frac{1}{2} + 25} = 48\frac{1}{2}$$

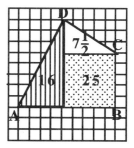

Solution   Thus, the area of the shaded region is $48\frac{1}{2}$.

EXAMPLE 6   These two congruent triangles could be glued together along entire matching sides to form different 4-sided regions. Which two sides should be glued together to form the region with the largest perimeter?

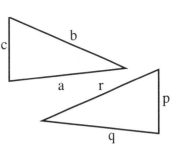

Strategy   Select any numbers for the side lengths: 5 for the shortest, 6 for the middle, and 7 for the longest. This will help you see the solution.

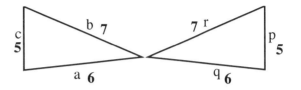

Visualize the 4-sided figure formed by all 3 possible combinations of gluing together equal sides.

Glue together the **7** sides.   Glue together the **5** sides   Glue together the **6** sides

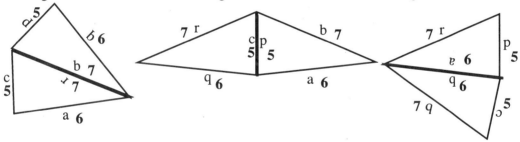

perimeter of quadrilateral   perimeter of quadrilateral   perimeter of quadrilateral

5 + 5 + 6 + 6 = 22   6 + 7 + 6 + 7 = **26**   7 + 5 + 7 + 5 = 24

Solution   Thus the largest perimeter, **26**, is obtained by gluing together the **shortest** sides, **c** and **p**, the **5** sides.

SUMMARY

1.   What is the difference between the radius and the diameter of a circle?

2.   What is the formula for the area of a circle?

3.   What is the formula for the circumference of a circle?

4.   How do you find the area of a circle with diameter 12 in.?

5.   How do you use a calculator to find the area of a circle with radius 25 cm if you use 3.14 for π?

6.   If each side of the square is 8, what is the length of the radius of the circle?

7.   If the radius of the circle is 6, what is the length of each side of the square?

Given: radius = 10

8.   How do you find the area of the circle?

9.   How do you find the area of the square?

10.   How do you find the shaded area?

For exercises 11-13 assume that there is a 3" border all around the shaded rectangle.

11.   How do you find the length and the width of the large rectangle ABCD?

12.   How do you find the area of the large rectangle ABCD?

13.   How do you find the area of the border between the two rectangles?

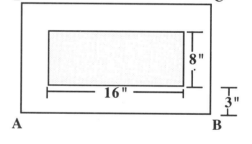

14.   How do you find the area of the shaded region? Is there more than one way to divide the region into triangles and rectangles?

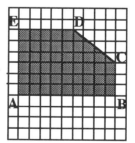

15.   These two congruent triangles can be glued together along matching sides to form different 4-sided figures. How do you find which sides can be glued together to form the region with the least perimeter?

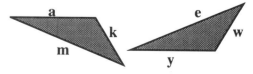

CLASSROOM PRACTICE

Find the area of each circle. Use $\pi = 3.14$.

1. radius: 4 cm   2. diameter: 8 km   3. radius: 12 ft

4. diameter: 18 m   5. radius: 11 ft   6. diameter: 16 in

Find the circumference of each circle. Use $\pi = 3:14$.

7. diameter: 5 yd   8. radius: 12 cm   9. diameter: 9 ft

The figure at the right shows a square inside a circle.
Find the area of the shaded region inside the square and outside the
circle for the given information. Express the area in terms of π.

10.   radius of circle: 8   11.   diameter of circle: 14   12.   side of square: 12

13.   Tanya has a 12" by 18" picture. She
       glues this picture to a mat board so
       that there is a 4" border all the way
       around her picture.
       The cost of the mat board is $0.05
       per square inch. Find the cost of the
       mat board.

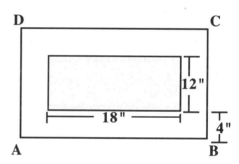

14.   The diagram shows a rug centered
       on a floor that measures 16 ft by 20 ft.
       There is a 1-ft border all around the room
       between the rug and the edges of the room.
       Find the area of the rug.

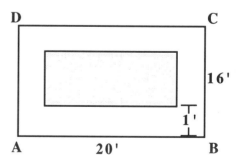

Find the area of the shaded region.

15.

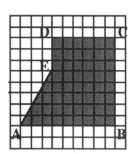

16.

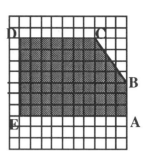

17.   A quadrilateral (4-sided figure) is
       formed by gluing together two
       matching sides of these congruent
       triangles. Which sides should be
       glued together to form a
       quadrilateral with least perimeter?

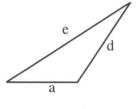

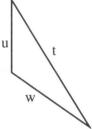

(A)   sides e and t   (B)   sides d and w

(C)   sides a and u   (D)   The perimeters are always the same.

WRITTEN EXERCISES

Find the area of each circle. Use $\pi = 3.14$.

   1.   radius: 7 cm   2. diameter: 10 km   3. radius: 17 ft
   4.   diameter: 24 m   5. radius: 19 ft   6. diameter: 26 in

Find the circumference of each circle. Use $\pi = 3.14$.

   7.   diameter: 32 yd   8. radius: 21 cm   9. diameter: 39 ft

The figure at the right shows a square inside a circle.
Find the area of the shaded region inside the square and outside the
circle for the given information. Express the area in terms of π.

10.   radius of circle: 7   11.   diameter of circle: 20   12.   side of square: 8

13.	Gina has a 14" by 20" picture. She glues this picture to a mat board so that there is a 2" border all the way around her picture.
The cost of the mat board is $0.07 per square inch. Find the cost of the mat board.

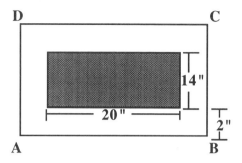

14.	The diagram shows a carpet centered on a floor that measures 21 ft by 30 ft. There is a 3-ft border all around the room between the rug and the edges of the room. If carpeting costs $29.95 a square yard, find the cost of the carpet.

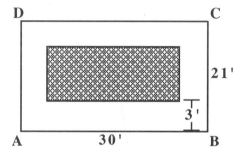

Find the area of the shaded region.

15.

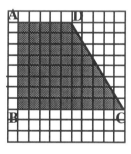

16.

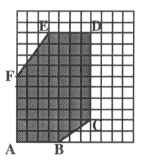

17.	A quadrilateral is formed by gluing together two matching sides of these congruent triangles. Which sides should be glued together to form a quadrilateral with greatest perimeter?

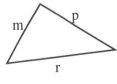

OPEN-ENDED QUESTION

18.   Which figure below appears to have the larger shaded area?

Make up possible numerical values for DE and EC in each figure.

Defend your conclusion by using these values to actually compute the shaded area of each of the two figures.

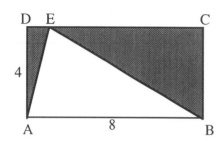   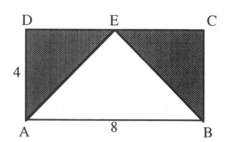

REVIEW

1.   Which is the closest approximation to $\sqrt{4000}$?

(A)   20   (B)   50   (C)   63   (D)   2000

2.   Which could represent the product of the numbers represented by P and M?

(A)   L   (B)   K

(C)   W   (D)   R

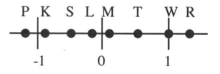

3.   Which of the choices below will make the statement 1.7^8 ___ 5.1^2 true?

(A)   <   (B)   =   (C)   >   (D)   is 3 times

4.   The larger of two numbers is 4 less than 3 times the smaller. Which of the following is a representation of the larger?

(A)   3x + 4   (B)   4x - 3   (C)   3x - 4   (D)   4 -3x

5.   Tina scored a hit $\frac{1}{3}$ of the time when at bat in softball. She batted 417 times. How many were hitless at-bats?

6.   If $P = \frac{4}{5}R - 10$, then what is the value of P if R = 5?

12.5   Ratios of Perimeters and Areas of Similar Figures

OBJECTIVES   To solve problems involving ratios of perimeters of similar figures

To solve problems involving ratios of areas of similar figures

Recall that two triangles are **similar** if corresponding angles have equal measures. Then the corresponding sides will be proportional, in the **same ratio.**

Similar geometric figures have the **same shape** but **not** the same size.

   $\triangle ABC$ **is similar to** $\triangle PQR$

   $\triangle ABC$ ~ $\triangle PQR$

     m $\angle A$ = m $\angle P$ = 52

     m $\angle B$ = m $\angle Q$ = 48

     m $\angle C$ = m $\angle R$ = 80

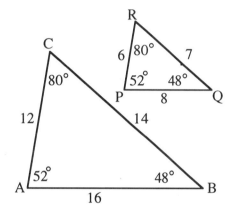

$$\frac{AB}{PQ} = \frac{16}{8} = \frac{2}{1} \qquad \frac{BC}{QR} = \frac{14}{7} = \frac{2}{1} \qquad \frac{CA}{RP} = \frac{12}{6} = \frac{2}{1}$$

Corresponding angles have **equal** measure **AND** corresponding sides have the **same ratio.**

DISCOVERY

Find the perimeter of each triangle.

Find the ratio $\dfrac{\text{perimeter triangle ABC}}{\text{perimeter triangle PQR}}$.

How does this ratio compare with the ratio of corresponding sides?

What does this suggest about the ration of the perimeters of two similar triangles?

Do you think that this will work with other similar figures, such as rectangles?

EXAMPLE 1   What is the ratio of the
lengths of the sides ABCD
to PQRS?
Show that the two
rectangles are similar.

What is the ratio of the
perimeter of ABCD to
PQRS?

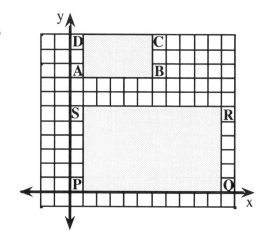

Strategy   **1.** First find the lengths of the
corresponding sides of the
two rectangles.
AB = 5, BC = 3
PQ = 10, QR = 6

2. Find the ratio of the lengths
of the sides.

$\dfrac{AB}{PQ} = \dfrac{5}{10} = \dfrac{1}{2}$

$\dfrac{CB}{RQ} = \dfrac{3}{6} = \dfrac{1}{2}$

All the angles have the same measure.

Corresponding sides are in the same ratio: $\dfrac{1}{2}$.

3. So, the rectangles are similar.
Find the perimeter of each rectangle.
perimeter of ABCD: 5 + 3 + 5+ 3 = 16
perimeter of PQRS: 6 + 10 + 6 + 10 = 32

Find the ratio of the perimeters: $\dfrac{\text{perimeter of ABCD}}{\text{perimeter of PQRS}} = \dfrac{16}{32} = \dfrac{1}{2}$

Solution   So, the ratio of the sides of the similar rectangles is the same as the
ratio of the perimeters, 1 : 2.

The results of Example 1 and the DISCOVERY of the first page of this lesson suggest the following property for similar figures.

PERIMETER PROPERTY FOR SIMILAR FIGURES

If two geometric figures are similar, then the ratio of their perimeters is the same as the common ratio of their corresponding side lengths.

EXAMPLE 2   Corresponding side lengths of two similar figures are in the ratio of 2 : 3 . The larger perimeter is 27. Find the perimeter of the smaller figure.

Strategy   Let p = the perimeter of the smaller figure.

Write a proportion.

Compare smaller to larger.

$$\frac{2}{3} = \frac{p}{27} \qquad \frac{\textbf{smaller}}{\textbf{larger}}$$

$$2 \cdot 27 = 3 \cdot p \qquad \textbf{Cross multiply.}$$

$$54 = 3p$$

$$18 = p$$

Solution   Thus, the perimeter of the smaller figure is 18.

If the ratio of the sides of two similar figures is 1 : 2, you might want to guess that the ratio of their areas is also 1 : 2. But be careeful!

DISCOVERY

Find the ratio of the areas of the two rectangles of Example 1 on the previous page. Is this ratio the same as the ratio of the corresponding sides or perimeters?

You have just seen that the ratio of the perimeters of two similar figures is **NOT** the same as the ratio of their areas. The following examples will lead you to discover a pattern.

EXAMPLE 3   If each side of a rectangle is tripled, is the area also tripled?

If not, how does the new area compare with the original area?

Strategy   **1.**   Draw a rectangle with any dimensions, say 2 by 3.

Then draw the rectangle with sides double those of the first rectangle.

Compare the new area with the original area.

2.   Find the two areas.

The areas are **6** and **54**.

$54 \div 6 = 9$.

sides triple those of
the **2-by-3 rectangle**

Solution   **3.**   Thus, the new area is **9** times   Areas: $3 \cdot 2 = 6$ and $6 \cdot 9 = 54$
the original area.

EXAMPLE 4   If each **side** of this rectangle is multiplied by

2, what is the **area** multiplied by?

3, what is the **area** multiplied by?

4, what is the **area** multiplied by?

Strategy   Draw a diagram of each of the resulting rectangles.

Label their side lengths. Find the area of each.

Multiply each side: x 2   x 3   x 4

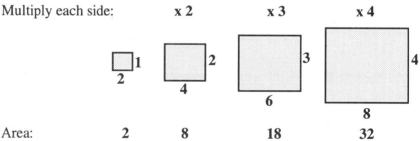

Area: 2   8   18   32

So, when the sides are multiplied by:

2   the area is multiplied by **4**. $8 \div 2 = 4$

3   the area is multiplied by **9**. $18 \div 2 = 9$

4   the area is multiplied by **16**. $32 \div 2 = 16$

Solution

We can use the results of example 4 to find a pattern.

If the sides of a geometric figure are multiplied by: 2,   3,   4

the area is multiplied by: 4,   9,   16

Notice the pattern: $2^2 = 4$ $3^2 = 9$ $4^2 = 16$

In each case the **multiplier** is **squared**.

So, if the sides of a geometric figure are multiplied by 5,

the area is multiplied by: 5^2, or **25**.

These results suggest the following property for similar figures.

AREA PROPERTY FOR SIMILAR FIGURES

If two geometric figures are similar, then the ratio of their areas is the same as the **square** of the ratio of their corresponding side lengths (or perimeters).

EXAMPLE 5   The ratio of the corresponding side lengths of two similar triangles is
3 : 4.
Find the ratio of the areas.

Strategy   Write the ratio of the side lengths as a fraction, $\frac{3}{4}$.

Use the Area Property for Similar Figures: ratio of the areas is the ratio of the square of the side lengths ratio.

$$(\frac{3}{4})^2 = \frac{3}{4} \cdot \frac{3}{4} = \frac{9}{16}$$

Solution   So, the ratio of the areas is $\frac{9}{16}$ or 9 : 16.

EXAMPLE 6   The perimeters of two similar triangles are in the ratio 2 : 3.
The area of the smaller triangle is 16. Find the area of the larger triangle.

Strategy   Let **a** = area of the larger triangle.
Write a proportion.
Compare areas. Remember: ratio of areas is **square** of ratio of side
lengths or perimeters.

Ratio of perimeters: $\frac{2}{3}$

Ratio of areas: $(\frac{2}{3})^2 = \frac{2}{3} \cdot \frac{2}{3} = \frac{4}{9}$

Proportion: $\frac{16}{a} = \frac{4}{9}$ **Compare:** $\frac{\textbf{smaller}}{\textbf{larger}}$

$$16 \cdot 9 = a \cdot 4$$
$$144 = 4a$$
$$36 = a$$

Solution   Thus, the area of the larger triangle is 36.

It can be shown that all circles are similar to each other. They all have the same shape.

The ratio of their circumferences is the same as the ratio of their radii.

EXAMPLE 7   The radius of a circle is 4. If the radius is multiplied by 3, show that the
circumference is multiplied by 3.

Strategy   Use the formula $C = 2\pi r$.
Circumference of circle with r = 4 : $C = 2 \cdot \pi \cdot 4 = 8\pi$
Circumference of circle with r = **3** · 4, or 12: $C = 2 \cdot \pi \cdot 12 = 24\pi$

Now, 24π is 3 times 8π.

Solution   So, the circumference is multiplied by **3.**

As with similar figures in general, if the radius of a circle is multiplied by some number, say 3, the area should be multiplied by the **square** of this multiplier. So, the area should be multiplied by 3^2, or 9. This is verified in the next example.

EXAMPLE 8   The radius of a circle is 4. If the radius is multiplied by 3, show that the area is multiplied by 3^2, or 9.

Strategy   Use the formula $A = \pi r^2$.

Area of circle with r = 4 : $A = \pi \cdot 4^2 = \pi \cdot 16 = 16\pi$

Area of circle with r = **3** · 4, or 12: $A = \pi \cdot 12^2 = \pi \cdot 144 = 144\pi$

Now, $144\pi \div 16\pi = 9$

Solution   So, the area is indeed multiplied by **9**.

SUMMARY

1. If you are given the ratio of corresponding side lengths of two similar figures, how do you find the ratio of the perimeters?

2. If you are given the ratio of corresponding side lengths of two similar figures, how do you find the ratio of the areas?

3. Corresponding side lengths of two similar figures are in the ratio 4 : 5. The larger perimeter is 30. How do you find the smaller perimeter?

4. Corresponding side lengths of two similar figures are in the ratio 4 : 5. The larger area is 50. What equation do you write to find the smaller area?

5. If the length of each side of a triangle is multiplied by 4, how do you find the effect of this on the area?

6. The ratio of the corresponding side lengths of two similar rectangles is 2 : 5. How do you find the ratio of the areas?

7. The perimeters of two similar triangles are in the ratio 3 : 4. The area of the smaller triangle is 32. How do you find the area of the larger triangle? What equation do you write?

8.   If the radius of a circle is multiplied by 5, how does this effect the area of the circle?

CLASSROOM PRACTICE

For the two rectangles shown, find each:
1.   the lengths of the sides
2.   the ratio of the side lengths
3.   the perimeters
4.   the ratio of the perimeters
5.   the areas
6.   the ratio of the areas

For the two rectangles shown, find each:
7.   the lengths of the sides
8.   the ratio of the side lengths
9.   the perimeters
10. the ratio of the perimeters
11. the areas
12. the ratio of the areas

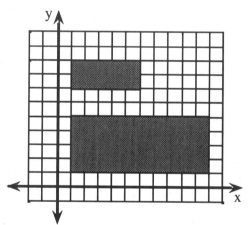

13. The ratio of the side lengths of two similar rectangles is 2 : 7. What is the ratio of the areas?

14. Corresponding side lengths of two similar figures are in the ratio 2 : 5. The larger perimeter is 25. Find the smaller perimeter.

15. Corresponding side lengths of two similar triangles are in the ratio 5 : 4. The larger perimeter is 32. Find the smaller perimeter.

16. The perimeters of two similar figures are in the ratio 4 : 3. Find the area of the larger figure if the area of the smaller figure is 27.

17. If the length of the radius of a circle is doubled, what is the effect on the area?

WRITTEN EXERCISES

For the two rectangles shown, find each:

1.   the lengths of the sides
2.   the ratio of the side lengths
3.   the perimeters
4.   the ratio of the perimeters
5.   the areas
6.   the ratio of the areas

For the two rectangles shown, find each:

7.   the lengths of the sides
8.   the ratio of the side lengths
9.   the perimeters
10.   the ratio of the perimeters
11.   the areas
12.   the ratio of the areas

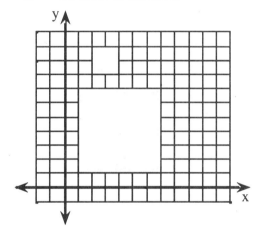 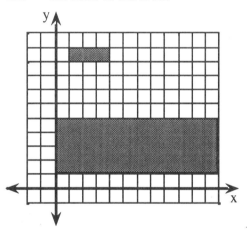

13.   The ratio of the side lengths of two similar rectangles is 3 : 8. What is the ratio of the areas?

14.   Corresponding side lengths of two similar figures are in the ratio 3 : 5. The larger perimeter is 45. Find the smaller perimeter.

15.   Corresponding side lengths of two similar triangles are in the ratio 2: 3. The larger area is 36. Find the smaller area.

16.   The perimeters of two similar figures are in the ratio 7 : 3. Find the area of the larger figure if the area of the smaller figure is 18.

17.   If the length of the radius of a circle is multiplied by 5, what is the effect on the area?

18.   The diameter of a circle is 8. If the length of the radius is tripled, find the area of the new circle.

19.   A square is 4 cm on a side. Find the area of the square if the sides lengths are doubled.

20.   A triangle is drawn with perimeter
       twice that of the one at the right.
       Find the perimeter of this new
       triangle.

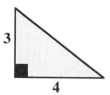

21.   The ratio of the areas of two squares is 16 : 25. Find the ratio of the perimeters.

OPEN-ENDED QUESTION

22.   A T.V. salesman argues that a television with a rectangular screen with diagonal
       of length 30 inches provides a picture 4 times the size of another television with
       the length of the diagonal only 15 inches. The customer maintains that the
       larger screen is only twice that of the smaller one since 30 is twice 15.
       Who is right? Support your answer with numerical proof.

REVIEW

1.   Three partners, Ms. Johnson, Mr. Roberts, and Ms. Tomlinson, share in their
      company's profits, respectively, in the ratio 3 : 4 : 5. This year's profits were
      $36,000. What is Mr. Robert's share?

2.   A team won 3 out of x games. What fraction of the games was lost?

3.   Jake mistakenly divided a number by 8 instead of multiplying by 8. If the
      incorrect answer displayed on his calculator was 6, what is the correct answer?

4.   The graph of y = 2x + 1 is shown at the
      right. Which of the statements below
      are true about the graph of y = 2x + 4?

      I   It is a translation (slide) of the
             graph of y = 2x + 1 up 4 units.
      II   It is parallel to the graph of
             of y = 2x + 1
      III   It is a translation (slide) of the
             graph of y = 2x + 1 up 3 units.

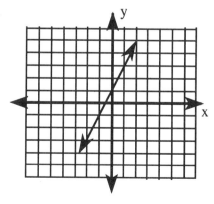

      (A)   I only   (B)   II·only   (C)   I and II   (D)   II and III

12.6 Volume

OBJECTIVES   To solve problems involving volume

To solve problems involving ratio and volume

Recall that the area of a rectangle measures the number of squares in the rectangle. The rectangle at the right contains **3 rows** of **4 squares** each for a total of

3 · 4, or **12** squares.

The area is A = **L** · **W**.

Let's now extend this idea to **three** dimensions.

The diagram below represents the three stages of constructing a new office building.

First floor:

4 · 4 or 16 rooms   Add a second floor.   Add a third floor.

2 floors of 16 rooms each   **3** floors of 16 rooms each

4 · 4 · **2** or 32 rooms   4 · 4 · **3** or 48 rooms

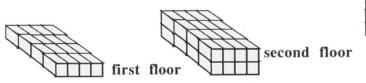

Thus, there are 4 · 4 · **3** or 48 rooms in the building of 3 floors.

There are 4 · 4 · **3** or 48 blocks in the third diagram.

In 3 dimensions, this is referred to as finding **volume.**

The formula for the volume of a rectangular solid: **box.**

V = **L**· **W** · **H**

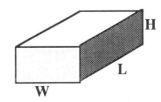

Notice the following pattern contrasting area and volume.

SQUARE   **CUBE**

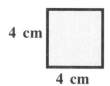

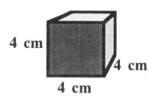

Area: $4\,cm \cdot 4\,cm$ Volume: $4\,cm \cdot 4\,cm \cdot 4\,cm$

      $4 \cdot 4 \cdot cm \cdot cm$ $4 \cdot 4 \cdot 4 \cdot cm \cdot cm \cdot cm$

      $16 \cdot cm^2$ $64 \cdot cm^3$

      $16\,cm^2$ $64\,cm^3$

      16 cm **squared**   64 cm **cubed**

So, area is measured in terms of **square**   So, volume is measured in terms of **cubic**
units. (Think of a **square**.)   units. (Think of a **cube**.)

The formulas for the volumes of a cylinder, cone, and sphere are given below.

Cylinder   **Cone**   **Sphere**

$V = \pi r^2 h$ $V = \frac{1}{3}\pi r^2 h$ $V = \frac{4}{3}\pi r^3$

EXAMPLE 1   Find, in terms of π, the volume of a cone with radius 6 in and height 4 in .

Strategy   Use the formula $V = \frac{1}{3}\pi r^2 h$

                            $V = \frac{1}{3}\pi \cdot 6 \cdot 6 \cdot 4$

                            $V = \frac{1}{3} \cdot 6 \cdot 6 \cdot 4 \cdot \pi$

Solution $V =\ 2\ \cdot 6 \cdot\ 4 \cdot \pi = 48\pi$

EXAMPLE 2   This block measures 2 inches by 2 inches
by 2 inches and weighs 24 pounds. Find the
weight of a block of the same material that
measures 3 inches by 3 inches by 3 inches.

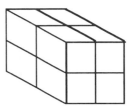

Strategy   **1.** Find the **volume** of each box.

First volume: $V = 2 \cdot 2 \cdot 2 = 4 \cdot 2 = \mathbf{8}$

Second volume: $V = 3 \cdot 3 \cdot 3 = 9 \cdot 3 = \mathbf{27}$

The ratio of the volumes will be the same as the ratio of the weights.
Let W = the weight of the 3 by 3 by 3 box.

Write a proportion.

2. $\dfrac{8}{27} = \dfrac{24}{W}$ $\dfrac{\textbf{weight of 2 b 2 by 2 box}}{\textbf{weight of 3 by 3 by 3 box}}$

$8 \cdot W = 27 \cdot 24$ **Cross multiply to solve the equation.**

3. $8W = 648$

$W = 81$ **Divide each side by 8.**

Solution   Thus, the 3-by-3 by 3 block weighs 81 pounds.

Recall the Area Property for similar figures.

If two geometric figures are similar, then the ratio of the **areas** is the same as the **square**
of the ratio of their corresponding side lengths.

The following DISCOVERY activity will help you extend this idea to volumes.

DISCOVERY

For the rectangular solid L = 2, W = 3, h = 4

Find the volume.

Find the volume of the solid if each of the dimensions is
multiplied by:

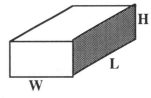

(a)   2   (b)   3   (C)   4

Look for a pattern that uses **exponents** in comparing

each volume with the volume of the original 2 by 3 by 4 solid.

You saw from the DISCOVERY that the volume of the 2 by 3 by 4 box was 24.

Volume for box with side lengths multiplied by 2: 192

Volume for box with side lengths multiplied by 3: 648

Volume for box with side lengths multiplied by 4: 1536

Now compare each of these volumes with the original, **24.**

Multiply original dimensions by **2:** $192 \div 24 = 8$ $= 2^3$ ratio^3

Multiply original dimensions by **3:** $648 \div 24 = 27$ $= 3^3$ ratio^3

Multiply original dimensions by **4:** $1536 \div 24 = 64$ $= 4^3$ ratio^3

These results suggest the following property.

VOLUME PROPERTY FOR SIMILAR FIGURES

If two geometric figures in three dimensions are similar, then the ratio of their **volumes** is the same as the **cube** (ratio^3) of the ratio of their corresponding dimension.

EXAMPLE 3   For a cylinder, r = 3 and h = 8.

A cylinder similar to this has r = 12 and h = 32.

Find the ratio of their **volumes**.

Strategy   First find the common raio of their dimensions.

For the radii: $12 \div 3 = 4$

For the heights: $32 \div 8 = 4$

So, the ratio of the dimensions is **4.**

By the property above, the ratio of the volumes must now be

Solution $4^3 = 64.$

Example 3 suggests that multiplying each of the dimensions of a cylinder by **4** results in multiplying the **volume** by 4^3, or **64.**

SUMMARY

What is the formula for the volume of each of the following?

1. rectangular solid   2. cylinder   3. cone   4. sphere

5. If the dimensions of a three-dimensional figure are multiplied by some number, how do you find the effect of this on the volume?

CLASSROOM PRACTICE

Find each volume.

1.   L = 4 cm, w = 6 cm, H = 9 cm
2.   L = 5 ft, w = 8 ft, H = 10 ft
3.   L = 3 m, w = 7 m, H = 13 m

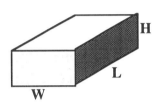

Find each volume in terms of π.

4. r = 4 cm, h = 8 cm   6. r = 3 ft, h = 7 ft   8. r = 6 m
5. r = 4 yd, h = 7 yd   7. r = 2 in, h = 9 in   9. r = 7 cm

10.   This block measures 2 inches by 4 inches by 5 inches and weighs 80 pounds. Find the weight of a block of the same material that measures 6 inches by 12 inches by 15 inches.

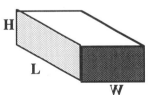

11.   For a cylinder, r = 5 and h = 6.
      A cylinder similar to this has r = 10 and h = 12.
      Find the ratio of their **volumes**.

12.   If the length of the radius of a sphere is tripled, what is the effect on the volume?

WRITTEN EXERCISES

Find each volume.

1. L = 5 cm, w = 8 cm, H = 7 cm
2. L = 4 ft, w = 9 ft, H = 11 ft
3. L = 3 m, w = 8 m, H = 14 m

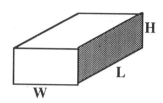

Find each volume in terms of π.

4. r = 5 cm, h = 9 cm
5. r = 6 yd, h = 8 yd

6. r = 5 ft, h = 7 ft
7. r = 4 in., h = 11 in.

8. r = 9 m
9. r = 12 cm

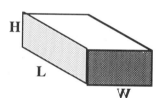

10. This block measures 3 inches by 5 inches by 7 inches and weighs 90 pounds. Find the weight of a block of the same material that measures 9 inches by 15 inches by 21 inches.

11. For a cylinder, r = 4 and h = 8. A cylinder similar to this has r = 8 and h = 16. Find the ratio of their **volumes**.

12. If the length of the radius of a sphere is doubled, what is the effect on the volume?

OPEN-ENDED QUESTION

13. The figure at the right is rotated 360° about $\overline{AB}$. Describe the shape of the figure formed. Find its volume.

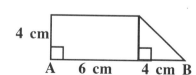

THREE DIMENSIONAL VISUALIZATION ACTIVITY

EXAMPLE   The large cube at the right has some small
cubes removed from it. How many cubes
have been removed?

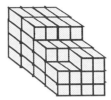

Strategy   Think: how many blocks would it take to put the whole cube back together?
How many blocks would be needed for the third layer?

Two blocks needed.

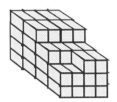

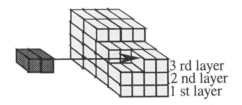

3 rd layer
2 nd layer
1 st layer

Now find the number of blocks needed to fill up the fourth level.

8 blocks needed

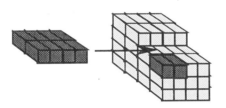

TOTAL of 8 + 2 = 10
blocks needed

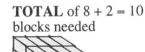

Solution   Thus, 10 blocks have been removed.

PRACTICE

Each large cube below has had some small cubes removed from it. In all, how many have
been removed?

1.

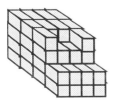

2.

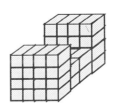

PRACTICE FINAL EXAM   CHAPTERS 1-12

MATHEMATICS PART I

DIRECTIONS FOR QUESTIONS 1-14: Record your answer choices in the spaces provided on the answer sheet given to you by your teacher. When you have finished questions 1-14, go on to questions 15-20. Read the directions for those questions carefully. Unless you are told to do so in the questions, do not include sales tax in your answers to questions involving purchases.

1.   Compare the following.

> I   This month, Ace Video sold 120 RCA'S and 30 GE's.
>
> II   This month, the number of GE's sold by Ace Video was 25% of the number of RCA's sold.
>
> III This month Ace Video sold 5 times as many RCA's as GE's.

Which statements above are equivalent to one another?

(A)   I and II only

(B)   I and III only

(C)   II and III only

(D)   I, II, and III

2.   Tanya has indicated that she wants to withdraw money from her bank's automatic teller. The computer screen displays **"ENTER MULTIPLES of 20."** Which entry below would not be acceptable to the computer?

(A)   3000   (B)   40

(C)   105   (D)   200

3.   The width of a rectangular lot is W meters, and its length is 4 times its width. Which of the following represents the perimeter of that lot?

(A)   4W

(B)   5W

(C)   2W + 2(4W)

(D)   2W + 2(W - 4)

4.   The arrangements below show the first three terms of a pattern.

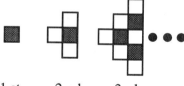

1 st   2 nd   3 rd
Term   Term   Term

How many squares would be in the arrangement representing the fifth term of this pattern?

(A)   16

(B)   25

(C)   36

(D)   41

Use the graph below to answer question 5 .

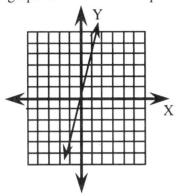

5.   The graph of y = 4x is shown above.
      Which statement below is true about
      the graph of y = 4x + 5?
      (A)   It is a translation (slide) of the
             graph of y = 4x five units up.
      (B)   It is perpendicular to the graph
             of y =4x.
      (C)   It is a translation (slide) of the
             graph of y = 4x five units to the
             right.
      (D)   It intersects the graph of y = 4x
             at the origin.

6.   Monique got an answer of 6.9
      (rounded to the nearest hundredth)
      when she entered 48 on her calculator
      and pressed √‾ . She tried to estimate
      the answer as a check. Which of the
      following is the most likely reason why
      the answer is or is not reasonable?
      (A)   It is not reasonable, because the
              answer should be only slightly
              more than 6.
      (B)   The answer is reasonable,
              because 48 is an even number.

(C)   It is not reasonable, because the
       answer should be a whole
       number.
(D)   It is reasonable, because 6
       squared is 36, and 7 squared is
       49, and 48 is between 36 and
       49.

7.   The average price of a home in Colts
      Neck is $435,000. The average price
      of a home in West Long Branch is
      $323,000.
      In both cities, the average home price
      is six times the average income.
      About how much more is the average
      income in Colts Neck than in West
      Long Branch?
      (A) $112,000   (B) $128,000
      (C) $18,000   (D) $10,000

Use the figure below to answer question 8.

8.   PQ = 2m and QR = m.
      Find the length of PR.

      (A) $3m^2$ units
      (B)   3m units
      (C)   2m units
      (D)   m units

9.   If a = -7, which of the following does
      NOT equal 49?
      (A) $-a^2$ (B) $(-a)^2$
      (C)   -7a   (D)   (-a)(-a)

10.   Rain turns to snow when the temperature drops to 32° Fahrenheit (0° Celsius).
        The opposite extreme is that water boils when the temperature rises to 212° Fahrenheit
        (100° Celsius). If a thermometer displays a temperature of 20° Celsius, to what would
        this be equivalent in degrees Fahrenheit?

        (A)   40°   (B)   50°   (C)   68°   (D)   none of these

HINT: Let x = temperature in degrees Fahrenheit. Set up a data table and solve for x as you learned in lesson 11.3.

Fahrenheit	Celsius
?	?
?	?
x	20

Use the advertisement pictured below to answer question 11.

11.   A deluxe sundae costs $4.90.
        Its toppings are strawberries,
        hot fudge, sliced bananas,
        walnuts, and whip cream. In terms
        of price only, which is a better
        deal: a deluxe sundae or the same
        toppings purchased separately?

KOOL ICE CREAM PARLOR

Delicious ice cream sundaes
$2.50 for the ice cream plus $0.60 for each
topping up to 3 and $0.30 for each additional
topping beyond 3

Toppings

strawberries   walnuts
M and M's   hot fudge
hot butterscotch   whip cream
sliced bananas   cushed cherries

        (A)   ice cream with toppings priced separately

        (B)   They are both the same price.

        (C)   deluxe sundae

        (D)   You need more information to solve the problem.

12.   How many unit cubes must be added to make one large
        4-by-4-by-5 solid block at the right?

        (A)   52

        (B)   48

        (C)   40

        (D)   28

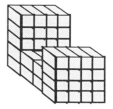

13.   Examine this pattern: **ARITHARITHARITH . . .**

If this pattern keeps repeating, what symbol will be in the 46th position?

(A)   R   (B)   I   (C)   A   (D)   H

14.   The speed of Car B is what percent of   NUMBER OF SECONDS TO REACH A

the speed of Car A at 10 seconds?   GIVEN SPEED IN MPH

(A)   70%

(B)   35%

(C)   14.3%

(D)   50%

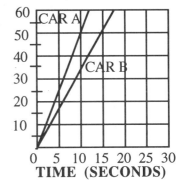

15.   Solve the following equation for x:

5x + 8 = 48 - 3x

16.   If a sheet of paper is cut in half, one of the pieces is $\frac{1}{2}$ of the original sheet. Imagine now cutting one of these pieces in $\frac{1}{2}$. One of those two pieces is $\frac{1}{4}$ of the original sheet of paper. Suppose this cutting is continued for a total of four times. What fractional part of the original sheet is the last piece?

DIRECTIONS FOR QUESTIONS 15-16: These two questions are not multiple-choice. Write your actual answers.

DIRECTIONS FOR QUESTIONS 17-20: Write your answers on the answer sheet provided by your teacher. For each question, give enough explanation so that the scorer can understand your solution, and write your response in the appropriate space. You will be graded on the quality of your thinking, as reflected in your explanations, as well as on the correctness of your responses.

17.   For a T.V. sale, the owner of an appliance store lowered the price of a 41" T.V. by 30%. After the sale the clerk was told to raise the price back up 30% of its sale price. The clerk decided this was the same as marking the original price. Was the clerk right? Present a convincing argument to support your answer. Include a specific example.

A **fractal** is a complex geometric shape which can be thought of as having been produced by repeating some geometric process over and over and over again forever. The drawing at the right illustrates the first three stages of forming a fractal.

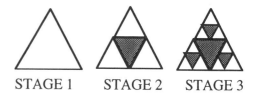

STAGE 1   STAGE 2   STAGE 3

Exercise 18 below asks you to predict the third stage of a **fractal** that you will draw on your own.

18.   Draw a square as shown in Stage 1 at the right. Divide it into nine congruent squares and shade the center one as shown in Stage 2. Now, think of **repeating** this process. Divide each unshaded square into nine congruent squares and shade the **center** one. Draw this third stage. How many shaded squares will be contained in the third stage?

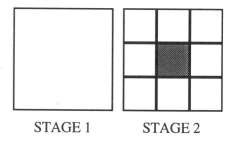

STAGE 1   STAGE 2

19.   A baseball player got 36 hits last season. His batting average for the season was .400. A batting average is the ratio of the number of hits to the number of times at bat. Find the number of times he was at bat last season.

20.   A small Basic Skills math class took a standardized test that had 140 questions. Below are the number right for each of the ten students.

Juan	26	Jose	76
Ronald	92	Twanna	140
Jamal	92	Joel	22
Rita	82	Mat	85
Jasmine	80	Tom	84

What are the mean, the median, and the mode of the scores?

Which of the three statistics seems to be the most reliable for discussing the typical score of that class of ten students?

MATHEMATICS PART II

DIRECTIONS FOR QUESTIONS 21-36: Record your answer choices in the spaces provided on the answer sheet given to you by your teacher. When you have finished questions 21-36, go on to questions 37-40. Read the directions for those questions carefully.

Unless you are told to do so in the questions, do not include sales tax in your answers to questions involving purchases.

21.   The square at the right is congruent to all the squares shown below. Which of the squares below seems to have the same fractional part of its interior shaded as the one drawn at the right?

        I   **II**   **III**   **IV**

    (A)   I and II only   (B)   II and IV only

    (C)   I and III only   (D)   all of them

22.   Four different shapes appear in the spiral at the right. They are labeled E, F, G, and H in the order in which they first appear at **Start**. What letters represent the two missing figures in this spiral?

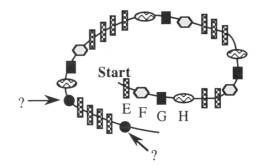

    (A)   EH

    (B)   EE

    (C)   HE

    (D)   EF

23.   Which inequality would be appropriate in solving the problem below?

        John is buying lunch for himself and his friend. Hot dogs cost $1.95 each and sodas cost $.85 each. John has only $12 to spend. He orders 2 sodas. He wants to buy as many hot dogs as possible. How many hot dogs could he now order?

    (A) $x + 1.70 \le 12$ (B) $.85x + 1.95 \le 12$

    (C) $1.70x + 1.95 \le 12$ (D) $1.95x + 1.70 \le 12$

24. Performing which set of transformations on the lightly shaded triangle will **NOT** result in the lightly shaded triangle completely covering the heavily shaded triangle?

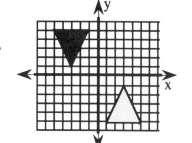

   (A) translation 6 units to the left followed by reflection in the x-axis

   (B) translation 3 units to the left followed by reflection in the x-axis

   (C) rotation of 180° about the origin

   (D) reflection in the x-axis followed by reflection in the y-axis

25. Which of the following points lies on the graph of $4x - y = 10$?

   (A)   (3, -2)   (B)   (3, 2)   (C)   (2, 2)   (D)   (-1, 6)

26. 6 is not a factor of 50 because

   (A)   6 is an even number   (B)   2 is not a factor of 50

   (C)   3 is not a factor of 50   (D)   5 is not a factor of 6

27. Which of the following is not equal to the other 3?

   (A) $\frac{1}{5}$ of 75   (B) $5\sqrt{9}$ (C) $3 \div \frac{1}{5}$ (D)   40% of 30

28. What is the units digit in the 49th term of the pattern below?
    $8^1, 8^2, 8^3, 8^4, ...$

   (A)   2   (B)   4   (C)   6   (D)   8

29. Which spinner below would give you the best probability of spinning an A?

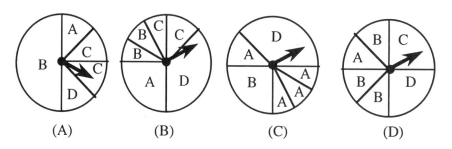

       (A)   (B)   (C)   (D)

30. A particular plant starts as a single stem. At the beginning of the second year, it grows three branches and therefore has four tips growing. Each year every branch does the same thing, that is, it grows three branches and continues to grow itself. How many tips are there on that plant in the fifth year if no tip or branch has died?

(A)   24   (B)   64   (C)   256   (D)   1024

31. The radius of the circle is 8. In terms of π, what is the area of the shaded region inside the square and outside the circle?

(A) $64\pi - 256$ (B) $16 - 64\pi$
(C) $32 - 64\pi$ (D) $256 - 64\pi$

32. The figure at the right shows a floor measuring 16' by 25'. There is a carpet centered on the floor with a 2' border all the way around the carpet. If carpet cost $10 a square yard, find the cost of the carpet.

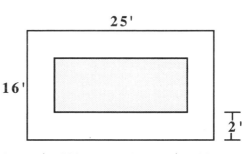

(A) $3,220   (B) $280   (C) $4,000   (D) $8,000

33. Given: P(6, 1), Q(12, 1), R(6, 10)
What kind of triangle is formed by connecting the points P, Q, and R?
(A)   acute   (B)   obtuse   (C)   right   (D)   isosceles

34.   Find the area of the rectangle.

(A)   80   (B)   40
(C)   24   (D)   48

35.   The Blazers USA company ordered 260 of a new popular type of monogrammed blazer.
      65 of them were sold the first day. About what percent of the 260 have not yet been sold?

(A)   25   (B)   33 (C)   75   (D)   1.33

36.   The graph at the right corresponds to Mrs.
      DeCuzzi's automobile trip between Audubon
      and Atlantic City. What was most likely
      happening between 2:00 and 3:00 P.M.?

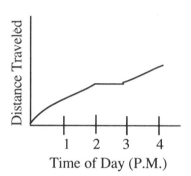

(A)   She was traveling on a highway.
(B)   She had stopped for a late lunch.
(C)   She was looking for a parking place.
(D)   She was driving very slowly.

**DIRECTIONS FOR QUESTIONS 37-40: Write your answers on the answer sheet
provided by your teacher. For each question, give enough explanation so that the scorer
can understand your solution, and write your response in the appropriate space. You will
be graded on the quality of your thinking, as reflected in your explanations, as well as on
the correctness of your responses.**

37.   Plot the following points on graph paper: P(3, 9), Q(3, 4), R(11, 21).
      Draw the triangle PQR. Find the perimeter of the triangle.
      Explain how you found the perimeter.

38.   Tina works a six-hour shift at Burger Delight. When she begins the shift at 2:00 P.M.
      there is $60 in the cash register drawer. Draw a graph that reasonably shows the amount
      of money in her cash register drawer as she works for the six hours.
      Clearly explain what your graph shows and why.

39.   Estimate 289.76 x 403 in your head. Explain in writing what your estimate is
       and how you got your answer.

40.   Use a ruler to determine the lengths of the sides of the figure below.
       Copy the figure on a sheet of paper. Label the corresponding sides of your sketch
       with the measurements you found.
       Use these measurements to find the perimeter and area of the figure below.
       Show all your work clearly.

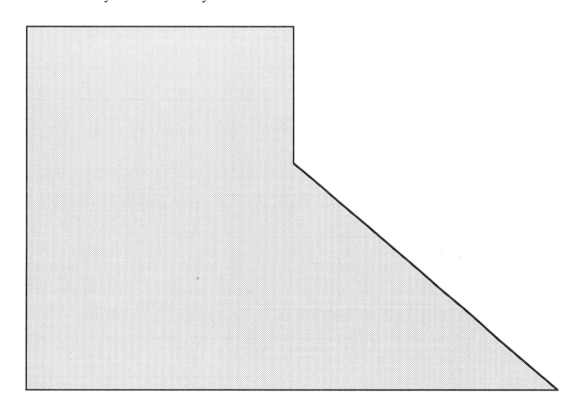

Glossary

Glossary

Acute angle   An angle whose measure is less than 90°.

Acute triangle   A triangle in which each angle measures less than 90°.

Addition Property of Equality   If a = b is true, then a + c = b + c is also true for all numbers a, b, and c.

Addition Property for Inequalities   If a < b, then a + c < b + c for all numbers a, b, and c.

Adjacent angles   Two angles with a common vertex, a common side, and no common interior points.

Alternate interior angles   Two inside angles on the opposite side of a transversal that cuts both lines.

Altitude (of a triangle)   A segment that originates at a vertex of the triangle and is perpendicular to the line containing the opposite side.

Area   The measure of a plane region in terms of square units.

Associative Property of Addition   For all numbers a, b, and c,
(a + b) + c = a + (b + c).

Associative Property of Multiplication   For all numbers a, b, and c, (a · b) · c = a · (b · c).

Average   The number found from adding several numbers and then dividing the sum by the number of numbers added.

Bar graph   A method of comparing quantities by the use of solid bars.

Binomial   A polynomial with 2 terms.

Bisect   To divide into two congruent parts.

Circle   Closed curve in a plane (flat surface) such that every point on the curve is the same distance from the center.

Circumference   The measure of the distance around a circle.

Coefficient   A number multiplied by a variable. Example: In 4x, 4 is the coefficient.

Collinear points   Points that are contained in one line.

Commission   Income based on a percentage of sales.

Commutative Property of Addition
a + b = b + a.

Commutative Property of Multiplication
a · b = b · a.

Complementary angles   Two angles whose sum of their measures is 90°.

Complete factorization   A number shown as a product of prime numbers only:
$36 = 3 \cdot 3 \cdot 2 \cdot 2$.

Congruent   Equal in size and shape.

Coplanar   Contained within the same plane.

Coordinate   A number assigned to a point on a number line.

Coordinate plane (system)   Two perpendicular number lines in a plane. Each point in a coordinate plane (system) corresponds to an ordered pair of numbers.

Corresponding angles   Two angles on the same side of a transversal, one on the inside and one on the outside.

Counting principle   One event can happen in x ways. Another event can happen in y ways. The total number of ways that both events can happen is $x \cdot y$ ways.

Cube   A three-dimensional solid with all faces squares.

Decagon   A polygon with ten sides.

Decimal   Number with decimal points used to indicate place value.

Degree (°)   A unit of measure for angles. $\frac{1}{90}$ of a right angle.

Denominator   The number below the fraction bar is the denominator. For example, in the fraction $\frac{3}{7}$, 7 is the denominator.

Dependent events   Two events where the outcome of one event affects the outcome of the other.

Diameter   A line segment whose end-points are on the circle and which contains the center of the circle.

Discount   A reduction in the price of an item.

Distributive Property of Multiplication   For all numbers a, b, and c,
$a \cdot (b + c) = a \cdot b + a \cdot c$.

Divisible   Can be divided by a number with a remainder of zero.

Divisor   The number by which you are dividing. For example, in $21 \div 7$, the divisor is 7.

Equation   A mathematical sentence in which the = symbol is used. $3x = 15$ and $x + 6 = 14$ are examples of equations.

Equation of a line $y = mx + b$ is an equation of a line. m is the slope of the line, and b is the y-intercept.

Equilateral triangle   A triangle whose sides are equal in length.

Even number   Any whole number divisible by 2 is an even number.

Exponent   In 2^4, 4 is the exponent. It tells how many times 2 is a factor in the product of $2 \cdot 2 \cdot 2 \cdot 2$.

Factor A number that divides into another number so that the remainder is zero.

$5 \cdot 2 = 10$. 5 and 2 are factors of 10.

Formula A general fact or rule expressed by using symbols. For example, the area of a circle (A) with radius r is found using the formula $A = pr^2$.

Frequency The number of times that a number appears in a set of data.

Gram (g) A metric unit of mass, 0.001 of a kilogram.

Greatest Common Factor (GCF) The largest number by which each of a given set of two or more numbers is divisible. For example 4 is the GCF of 8, 16, 20.

Hexagon A polygon with 6 sides.

Hypotenuse The side opposite the right angle in a right triangle.

Independent events Two events where the outcome of one does not affect the outcome of the other.

Inequality A mathematical sentence that has the symbol > or < in it.

Integer A directed whole number, positive or negative or zero.

Isosceles triangle A triangle with at least two congruent sides.

Irrational number A number named by a nonterminating, nonrepeating decimal. For example: $1.424224222....$, $\sqrt{2}$, π.

Least Common Denominator (LCD) The same as the least common multiple.

Least Common Multiple (LCM) The smallest number of which each of two or more given numbers is a factor. The LCM of 3, 5, and 2 is 30. 30 is the smallest number that has 3, 5, and 2 as factors.

Line segment Segment $\overline{AB}$ is the set of points on a line including A and B and all the points in between.

Liter (L) A metric unit of volume, 1,000 mL.

Mean Average. To find the mean, add the numbers and divide the sum by the number of numbers.

Median The middle number in a set of numbers arranged from least to greatest. If there is an even number of items, the median is the mean of the two middle numbers.

Meter A metric unit of length that is equal to 100 centimeters.

Metric system A system of measurement based on the number 10.

Mixed number A number that consists of the sum of an integer and a fraction. For example $4\frac{2}{3}$.

Mode   The number occurring more frequently than any other number in a set. A set may have more than one mode.

Monomial   A polynomial with one term.

Multiple   Any product of a given number and a whole number.

Multiplicative Identity   See Property of 1 for Multiplication.

Non-collinear points   Three or more points that are not contained in the same line.

Number line   A line in which the numbers and the points have been matched one-to one.

Numerator   In a fraction, the number above the fraction line is the numerator. In the fraction $\frac{5}{7}$, 5 is the numerator.

Obtuse angle   An angle whose measure is between 90º and 180º.

Obtuse triangle   A triangle that has one obtuse angle.

Odd number   Any whole number not divisible by 2.

Ordered pair   Two numbers that correspond to exactly one point in a coordinate plane.

Origin   The point corresponding to zero on a number line or the point (0,0) in a coordinate plane.

Palindrome number   A number that reads the same backwards as forwards. For example, 2332.

Parallel lines   Lines that lie in the same plane and do not intersect.

Parallelogram   A quadrilateral with two pairs of opposite sides parallel.

Percent (%)   A number that indicates how many out of 100. 42% means 42 out of a 100.

Perfect square   A number whose principal square root is a whole number.

Perimeter   The distance around a polygon.

Perpendicular lines   Lines intersecting at right angles.

Pi (π)   The number, approximately equal to 3.14, used in finding the circumference or area of a circle. π is the ratio between the circumference and twice the radius.

Pictograph   A graph that uses pictures to represent data.

Plane   A two-dimensional flat surface.

Polygon   A geometric figure with 3 or more sides.

Prime number   A whole number greater than one having only two factors, 1 and itself. For example, 7 is a prime number. The only factors of 7 are 7 and 1.

Principal square root   The positive square root of a number. For example, 5 is the principal square root of 25. $\sqrt{25} = 5$

Probability   The number of favorable outcomes divided by the total number of all possible outcomes.

Property of 1 for Multiplication   The product of any number and 1 is that number.

$x \cdot 1 = x$.

Proportion   An equation that states that two ratios are equal.

$\frac{a}{b} = \frac{c}{d}$ or $a : b = c : d$.

Protractor   An device used to measure angles.

Pythagorean Theorem   In any right triangle, the square of the length of the hypotenuse equals the sum of the squares of the lengths of the other two sides. If D ABC is a right triangle with c the hypotenuse, then

$a^2 + b^2 = c^2$.

Quadrilateral   A polygon with 4 sides.

Radical sign   The symbol used to indicate a nonnegative square root. $\sqrt{}$

Radicand   Any expression inside a radical sign.

Radius   A segment from a point on a circle to the center of the circle.

Range   The difference between the highest and lowest numbers in a set.

Ratio   A comparison of two numbers by division. Fraction are ratios, for example $\frac{a}{b}$.

Rational number   A number that can be named by a fraction. Examples are fractions, mixed numbers, and terminating and repeating decimals.

Ray   A part of a straight line that has a beginning point and continues infinitely in one direction.

Real numbers   All of the rational and irrational numbers.

Reciprocal Two numbers whose product is 1. 3 and $\frac{1}{3}$ are reciprocals because $3 \cdot \frac{1}{3} = 1$.

Rectangle   A four-sided polygon with four right angles.

Regular polygon   A polygon with all sides equal in length and all angles equal in measure.

Repeating decimal   A decimal that repeats a digit or group of digits forever.

Example: $0.4444.... = 0.\overline{4}$

Right angle   An angle whose measure is 90°.

Right triangle   A triangle that contains 1 right angle.

Scientific notation   A number written as the product of a number from 1 to 10 and a power of 10.

Similar figures   Figures with the same shape, but not necessarily the same size.

Slope of a line The steepness of a line.

$$\frac{\text{Difference of y-coordinates}}{\text{Difference of x-coordinates}}$$

Sphere A round three-dimensional figure shaped like a baseball or basketball. All points on the surface of the sphere are the same distance from the center.

Square A quadrilateral in which all sides have the same measure and all angles are right angles.

Square root If $x \cdot x = n$, then x is a square root of n.

Straight angle An angle with a measure of $180°$.

Supplementary angles Two angles the sum of whose measures is $180°$.

Symmetry with respect to a line The property of a figure such that it coincides with its reflected image over a line.

Systems of equations Two equations with two variables. Example: $y = 2x - 5$
$y = -3x + 5$

Transversal A line that intersects two or more lines.

Trapezoid A quadrilateral with exactly one pair of parallel sides.

Variable A letter or symbol that can be replaced by numbers.

Vertex The common endpoint of two rays of an angle.

Vertical angles Angles formed by two intersecting lines that are opposite each other; they have the same measure.

Volume The measure of the amount of space occupied by a figure in 3 dimensions.

Weight A measure of the mass of an object.

Whole number The numbers 0, 1, 2, 3, 4, ...

x-axis The horizontal number line in a coordinate plane.

x-coordinate The first number in an ordered pair of numbers.

x-intercept The x-coordinate of the point of ntersection of a line with the x-axis.

y-axis The vertical number line in a coordinate plane.

y-coordinate The second number in an ordered pair of numbers.

y-intercept The y-coordinate of the point of intersection of a line with the y-axis.

Index

Index

Selected Answers

Selected Answers

CHAPTER 1

Lesson 1.1
Written Exercises, pg 6
1. 15   3. 10   5. 243   7. 850   9. 52
11. 158   13. 54687   15. 1364   17. 5163264
19. The next number is 35 + 32 = 67; the eighth term is 67 + 64 = 131. The pattern is to add the double of the number added last time. Accept reasonable explanations.

Lesson 1.2
Written Exercises, pg 12-13
1. 5   3. 24   5. 8   7. 42   9. circle, square
11. 14   13. 16

Review, pg 13
1. 20   3. 127   5. 125

Lesson 1.3
Written Exercises, pg 17-18
1. P   3. R   5. F   7. 4994   9. 440044
11. 1257521   13. 400004

Review, pg 18
1. 16   3. 32   5. 4006   7. 24

Lesson 1.4
Written Exercises, pg 25-27
1. 6.   3. 4   5. F   7. B   9. B   11. D
13. The side opposite 8 must say 10 - 8 = 2; the side opposite 4 must say 10 - 4 = 6; the side opposite 2 must say 10 - 2 = 8. 2 + 6 + 8 = 16.

Review, pg 27
1. H   3. 143   5. 109

Lesson 1.5
Written Exercises, pg 33-34
1. <   3. >   5. 64   7. 343   9. $\frac{64}{125}$
11. $\frac{64}{729}$ 13. >   15. 9   17. 500   19. 600
21. 32; 26.94891777

REVIEW: Chapter 1 pg 35

1. 20	3. 91	5. 286	7. 752877568	9. N
11. 257000752		13. 1	15. >	17. S	19. T
21. D	23. 36	25. 845.8700491		27. >
29. 256; 252.8403305		31. 9	33. C

CHAPTER 2

Written Exercises pg 43

1. 60	3. 42	5. 16	7. 5	9. 8

11. 512	13. 18	15. $\frac{4}{9}$	17. 541

Review pg 43

1. 29   3. 688

Written Exercises pg 49

1. 38	3. 50	5. 38	7. 36	9. 144
11. 22	13. 36	15. 12,839	17. 215.7384	19. .02
21. B	23. 82 in.	25. T = 6N + 85		27. B	29. D

Review pg 51

1. I   3. 4

Written Exercises pg 58

1. C	3. +$0.10	5. +7	7. +1	9. $-3\frac{1}{2}$
11. -6	13. Pt. at -7	15. Pt at $-3\frac{1}{2}$	17. <	19. >

21. Subtract -20 from 10. The difference is 30. Count the number of subdivisions between -20 and 10. It is 15. Divide 30 by 15. Each subdivision is 2. Count by 2's from -20. Arrow points to -6.

Review pg 59

1. 256   3. 16   5. 1

Written Exercises pg 62

1. -10	3. -4	5. -13	7. 3	9. 9
11. -7	13. 5	15. -4	17. 0	19. 0
21. -127	23. 115	25. -1.166		

27.
5 + (-8) = -3	-5 + 9 = 4	Get numerical answer by subtraction.
5 + (-9) = -4	-5 + 10 = 5	Use sign of larger number.
5 + (-10 = -5	-5 + 14 = 9	Since signs are different, subtract 19
5 + (-12) = -7	-5 + 16 = 11	from 43 and use the sign (positive) of the larger. Answer is 24.

Review pg 63
  1. 54 ft   3. 38   5. 113.04 cm^2 7. 60   9. 12   11. C

Written Exercises pg 70
  1. 13   3. -10   5. -19   7. -40   9. 17   11. -64
  13. -70   15. -60   17. -8.09   19. -2.66   21. -4 lb

Review pg 70
  1. 24   3. There will be 27 unshaded triangles at stage 4 because each new
              stage creates 3 unshaded triangles for every one that existed in the
              previous stage.

Written Exercises pg 73
  1. -6   3. -15   5. 15   7. -12   9. -10   11. -15
  13. 2   15. -46   17. -62   19. -24   21. -197 ft

Review pg 74
  1. 13   3. 9

Written Exercises pg 80
  1. -56   3. 28   5. -81   7. -72   9. 24
  11. -63   13. -15   15. -9   17. -150   19. -128
  21. 64   23. 343   25. 216   27. R
  29. $(-1)^1$ = -1 $(-1)^{75}$ = -1 because 75 is odd and the odd powers of
      $(-1)^2$ = 1   -1 are negative.
      $(-1)^3$ = -1 $(-1)^{24}$ = 1 because 24 is even and the even powers of
      $(-1)^4$ = 1   -1 are positive.
      $(-1)^5$ = -1
      $(-1)^6$ = 1
      $(-1)^7$ = -1

Review pg 81
  1. -3   3. -2

Written Exercises pg 86
  1. 2   3. -4   5. -4   7. 1   9. -10   11. -6
  13. .6   15. $-\frac{1}{2}$ 17. $-\frac{1}{16}$ 19. -20   21. $-\frac{4}{3}$ 23. D

25.

n	(n + 1)(n - 1)
5	24
8	63
12	143
7	48
10	99
-99	9800
3	8
15	224
0	-1

When you multiply 1 more than a given number by one less than the number, you get 1 less than the square of the number. Therefore to get the number in the second column you square the number in the first column and subtract 1. To get a number in the first column you add 1 to the number in the first column and take the square root.

REVIEW: Chapters 1-2 pg 87

1. >	3. 40	5. C	7. 13	9. 4	11. 27
13. 44 cm	15. B	17. A	19. C	21. $-1\frac{1}{2}$	23. >
25. -15	27. -30	29. 224	31. -15	33. 13	35. 64
37. B	39. 2	41. 97			

41. 97 The number added to get the next term is 1 less than the number in the term. The numbers added are 3, 6, 12, 24,... Each number added is 2 times the number previously added. To get any term from the previous one you could double the given term and subtract one.

CHAPTER 3

Written Exercises pg 98

1. 13	3. 14	5. 20	7. 7	9. -11
11. -8	13. -9	15. 42	17. -2	19. -4.5
21. 8.6	23. -3,616	25. -2.67127		

Review pg 98

1. D	3. -13	5. -243

Written Exercises pg 105

1. 3	3. 2	5. 72	7. 88	9. 3
11. -13	13. -78	15. -63	17. 6	19. 32
21. -20	23. -21	25. 225.1111111	27. -11,771	29. 3,434.565217

Review pg 105

1. <	3. <	5. D	7. 35	9. 26

11. The row sums are 1, 2, 4, 8, 2^4, 2^5, ...where the exponent is 1 less than the row number. Therefore the answer is 2^9 or 512.

Written Exercises pg 111
1. 5   3. 7   5. 7   7. 12   9. 5
11. $\frac{1}{2}$ 13. $\frac{3}{4}$ 15. 4   17. 3.73   19. 55.39
21. Add 2 pyramids and 2 blocks to the left side and the two sides will be identical. Could have added 1 pyramid and 6 blocks to the left side or just 8 blocks. There are many ways to balance the scales.

Review pg 112
1. B   3. -35   5. 143

Written Exercises pg 116
1. w - 7   3. x - 50   5. b + 18   7. k - 14   9. 2x - 8
11. T + 9   13. 2H - 25   15. 34 + 2n   17. 3M - 12   19. 2P + 12
21. 2w - 4   23. 34 + 5n

Review pg 116
1. 7   3. 10   5. 42   7. -32

Written Exercises pg 122
1. 22   3. $95   5. 13   7. 6   9. 15   11. 20
13. 20 in.   15. 3.5   17. C

REVIEW: Chapters 1-3 pg 124
1. 19   3. -2   5. -48   7. 10   9. 4   11. .41
13. 8   15. 8   17. D   19. T   21. -80   23. -64
25. 7   27. 2   29. C   31. B   33. -5   35. B
37. A   39. 81   41. 7   43. G
45. There are four possibilities: L = 6, W = 5; L = 8, W = 3; L = 9, W = 2; and L = 10, W = 1. Find the perimeter, 22. Let W = 1 and solve the equation to find L. Repeat for W = 2, 3, and 5. Assumptions are that only whole numbers will be used and that L > W.

CHAPTER 4

Written Exercises pg 136
1. $\frac{7}{11}$ 3. $\frac{5}{10}$ (or $\frac{1}{2}$)   5. $\frac{8}{15}$ 7. $\frac{B - 3}{B}$ 9. 12
11. $18\frac{1}{3}$ 13. $19\frac{2}{7}$ 15. $\frac{1}{5}$ 17. $55.11

Review pg 136
1. -5   3. 7   5. 17 m

Written Exercises pg 146

1. 114	3. 37 (or 38)	5. $1080	7. A	9. $32.40
11. 425	13. Video Shack; $10		15. C	17. B
19. A	21. D			

Review pg 148

1. T   3. -2   5. -8

Written Exercises pg 155

1. 2.4	3. 80	5. 40%	7. 20	9. 20	11. 53
13. 81	15. 36	17. 20%	19. 75%	21. $57\frac{1}{7}$ %	

23. Probably not. It is likely that the BEST DEAL STORE was very close to the lowest price (or they wouldn't want to advertise such a policy). For example, BEST DEAL price is $99.50 and other store will sell for $98.99. 5% of ($99.50 - $98.99) would be about $.03.

Review pg 156

1. <   3. B   5. 25   7. 7

Written Exercises pg 164

1. $90	3. $250	5. 75%	7. 80%	9. 50%
11. $9.85	13. 13%	15. 20	17. 10	19. 60%

21. She is right. 80% of Forester students passed on the first try while only 50% of Clinton students and 73% of Windsor West students did.

Review pg 166

1. .48   3. 175

Written Exercises pg 174

1. 250	3. 1050	5. 75%	7. 20	9. 15	11. 150

13. Place activity names across the bottom.   15. 48 mi   17. $2\frac{1}{2}$ hr
Place range numbers, 33-38, 39-44,
45-50, 51-56, up the left side.
The heights of the bars will be:
bicycling 4, softball 2,
swimming 3, volleyball 1.

REVIEW: Chapters 1-4 pg 176

1. $\frac{9}{12}$ or $\frac{3}{4}$	3. 21	5. 42	7. $47.70	9. $12
11. 60%	13. 10%	15. $350	17. 60%	19. 10.36%
21. 20	23. 1	25. 81 mi	27. 7	29. 18 cm
31. >	33. 56	35. 2	37. M	39. 7
41. 27	43. 9	45. 2002	47. C	49. -250

CHAPTER 5

Written Exercises pg 188
1. R 7, U 2   3. L 3, D 5   5. R 0, D 8   7. L 9, D 8   9. (0,6)
11. (-7, 3)   13. (-6,0)   15. (1,2)   17. (7,-1)   19. (3,-6)
21. D(2,9)

Review pg 189
1. $17.40   3. 140°

Written Exercises pg 199
1. 20; 21   3. 32; 55   5. 30 in.   7. 102 cm^2 9. 144 m^2
11. 133 yd^2 13. $2220.40   15. Make L and W any 2 numbers whose sum is 9.
17. $16800

Review pg 200
1. $3\frac{1}{3}$ lb   3. C   5. D   7. 20%

Written Exercises pg 206
1. 56j   3. 36m   5. 30a + 24   7. 56b + 28   9. 42k - 35
11. 24k + 40; 112   13. 20m-10; 110
15. 47307j + 9555; 3415659   17. $29.94   19. 776

Review pg 206
1. 1   3. -7   5. 106

Written Exercises pg 211
1. 13x   3. 10b   5. 5x   7. not possible 9. 18x
11. 7y + 4   13. 9m   15. -4x + 1   17. -a - 5   19. 10a - 24
21. 21h - 15

Review page 211
1. 14   3. 24; 35   5. 24

Written Exercises pg 217
1. 4   3. 7   5. 7   7. 11   9. 6
11. 2   13. 2   15. 12; 4   17. 29   19.$23.20
21. 2L + B = P. 2(2x - 4) + 6 = 22. Distribute 2. 4x - 8 + 6 = 22.
   Combine like terms. 4x - 2 = 22. Add 2 to each side. 4x = 24.
   Divide each side by 4. x = 6. AC = 2x - 4. AC = 2(6) - 4. AC = 8.

Review pg 218
1. $\frac{n - 3}{n}$ 3. 0

Written Exercises pg 225

1. 30 m,6 m   3. 18 cm, 9 cm   5. 26,8   7. C   9. 19 in., 11 in.
11. $420,$140 13. 53 m,10 m
15.   Let x = width   length depends on width
         3x - 2 = length $2(3x - 2) + 2x = 44$ 2L + 2W = p
      6x - 4 + 2x = 44;   Distribute 2
         8x - 4 = 44;   Combine like terms
         8x = 48;   Add 4 to both sides
         x = 6   Divide both sides by 8
      width = 6 cm
      length = 16 cm   3(6) - 2 = 16

Review pg 226

1. 10   3. 150   5. 159

Written Exercises pg 237

1. C   3. 6   5. A   7. D   9. A
11. 813.   15. 3, a common factor of 12 and 30 does not divide into 8,456 exactly.

REVIEW: Chapters 1-5 pg 239

1. 26; 42   3. $778.50   5. $10,080   7. 15x + 24   9. 32
11. 4   13. -9m   15. 2   17. 5   19. 7; 5
21. 24,8   23. 6   25. 3 not a factor of 320   27. B
29. B   31. $9\frac{1}{3}$ lb   33. 2   35. 44   37. B
39. 60%   41. <   43. $340   45. $85   47. $66\frac{2}{3}$ %
49. 2 hr   51. r   53. 3   55. 5

57.

L	W	A
11	1	11
10	2	20
9	3	29
8	4	32
7	5	35
6	6	36

Largest area is produced when L = 6, W = 6

CHAPTER 6

Written Exercises pg 251
1. $\overleftrightarrow{YR}$ 3. TJ   5. $\overleftrightarrow{DM}$ 7. 2   9. 3
11. 3   13. 9   15. 10   17. 4   19. $2\frac{5}{8}$
21. $2\frac{1}{4}$ 23. 1 or -11; could go 6 left or right

Review pg 252
1. 34   3. D   5. 34; 72   7. $1509.90

Written Exercises pg 258
1. 18   3. 18   5. 8   7. $6\frac{1}{3}$ 9. 15
11. 2   13. 13   15. 1 ft; $1\frac{1}{2}$ ft   17. 80%   19. 4 mi; No

Review pg 260
1. -37   3. 10m - 30   5. -8   7. 7 cm   9. 3

Written Exercises pg 267
1. 21   3. 18   5. 15 yd   7. 15 cm   9. 14 in.
11. 15   13. 20 cm   15. 2x + 5x = 49; 7x = 49; x = 7; More than one
   answer because you don't know whether RQ was 2x or 5x. So RQ is 14 or 35.

Review pg 268
1. 40   3. D   5. 25%

Written Exercises pg 274
1. $2\frac{2}{5}$ 3. $3\frac{3}{7}$ 5. 32,000   7. 69   9. $2.88
11. 100 mi   13. 84 mi   15. 16 mpg   17. 16 lph   19. D

21. To find how many miles, let $\frac{20}{\frac{1}{2}} = \frac{x}{6}$; x = 240. To find gallons, let $\frac{240}{x} = \frac{30}{1}$; x = 8.

   Cost is 8 · $1.12; Cost is $8.96. Multiply by 2 for the round trip. Total cost $17.92.

Review pg 276
1. C   3. 226   5. B

Written Exercises pg 282
1. 6.5   3. 7.5   5. 2   7. -1   9. 5.4
11. -2.6   13. 29   15. 65   17. 15   19. 168   21. B

Review pg 283
1. Richmond   3. 254.34 cm^2

Written Exercises pg 290

1. 8.1	3. 9	5. 44	7. 48	9. 96.8
11. 98,100	13. 9.1	15. 10	17. median	19. 69.7
21. 60,66				

23. Median. Modes are too low. Mean is too high because of 94 and 100
25(a). Mean 146.32; median 131; mode 131
25(b). Frequencies for given ranges are: 1, 7, 7, 4, 4, 2
25(c). Median or mode are best. Mean is too high because of 250 and 300.

REVIEW: Chapters 1-6 pg 292

1. $\overline{GP}$	3. $\overleftrightarrow{RL}$	5. $4\frac{1}{6}$	7. $8\frac{3}{4}$	9. 5
11. 20	13. 2 ft	15. 3	17. 25,000	19. 18 gal
21. 4 mpg	23. A	25. -6	27. 30	29. 65
31. 45	33. $1.80	35. 60	37. D	39. B
41. 22; 24	43. $1501.50	45. 40	47. $287.50	49. 12 ft
51. C	53. e	55. 3 hr	57. 7	59. 8

CHAPTER 7

Written Exercises pg 303

1. right from -8	3. left from -2		5. left from -5
7. line; $\overleftrightarrow{US}$	9. $\overrightarrow{YW}$, $\overrightarrow{YR}$	11. $\overrightarrow{RW}$, $\overrightarrow{RY}$, $\overrightarrow{RM}$	13. $\overrightarrow{BN}$, $\overrightarrow{BQ}$, $\overrightarrow{BH}$
15. $\overrightarrow{TJ}$, $\overrightarrow{TZ}$, $\overrightarrow{TA}$, $\overrightarrow{TY}$	17. x ≤ 7, x ≥ 2. Rays must overlap.		

Review pg 304

1. 2	3. 4 is factor of 12 and 16 but not 282	5. 28	7. B

Written Exercises pg 309

1. left from 5	3. left from 3	5. right from 5	7. right from 2
9. left from -4	11. right from 4	13. left from -2	15. right from 3
17. left from 5	19. D		

Review pg 310

1. $353.41   3. $\frac{2}{3}$ lb

Written Exercises pg 317
1. 180 3. 90 5. ∠P, ∠2, ∠APT, ∠TPA 7. ∠T, ∠1, ∠GTW, ∠WTG
9. 130 11. ∠L, ∠3, ∠MLK, ∠KLM 13. Right 15. 60
17. Right 19. Straight 21. 27.5 < x < 50 23. 50 25. No

Review pg 319
1. D 3. left from -9 5. 8

Written Exercises pg 326
1. 81 3. 41 5. 22 7. 20 9. 12
11. 46 13. 54 15. 50

Review pg 327
1. C 3. B 5. C 7. left from 3

Written Exercises pg 333
1. 360 3. 15 5. 84 7. 177 9. 57.6 11. 18
13. 158.4 15. 200 17. 20 19. 75 21. B

Review pg 335
1. Acute 3. Obtuse 5. 32

Written Exercises pg 342
1. 24 in. 3. 28 ft 5. C 7. A
9. B 11. 31.4 in., 62.8 in., 94.2 in.

Review pg 345
1. 22; 24 3. $316.92 5. 8 7. 81 9. 14

Written Exercises pg 353
1. $\frac{3}{5}$ 3. $\frac{1}{5}$ 5. $\frac{1}{10}$ 7. $\frac{1}{4}$ 9. $\frac{11}{36}$
11. $\frac{2}{5}$ 13. $40.83 15. $\frac{1}{2}$ 17. B

19. Make a proportion $\frac{x}{450} = \frac{2}{3}$. Cross-multiply and solve for x. x = 300.

Or multiply 450 by $\frac{2}{3}$ which also makes 300.

650

REVIEW: Chapters 1-7 pg 355

1. straight	3. obtuse	5. right of -4	7. $\overrightarrow{JW}, \overrightarrow{JA}, \overrightarrow{JY}$	9. $17.5 < x < 40$
11. -162	13. 24	15. 53	17. 20	19. 35%
21. 36	23. 56 cm	25. $\frac{1}{5}$	27. $\frac{1}{3}$	29. $\frac{4}{9}$
31. C	33. B	35. C	37. n	39. $6\frac{1}{4}$
41. 16 cm	43. 20 mpg	45. $6.40	47. 79.6	49. 100

51. mean because it is close to the median. There are 5 high scores not just one or two.
53. A(0,0) B(12,0) C(12,8) D(0,8). There are many ways to do this. The base and height could be reversed. The rectangle could be shifted in any direction.

CHAPTER 8

Written Exercises pg 368

1. 41	3. 90 - m	5. 36	7. 51	9. 54
11. 36	13. 70	15. $\frac{1}{4}$		

Review pg 369

1. B   3. 75%

Written Exercises pg 376

1. 138	3. 180 - 5x	5. 68	7. Yes, st line	9. 66
11. 65	13. 98	15. 110	17. 126	19. 20 21. 94

Review pg 377

1. 48   3. 16   5. -9   7. 4
9. 4 (a common factor of 8 and 12) is not a factor of 302   11. B   13. C

Written Exercises pg 383

1. 10	3. -8	5. -9	7. 4	9. 15
11. 1	13. 9	15. 4	17. 12	19. D 21. 60°C

Review pg 384

1. D   3. $1110

Written Exercises pg 389

1. 54	3. 54	5. 122	7. 33	9. 112
11. 29	13. 32	15. 22	17. 40	19. 144

21. $\angle 1$ and $\angle 2$ are complementary because of the perpendicular lines. $m\angle 1 + m\angle 2 = 90$. $4x + 5x = 90$. $x = 10$. $m\angle 2 = 5x = 50$. $m\angle 3 = m\angle 2$ because of vertical angles. $m\angle 3 = 50$.

Review pg 390
1. k   3. 979   5. 18; 8   7. 445   9. B

Written Exercises pg 400
7. D   9. C   11. C   13. A

REVIEW: Chapters 1-8 pg 402
1. 54   3. 41   5. Yes, st line   7. 51   9. 126
11. 104   13. 105   15. 51   17. horizontal cylinder

19. vertical cone   21. $5\frac{1}{2}$ 23. A   25. A

27. 75%   29. 72   31. C   33. 33   35. 4
37. B   39. 14   41. D   43. Right   45. B
47. >   49. $\frac{1}{3}$ 51. 18   53. $5.12   55. 77.3   57. 80

59. Either, since they are very close. Two low scores are almost balanced by two high
    scores.
61. C   63. A   65. V   67. 240 mi

CHAPTER 9

Written Exercises pg 415
1. x; 5   3. y; 11   5. x; 10   7. x; 16   9. x; 5

11. x; 10   13. y; 11   15. y; 7   17. y; 15   19. x; $1\frac{1}{2}$

21. y; $5\frac{1}{4}$ 23. Yes, both = 9

25. (2,-1) Only one answer. Since $\overline{AC}$ ‖ to the x-axis, the x-coordinate must be 2.
    AB = 4 so C must be 4 up or 4 down from A. But B is 4 up so C must be 4 down.

Review pg 416
1. B   3. 104°

Written Exercises pg 425
1. (7,1)   3. (3,-8)   5. (-8,-4)   7. (9,-5)   9. P(8,3) Q(1,6)
11. P(5,7) Q(1,-9)   13. P(-6,8) Q(-3,-10)   15. S(-12,2) T(-3,8)
17. S(2,1) T(7,6)   19. P(-6,-6) Q(-1,-4) R(-4,-2)   21. $\overline{QR}$ 23. $\overline{QT}$
25. In the first quadrant, C(4,5) D(2,2) is obtained by flipping $\overline{AB}$ over the y-axis. In
    the third quadrant E(-4,-5) F(-2,-2) is obtained by flipping $\overline{AB}$ over the x-axis. In
    the fourth quadrant G(4,-5) H(2,-2) can be obtained by flipping $\overline{CD}$ over the x-axis
    or by flipping $\overline{EF}$ over the y- axis. The segments could also be obtained by flipping
    continuously in a clockwise or counter-clockwise direction.

Review pg 427

1. C   3. 44 mph   5. x; 7

Written Exercises pg 434

1. P(12,3) Q(2,3) R(4,10); AB=PQ=$2\frac{1}{2}$ in.; BC=QR=$1\frac{3}{4}$ in.; AC=PQ=$2\frac{3}{4}$ in.;
   m∠A=m∠P=41; m∠B=m∠Q=74; m∠C=m∠R=65.
3. HJ=PO; JE=OR; HE=PR; m∠H=m∠P; m∠J=m∠O; m∠E=m∠R.
5. FI=NO; IG=OW; FG=NW; m∠F=m∠N; m∠I=m∠O; m∠G=m∠W.
7. WE=RO; EB=OK; WB=RK; m∠W=m∠R; m∠E=m∠O; m∠B=m∠K.   9. AK
11. TU   13. m∠P   15. BN   17. EH   19. m∠D
21. P(8,-3) Q(10,-12) R(12,6)   23. QR   25. PQ   27. AC
29. Flip over the y-axis and then over the x-axis. Also over the x-axis and then the
    y-axis. Final points are (8,-2) (1,-2) and (10,-7).

Review pg 435

1. B   3. C   5. 48   7. 137   9. cylinder   11. $\frac{1}{10}$

Written Exercises pg 443

1. (2,1)(6,1)(6,5)(2,5)(2,4)(5,4)(5,2)(2,2)
3. (-2,1)(-6,1)(-6,5)(-2,5)(-2,4)(-5,4)(-5,2)(-2,2)
5. (-2,1)(-6,1)(-6,5)(-2,5)(-2,4)(-5,4)(-5,2)(-2,2)   7. No
9. (6,-2)(6,-6)(2,-6)(2,-2)(3,-2)(3,-5)(5,-5)(5,-2)
11. (3,-2)(3,-6)(7,-6)(7,-2)(6,-2)(6,-5)(4,-5)(4,-2)
13. #8 and #11; #9 and #12   15. B

REVIEW: Chapters 1-9 pg 445

1. y; 9   3. (4,7)   5. Trace on tracing paper and fold on the axis
7. (7,-1)(7,-5)(3,-5)(3,-1)(4,-1)(4,-4)(6,-4)(6,-1)
9. (2,-1)(2,-5)(6,-5)(6,-1)(5,-1)(5,-4)(3,-4)(3,-1)   11. #6 and #9; #7 and #10

13. P(14,2) Q(10,2) R(3,11); AB=PQ=1 in.; BC=QR=$2\frac{3}{4}$ in.; AC=PR=$3\frac{1}{2}$ in.;
    m∠A=m∠P=40; m∠B=m∠Q=128; m∠C=m∠R=12.

15. 30   17. 136   19. 51   21. Yes; sum 180   23. 56
25. 75   27. 42   29. 7   31. C   33. F
35. 22; 8   37. $182   39. 92   41. B   43. 15   45. C
47. D   49. 12   51. 30   53. $1740   55. 16 cm   57. B
59. I   61. 70   63. 44   65. A

67. $\frac{n-5}{n}$. Subtract the first number from the second number and then divide the result

by the second number.

CHAPTER 10

Written Exercises pg 459

1. 2,3 3. 1,3 or 2,4 5. 1,2 7. 4,5 9. 3,4

11. 5,7 13. 4,5 15. 1,2 17. 1,3 or 2,4

Review pg 460

1. B 3.8008

Written Exercises pg 470

1. If a car is a General Motors car, then it is a Chevrolet. False

3. 66 5. 67 7. 145 9. 135

11. 50 13. 80 15. 65 17. 28

19.

m∠1	x	y	x + y	
30	150	30	180	x and y are supplementary
40	140	40	180	
60	120	60	180	consecutive
80	100	80	180	

Review pg 471

1. D 3. 6

Written Exercises pg 479

1. 70 3. 41 5. 83 7. 93 9. 12

11. 63 13. 60 15. 30 17. 85 19. 130

Review pg 480

1. 143 3. C 5. A 7. B

Written Exercises pg 489

1. FH = $1\frac{1}{2}$ in.; HW = $2\frac{1}{2}$ in.; WP = $1\frac{1}{2}$ in.; PF = $2\frac{1}{2}$ in. 3. Yes, opp sides ∥

5. Each side is 8 7. Each appears to be 90° 9. Each side is $3\frac{1}{4}$ in.

11. Each appears to be 90° 13. AB = $2\frac{1}{2}$ in.; BC = $1\frac{3}{4}$ in.; CD = $1\frac{1}{4}$ in.; DA = 2 in.

15. No, both pairs opp sides not ∥ 17. 44 19. 55

21. ABCD is parallelogram (opp sides ∥) AC = 3 in.; BD = $2\frac{1}{8}$ in. Diagonals of parallelogram not always equal. Diagonals would be equal for any rectangle.

Review pg 491
1. D   3. C   5. D

Written Exercises pg 501

1. AB = 5; BC = 6; CD = 5; DA = 6   3. $\frac{5}{10} = \frac{6}{12}$

5. P(2,2) Q(12,2) R(4,14); PQ = $2\frac{1}{2}$ in.; QR = $3\frac{1}{2}$ in.; RP = 3 in.

7. Rectangles not similar. $\frac{4}{12}$ not = $\frac{6}{20}$ 9. $7\frac{1}{5}$

11. Yes, corresponding angles =; m∠1 = m∠4 (vert ∠s =), m∠3 = m∠5 and
    m∠2 = m∠6 (if lines ‖, alt int ∠s =)

13. $2\frac{6}{7}$ 15. 25   17. 125

19. 70; 80; 55; the triangles are similar; no; if two angles of one triangle are equal to
    two angles of another triangle, then the third angles must be equal and the triangles
    are similar.

REVIEW: Chapters 1-10 pg 503
1. 85   3. 102   5. 85   7. 35   9. 85
11. Yes, opp sides ‖   13. Square   15. 37

17. PQ = $1\frac{1}{4}$ in.; QR = $1\frac{3}{4}$ in.; RP = $1\frac{1}{2}$ in.

19. Similar, corr ∠s =, corr sides in same ratio but not =

21. $1\frac{5}{7}$ 23. 32   25. B   27. C   29. B   31. m
33. C   35. B   37. B   39. C   41. C   43. B
45. B   47. B

CHAPTER 11

Written Exercises pg 515

1. $\frac{2}{3}$ 3. $\frac{2}{3}$ 5. 1   7. -1   9. 0

11. $-\frac{2}{3}$ 13. Slopes of parallel lines are the same.

Review pg 515
1. C   3. B   5. C

Written Exercises pg 524

1. $\frac{5}{6}$; 2   3. $-\frac{5}{4}$; 3   5. $\frac{4}{5}$; -1   7. 3; -2   9. 2; -7

11. $-\frac{3}{5}$; -2   13. A   15. $y = \frac{1}{3}x + 2$ 17. Up 5; U1,R2
19. D

Review pg 526
1. A   3. B   5. 48

Written Exercises pg 531
1. 17   3. 23   5. 9   7. 6
9.   time   chirps
      50   40
      55   60   There will be
      70   120   400 chirps in
     140   ___   140 minutes

Review pg 532
1. 77°   3. C

Written Exercises pg 536
1. $200   3. 3   5. 50%   7. $450   9. 40
11. 10   13. $375

Review pg 537

1. $\frac{2}{3}$; -4   3. 70   5. C ,   7. A

Written Exercises pg 546
1. decreasing   3. constant   5. a to b; d to e   7. b to c   9. A

REVIEW: Chapters 1-11 pg 548

1. $\frac{1}{2}$ 3. $-\frac{2}{3}$ 5. Up 5; D3,R4   7. $y = \frac{1}{3}x + 2$

9. B   11. 11   13. $400   15. C   17. A
19. C   21. 68   23. 64   25. 85   27. Yes, opp sides =

29. Square   31. 76   33. (2,2) (12,2) (4,14); $2\frac{1}{2}$ in., $3\frac{1}{2}$ in., 3in.   35. 14

37. B   39. 31   41. D   43. 243   45. A   47. C

49. 729   51. $33\frac{1}{3}$ %   53. C   55. 32   57. 200 in.^{2}

CHAPTER 12

Written Exercises pg 563
1. centimeter   3. liter   5. kilometers   7. meter   9. 58 kg 100 g
11. 16 km 200 m   13. 5.412 km   15. 1.687 L   17. 2 hr 40 min
19. 38 yd   21. Change 7 km 400 m to 6 km 1400 m. Then you can subtract 3 km
                600 m and get 3 km 800 m

Review pg 565
1. C   3. C   5. 242

Written Exercises pg 574
1. 84 m^2 3. 44 m^2 5. 200 m^2 7. 234 m^2 9. 230 m^2
11. 95 in.^{2} 13. 216 in.^{2} 15. 120 in.^{2} 17. 17.6 m   19. <   21. 30 m

Review pg 575
1. 11x - 2   3. 32   5. 80%

Written Exercises pg 583
1. 5   3. 11.96   5. 9.4   7. A, between 9 and 10   9. 10.8
11. 4.5   13. 30; 30   15. 12.1 cm   17. C   19. 24   21. 46
23. AB = $2\frac{1}{2}$ in.; BC = 2 in.; CD = 1 in.; DA = $2\frac{1}{2}$ in.; p = 8 in.; A = $3\frac{1}{2}$ in.^{2}

Review pg 585
1. 1365   3. 5   5. D   7. p = 2L + 2(L - 3); p = 4L - 6
9. 77.9   11. 85   13. median; all but one quiz score was above the mean.

Written Exercises pg 594
1. 153.86 cm^2 3. 907.46 ft^2 5. 1133.54 ft^2 7. 100.48 yd
9. 122.46 yd   11. 400-100p   13. $30.24   15. 60   17. m and g

Review pg 596
1. C   3. C   5. 278

Written Exercises pg 605
1. 2,2: 6,6   3. 8; 24   5. 4; 36   7. 3,1; 12,4   9. 8; 32
11. 3; 48   13. 9 : 64   15. 16   17. Area is multiplied by 25
19. 64 cm^2 21. 4 : 5

Review pg 606
1. $12,000   3. 384

Written Exercises pg 612

1. 280 cm^3 3. 336 m^3 5. 288π yd^3 7. $\frac{176}{3}$π in.^{3} 9. 2304π cm^3

11. 1 : 8   13. Horizontal cylinder with a horizontal cone attached on the right
end. Volume = $\frac{352}{3}$π cm^3

Activity pg 613

1. 10

PRACTICE FINAL EXAM: Chapters 1-12 pg 614

1. A   3. C   5. A   7. C   9. A

11. B   13. C   15. 5

17. Clerk is wrong. If the original price was $1000, the sale price would have been
$700. Adding 30% of $700 onto $700 = $910.

19. A batting average of .400 means that the player got a hit 40% of the time.
.40x = 36. x = 90.

21. C   23. D   25. B   27. D

29. C   31. D   33. C   35. C

37. PQ = $1\frac{1}{4}$ in., QR = $4\frac{3}{4}$ in., PR = $3\frac{3}{4}$ in.; perimeter is the sum of the three sides.

$9\frac{3}{4}$ in.

39. Round 289.76 to 300 and 403 to 400. Multiply 300 by 400, giving 120,000.